Health: a vital investment for economic development in eastern Europe and central Asia

The European Observatory on Health Systems and Policies supports and promotes evidence-based health policy-making through comprehensive and rigorous analysis of health systems in Europe. It brings together a wide range of policy-makers, academics and practitioners to analyse trends in health reform, drawing on experience from across Europe to illuminate policy issues.

The European Observatory on Health Systems and Policies is a partnership between the World Health Organization Regional Office for Europe, the Governments of Belgium, Finland, Greece, Norway, Slovenia, Spain and Sweden, the Veneto Region of Italy, the European Investment Bank, the Open Society Institute, the World Bank, the London School of Economics and Political Science and the London School of Hygiene & Tropical Medicine.

Health: a vital investment for economic development in eastern Europe and central Asia

Marc Suhrcke

Lorenzo Rocco

Martin McKee

European
Observatory
on Health Systems and Policies

Keywords:
FINANCING, HEALTH
PUBLIC HEALTH - economics
ECONOMIC DEVELOPMENT
SOCIAL JUSTICE
DELIVERY OF HEALTH CARE
SOCIOECONOMIC FACTORS
EMPLOYMENT
HEALTH STATUS
HEALTH POLICY
EUROPE, EASTERN
ASIA, CENTRAL

ISBN 978 92 890 7282 3
Printed in the United Kingdom by The Cromwell Press, Trowbridge, Wilts.

Contents

List of tables, figures and boxes

Tables

Figures

Boxes

List of abbreviations

2SLS	Two-stage least squares
3SLS	Three-stage least squares
ACE	Angiotensin converting enzyme
AIDS	Acquired immunodeficiency syndrome
AMR	Adult mortality rate
CBA	Cost–benefit analysis
CEA	Cost–effectiveness analysis
CMH	Commission on Macroeconomics and Health
CVD	Cardiovascular diseases
DAH	Development assistance for health
DHS	Demographic and Health Survey
DALY(s)	Disability-adjusted life year(s)
EBRD	European Bank for Reconstruction and Development
ECHO	Educational Concerns for Hunger
EERC	European Roma Rights Centre
EVS	European Values Surveys
FE	Fixed effect(s)
GDP	Gross domestic product
GNI	Gross national income
HIPC	Highly indebted poor countries
HIV	Human immunodeficiency virus
HLE	Healthy life expectancy
IDA	International Development Association
IMF	International Monetary Fund
IMR	Infant mortality rate

I-PRSP	Interim-PRSP
IUD	Intrauterine device
IVs	Instrumental variables
JSAN	Joint Staff Advisory Note
LFP	Labour force participation
LLH	Living Conditions, Lifestyles and Health
LSMS	Living Standards Measurement Survey
MDG	Millennium Development Goal
MDR-TB	Multidrug-resistant tuberculosis
MICS	Multiple Indicator Cluster Surveys
NCD	Noncommunicable disease
NICE	National Institute for Clinical Excellence (United Kingdom)
NOBUS	National Survey of Household Welfare and Program Participation
ODA	Official development assistance
OECD	Organisation for Economic Co-operation and Development
OLS	Ordinary least squares
OOP	Out-of-pocket
OSI	Open Society Institute
p.a.	Per annum or per year
p.c.	Per capita or per person
PER	(World Bank's) Public Expenditure Review
PPP	Purchasing power parity
PRGF	Poverty Reduction and Growth Facility
PRSP	Poverty Reduction Strategy Paper
PSM	Propensity score matching
QALY	Quality-adjusted life year
RLMS	Russian Longitudinal Monitoring Survey
SDR	Standardized death rate
SPRED	State Program on Poverty Reduction and Economic Development

TFP	Total factor productivity
UNAIDS	Joint United Nations Programme on HIV/AIDS
UNICEF	United Nations Children's Fund
USAID	United States Agency for International Development
USSR	Union of Soviet Socialist Republics
VSL	Value of a statistical life
WHO	World Health Organization
WHOSIS	WHO Statistical Information Systems (web site)
WTP	Willingness to pay
WVS	World Values Surveys

Country categories

Baltic states	Estonia, Latvia, Lithuania
Caucasus	Armenia, Azerbaijan, Georgia
CEE	Central and eastern Europe: Czech Republic, Estonia, Hungary, Latvia, Lithuania, Poland, Slovakia, Slovenia
CEE5	Czech Republic, Hungary, Poland, Slovakia, Slovenia
Central Asia	Kazakhstan, Kyrgyzstan, Tajikistan, Turkmenistan, Uzbekistan
CIS	Commonwealth of Independent States: Azerbaijan, Armenia, Belarus, Georgia, Kazakhstan, Kyrgyzstan, Republic of Moldova, Russian Federation, Tajikistan, Turkmenistan, Ukraine, Uzbekistan
CEE-CIS	(Countries of) central and eastern Europe and the Commonwealth of Independent States
ECA	Europe and central Asia
EU	European Union
EU8	The eight central and eastern European countries that joined the EU in 2004: Czech Republic, Estonia, Hungary, Latvia, Lithuania, Poland, Slovakia, Slovenia

EU15	The 15 countries that made up the EU before 2004: Austria, Belgium, Denmark, Finland, France, Germany, Greece, Ireland, Italy, Luxembourg, Netherlands, Portugal, Spain, Sweden, United Kingdom
SEE	South-eastern Europe: Albania, Bosnia and Herzegovina, Bulgaria, Croatia, Republic of Moldova, Romania, Serbia and Montenegro (including the United Nations Administered Province of Kosovo (Serbia)), The former Yugoslav Republic of Macedonia
W-CIS	Western Commonwealth of Independent States: Belarus, Republic of Moldova, Russian Federation, Ukraine

Country names

ALB	Albania
ARM	Armenia
AZE	Azerbaijan
BUL	Bulgaria
BIH	Bosnia and Herzegovina
BLR	Belarus
CRO	Croatia
CZH	Czech Republic
EST	Estonia
GEO	Georgia
HUN	Hungary
KAZ	Kazakhstan
KGZ	Kyrgyzstan
LTU	Lithuania
LVA	Latvia
MDA	Republic of Moldova
MKD	See TFYR Macedonia
POL	Poland
ROM	Romania

RUS	Russian Federation
SRB-MNE	Serbia and Montenegro*
SVK	Slovakia
SVN	Slovenia
TFYR Macedonia	The former Yugoslav Republic of Macedonia
TJK	Tajikistan
TKM	Turkmenistan
UKR	Ukraine
UZB	Uzbekistan

---

* Many of the data for this report were collected and analysed before the Declaration of Independence adopted on 3 June 2006 by the National Assembly of Montenegro. All references to Serbia and Montenegro herein refer to the legal status preceding that date. At the time of writing, the Republic of Montenegro has applied for membership of the United Nations but has not yet deposited an instrument of acceptance of the World Health Organization's Constitution in order to join the World Health Organization.

About the authors

Marc Suhrcke, PhD, is an economist with the WHO Regional Office for Europe in Venice, Italy, where he is in charge of the Health and Economic Development workstream. His main current research interests are the economic consequences of health, the economics of prevention and the socioeconomic determinants of health.

Lorenzo Rocco, PhD, is Assistant Professor of Economics with the University of Padova in Italy. He obtained a PhD from the University of Toulouse I in 2005. His main current fields of research are development economics and health economics.

Martin McKee, CBE, MD, DSc, is Professor of European Public Health at the London School of Hygiene & Tropical Medicine (LSHTM), where he co-directs the School's European Centre on Health of Societies in Transition, and he is also a research director at the European Observatory on Health Systems and Policies. His main fields of research include health systems, the determinants of disease in populations and health policy, all with a focus on eastern Europe and the former Soviet Union.

WHO European Office for Investment for Health and Development

The WHO European Office for Investment for Health and Development, which coordinated the activities leading to this publication, was set up by the WHO Regional Office for Europe, with cooperation and support from the Ministry of Health and the Veneto Region of Italy. One of its key responsibilities is to provide evidence on and act upon the social and economic determinants of health. The Office systematically reviews what is involved in drawing together the concepts, scientific evidence, technology and policy action necessary to achieve effective investment for the promotion of health and synergy between social, economic and health development. The Office fulfils two interrelated main functions:

- to monitor, review and systematize the policy implications of the social and economic determinants of population health;

- to provide services to help Member States in the WHO European Region increase their capacity to invest in health by addressing these policy implications and integrating them into the agenda for development.

For more information, visit the web site of the WHO European Office for Investment for Health and Development
(www.euro.who.int/socialdeterminants).

Foreword

The 2001 report of the WHO Commission on Macroeconomics and Health (CMH) called attention to the two-way relationship between health and economic development. Investments in health not only reduce the burden of disease, but also stimulate economic growth, which in turn raises a society's ability to invest in health. The CMH focused much of its attention on the urgent public health crises of sub-Saharan Africa, a region ravaged by HIV, malaria and tuberculosis, rather different from the former socialist countries in eastern Europe and central Asia.

Following the work of the CMH, efforts by WHO with technical support from Columbia University have led to the formation of national macroeconomics and health commissions in many countries. These commissions examine ways to mutually enhance public health investment and economic development, based on the active cooperation of ministries of health and finance. Several of these national commissions have stressed that health concerns with macroeconomic consequences are not limited to infectious diseases, nutrition, and maternal health (the main areas of concern that formed the CMH agenda). Indeed, in many low- and middle-income countries, physical injury and noncommunicable diseases (NCDs) are of great and increasing significance.

The key contribution of this book is the extensive documentation of the economic implications of NCDs. The report focuses on eastern Europe and central Asia, a region too often ignored in the global health debate – unjustifiably so, as the book shows. Despite its focus on one region, the significance of the results is also relevant for other countries – both developing and developed ones – grappling with the challenge of NCDs. The authors have produced substantive original evidence to suggest that individuals, households and economies pay a heavy, unnecessary price for the existing and largely avoidable chronic disease burden, alongside the (re-) emerging infectious disease challenges that many of the countries are facing. At the macroeconomic level, there is a clear indication that the current favourable growth of many countries in this region will slow if the burden of ill health is not tackled effectively. Based on standard empirical growth model predictions the authors argue convincingly that improving population health (from historically low levels) could do a lot to contribute to sustaining growth rates over the medium and longer term. Such long-term growth will also be greatly needed to lift millions out of absolute poverty in this region, and to reach the primary Millennium Development Goal by 2015.

Clearly, the state of research on interventions to address the NCD burden in low- and middle-income countries is less developed than for communicable, maternal and child-related conditions. The CMH had the advantage of building on a large pool of evidence and experience of tackling these conditions in resource-constrained settings. Yet the evidence on cost-effective interventions for NCDs that are affordable and achievable in a low- and middle-income country context is growing, and the authors provide a useful summary of this evidence. They also add an important but still often ignored message that in some instances in this region the return on scaling up health care interventions can be reinforced and amplified by policy measures outside the boundaries of the traditional health care services, for instance by improving the quality of governance. This case, backed up by quantitative evidence in the book, appears particularly compelling in this region, where indicators of governance suggest significant scope for improvement, when compared to other countries at similar development levels.

The authors are to be commended for both the new and the synthesized evidence assembled in this book, and for the roadmap they provide. They point the way towards integrating health more firmly into the overall development strategy, thereby laying the groundwork for researchers and policy-makers, both domestic and international, to better the human and economic living standards of the people in this region.

Dr Nata Menabde
Deputy Regional Director
World Health Organization Regional Office for Europe

Acknowledgements

The work for this report has been coordinated and financially supported by the WHO European Office for Investment for Health and Development in Venice, Italy. Financial support from the Coordination of Macroeconomics and Health Unit of WHO is also gratefully acknowledged. Martin McKee's work has been supported by the United Kingdom Department for International Development's Health System Development Programme.

Elizabeth Goodrich and Nicole Satterley edited the report, and have greatly improved its readability and quality. Many thanks also to Giovanna Ceroni for her management of what has been a very swift and smooth publication process, and to Sarah Moncrieff for her design and layout work.

This report builds on and has benefited greatly from a large number of related global, European, subregional and country-specific projects that have been carried out by the Venice Office over the years, mainly in collaboration with the European Centre on Health in Societies in Transition (ECOHOST) at the London School of Hygiene & Tropical Medicine, as well as the Department of Economics of the University of Padova, Italy. The preceding work has shaped much of the content of the present report, and, hence, our gratitude goes to the institutions that have actively supported our work in this field: the Health & Consumer Protection Directorate General of the European Commission, the Council of Europe Development Bank, the Oxford Health Alliance, the World Bank and the WHO Country Office, Estonia.

The report also benefited from a number of background papers that had been prepared by external experts. We therefore acknowledge the particularly useful contributions of Martin Bobak, Ivana Bozicevic, Beatrice d'Hombres, Christopher Davis, Massimo Fiorin, Corinna Hawkes, Martina Kirchberger, Cecile Knai, Carole Maignan, Stefano Mazzuco, Catherine Michaud, Alberto Motta, Alfred Steinherr, Dieter Urban, Bernd Rechel, Britta Lokrantz Bernitz and Sarah Walters.

Special thanks go to the staff of the Venice Office and in particular to its head, Erio Ziglio, for his continued support and patience throughout the years; to Antonella Biasotto for helping to organize the reference list; and to Andrea Bertola for his invaluable support on a number of data issues.

The report has also benefited from comments and various contributions from Donata Favaro, Armin Fidler, Jenni Kehler, Patricio Marquez, Cem Mete and Dieter Urban. The peer-reviewers for the report were Shiyan Chao and Ruslan Yemtsov, whose guidance has been extremely useful in the final stages of preparing the report.

Despite the tremendous amount of help and guidance from many people, the responsibility for any errors will have to remain with the authors. Views expressed in the report are entirely those of the authors and do not necessarily reflect the official views of the institutions with which they are affiliated.

Executive summary

The breakdown of the socialist system late in the 20th century gave the countries of central and eastern Europe (CEE) and the Commonwealth of Independent States (CIS) (together: CEE-CIS) the opportunity to establish the prerequisites for sustainable economic development and improved human welfare. Many countries benefited from the new possibilities that became available, as exemplified by the 2004 accession to the European Union (EU) by eight formerly socialist countries and the 2007 accession of Bulgaria and Romania.

Outside the enlarged EU, however, progress was less smooth. Dramatic economic decline in the early 1990s produced widespread poverty. More than 100 million people (20% of the population) were living in absolute poverty by 1998/1999, according to the World Bank's definition of poverty for the Region (living on less than US$ 2.15 a day). Another 160 million people (about 33%) were economically vulnerable (living on between US$ 2.15 and US$ 4.15 a day). Some relief came between 1998 and 2003 as more than 40 million people moved out of poverty, bringing absolute poverty rates down to about 12%. Still, the figure for economically vulnerable people held firm. Today, more than 60 million remain poor and more than 150 million are economically vulnerable: a long road still lies ahead. That road will require developing economic growth that will be sustained over decades in order to lift large numbers of people out of poverty and vulnerability.

Yet a large share of the recent growth is likely of a transitory nature. According to the World Bank and other financial institutions, part of the remarkable recent growth is but a simple correction of the earlier huge economic decline, either caused by efficiency gains from partial market reforms that are thus far insufficient to affect the long-term rate of economic growth, or by windfalls from natural resources that are probably not being reinvested to maximize long-term growth. Expectations of sustained growth from these causes cannot be encouraged.

Where, then, can these countries turn for sustained improvements to their economies? The key message here is that investing in health offers a hitherto neglected opportunity to contribute to growth and poverty reduction in the CEE-CIS Region – albeit not the panacea. This discussion has four platforms as its base, as follows.

1. The Region's health status is unfavourable as shown by many standards.

- Health suffered substantially during the transition, when measured, for instance, by official life expectancy data. Comparing health status in western European high-income countries with that in the CEE-CIS Region reveals a widening gap, probably even wider than official figures suggest.

- Adult mortality – an important health indicator of the working-age population – is much higher in this Region than in other countries with a similar level of economic development.

- The transition health crisis tends to be portrayed as predominantly affecting male mortality, but female morbidity is also in crisis.

- Noncommunicable disease and injuries cause the greatest share of morbidity and mortality in the Region, although communicable diseases and child and maternal health concerns must also be taken seriously.

2. Neither domestic nor international policy has made sufficient effort to address the Region's health problems.

- Policies to improve health in this Region have been limited, leaving much scope for investing more in health and doing so more effectively, through the health system itself and other channels.

- Public expenditure in general and expenditure on health in particular declined in the Region in the 1990s to levels that make running a basic system virtually impossible in several countries. More recently, funding levels have stabilized or even increased, but significant improvements in health outcomes have not followed.

- One indication of a likely shortcoming of health policy can be seen in the significant and rising socioeconomic inequalities in health and health care access. Rising inequalities in access are largely due to rises in informal payments, but inequalities in health are only partly explained by unequal access. The available evidence suggests that public expenditures in CEE-CIS have done little to redress the inequities embodied in health systems, although this should be a primary aim.

- Catastrophic health expenditures threaten to impoverish households in certain subregions, such as the low-income CIS countries. Here, health systems rely heavily on household contributions, and households are largely poor. Outside the eight CEE countries that joined the EU in 2004, simulations suggest that catastrophic health spending can increase the size of the poor population by 3–9%.

- Comparing the development assistance for health received in these countries with that for other countries with similar levels of health need shows that the international community has neglected health in this Region. This neglect may spring from global neglect of noncommunicable disease in health targets defined, for example, in the Millennium Development Goals.

- There is significant opportunity to more firmly integrate health and health investment in the countries' national development strategies, as reflected in the Poverty Reduction Strategy Papers.

3. Health does matter for the economies of the CEE-CIS Region and beyond.

- This analysis offers abundant evidence from CEE-CIS that health significantly affects economic outcomes at individual and household levels, even when other relevant determinants are taken into account. Ill health is shown to play an important role in determining people's labour market performance, on top of other potentially important economic effects.

- Improving health, measured by reducing mortality rates, is projected to bring substantial macroeconomic benefits in terms of gross domestic product (GDP) per capita. Given the enormous expected economic benefits, any well-designed, effective initiative to invest in health in the Region is likely to be well worth the money.

- Improving health would also improve the population's welfare, a goal that should be the prime aim of economic policy.

4. Evidence-based, cost-effective interventions exist to improve the health situation through policy measures within and outside the health system.

- Even from a purely economic perspective, any government has a role to play in improving the health of its population. While such role has long been recognized in the domains of communicable disease and child and maternal health and with regard to the establishment of a health system, it also applies to noncommunicable disease.

- Countries of this Region need to develop a broader public health perspective that will allow them to identify existing and emerging health needs and to develop effective policies to address them.

- Much could be gained from investing in health in ways that go beyond the traditional forms of health care investment: investments in the quality of governance and in social capital are highlighted as two such examples.

In light of the evidence, national policy-makers – particularly those outside the health system – might achieve their economic objectives more efficiently by investing in health. While investing in health is not the panacea for achieving sustained economic growth and poverty reduction in the CEE-CIS Region, it should certainly be an integral component of the overall development strategy, not marginalized by decision-makers whose purview seems – at first glance – not to overlap with health concerns. The traditional view has been that health is but an automatic by-product of economic development, but the evidence here reveals a causal effect that also runs from health to economic outcomes. This bidirectional characteristic means that one problem cannot be solved without simultaneously solving the other. Thus, governments are better off investing a given amount of resources in both health and economies, rather than in just one, thereby creating a mutually reinforcing upward cycle. Thus far in CEE-CIS, the focus has been on traditional economic investment strategies.

In addition to national policy-makers, the findings here apply to the international community, which seems to be neglecting the Region's serious health challenges and thereby the attendant consequences for economic development. Both the health challenges and their consequences are a matter of vital interest to both the nearby EU and the United States, which has strategic interests in the Region. To the extent that the limited international efforts directed at these challenges are due to the global neglect of noncommunicable diseases in the international development agenda, the agenda must be broadened and interpreted more flexibly.

Chapter 1

Introduction

The breakdown of the socialist system in 1989–1991 offered the countries of central and eastern Europe (CEE) and the Commonwealth of Independent States (CIS) (together: CEE-CIS) the opportunity to put in place the pre-requisites for sustainable economic development and improved human welfare. Many countries benefited from the new possibilities, as exemplified by the 2004 accession to the European Union (EU) by eight formerly socialist countries and the 2007 accession of Bulgaria and Romania.

Outside the enlarged EU, progress evolved less smoothly. Dramatic economic decline in the early 1990s drove many families into poverty. Although reliable data on poverty rates from the early 1990s are scarce, it is undisputed that a far greater share of the population is now living in poverty than at the onset of political and economic transition. Despite a recent rebound in economic growth, the latest counts show that more than 60 million people in the CEE-CIS Region remain poor, and more than 150 million are economically vulnerable (Alam et al. 2005). The road that still lies ahead is long.

This book responds to the question whether investing in health would make a significant contribution to sustained economic growth and poverty reduction in CEE-CIS. While it focuses on the *economic* consequences of health, it in no way seeks to downplay the *intrinsic* importance of health in the Region and elsewhere. Discussing health and disease in financial terms should not be viewed as trivializing the human component.

This is the first comprehensive effort to focus on the nexus of health and economic development in the transition countries in this Region; it builds on and extends previous work that examined the economic importance of health in other regions. Recent years have seen an increasing body of work on the economic importance of health, much of it summarized by the Commission on Macroeconomics and Health (CMH), which focuses on the developing country context (CMH 2001; see also Prah Ruger, Jamison & Bloom 2001; López-Casasnovas, Rivera & Currais 2005). The need for specific evidence directly relevant to the CEE-CIS Region became apparent because extant work seemed to have only limited applicability to the context of transition countries. Although a number of CIS countries are in the same "low- and middle-income" category (World Bank definition[1]) as developing countries, a number of salient features distinguish the post-socialist, low-income countries from those traditionally called "developing countries". Some of these differences, such as in the socioeconomic contexts and health patterns, may critically affect the interrelationship between health and economic development in ways that call for a separate analysis.

As for the health situation, the most striking difference between this Region and the developing world is that in the former, noncommunicable diseases (and injuries) account for the vast majority of the disease burden. Only a comparatively minor share is due to the diseases that burden the world's poorest countries in sub-Saharan Africa: communicable disease and child and maternal health problems. Noncommunicable diseases typically occur later in life than most of the conditions hitting the developing world. Since noncommunicable diseases tend to occur towards the end of life or beyond working age, when individuals may have already "delivered" their lifetime economic contribution, some infer that there can only be a very limited, if any, economic loss associated with such diseases. As a result, the subject has thus far not attracted attention – attention that this book shows is needed.

The challenge of assessing the economic importance of health in CEE-CIS is to a large extent, but not exclusively, that of assessing the economic importance of noncommunicable diseases. This makes this book of potential relevance far beyond its primary geographical focus. Noncommunicable diseases have long ceased to be solely an issue for affluent high-income countries (Strong et al. 2005; Suhrcke et al. 2006) and are increasing rapidly in many low- and middle-income countries, too (WHO 2005a), killing large shares of these populations prematurely and unnecessarily. The international community has so far failed to respond adequately to this health threat (Beaglehole & Yach 2003).

---

1. The World Bank classifies countries on the basis of their gross national income (GNI) per capita as low income, middle income (subdivided into lower middle and upper middle), or high income. See Table 1.1 at the end of this chapter for the latest classification of the CEE-CIS countries.

Their more advanced socioeconomic context also distinguishes transition countries from developing countries, although, on the basis of per-capita income, three CIS countries are classified as low-income. However, income is only a portion of a country's wealth and this viewpoint overlooks inherited infrastructure, both physical (such as transport networks) and human (such as the population's education level).

Since the CEE-CIS countries are on average more developed, their overall health status (measured, for instance, by life expectancy and child mortality) tends to be higher. Higher health status might suggest that achieving health gains will be more difficult than in very poor settings. While the concept of decreasing marginal returns likely applies to health, this book shows that, in the CEE-CIS context, the scope for further health gains remains sizeable, albeit possibly smaller than in the poorest countries. Moreover, the idea that better health brings economic benefits only in poor settings, where infectious disease is rampant, was rejected by a recent study synthesizing the empirical evidence that health contributes significantly to the economy in the high-income European countries (Suhrcke et al. 2005). Although that study concerned only high-income countries, the evidence it assembled is of direct relevance to transition countries. This is because (1) in terms of the relative contribution of the main causes of morbidity and mortality, the CEE-CIS Region is strikingly similar to rich European countries, and (2) the socio-economic context tends to be more comparable to European high-income countries than to developing countries, at least when assessed by some key socioeconomic indicators (such as degree of industrialization or literacy).

Structurally, this book presents its information on the Region's economic and health situation in three main chapters, followed by a conclusion: Chapter 2 presents the economic challenge that the CEE-CIS countries face, beginning by showing the widespread scale of income poverty across the Region. Apart from being a tragedy in its own right, such poverty puts the Region far off track in reaching the first and principal goal of the eight Millennium Development Goals (MDGs): halving the 1990 income poverty rate by 2015. Chapter 2 also examines the recent trends in poverty and national per-capita income as well as the factors driving them, in particular the economic growth in parts of the Region since 1998 – growth that may not be sustained under current policy.

If health improvement in CEE-CIS is possible and health does affect economic development in this Region, a well-designed health investment strategy would be expected to make a valuable contribution to economic growth in the Region. Chapter 3 assesses the scope for health improvement, exploring the current health status in CEE-CIS and efforts directed toward health there. The evidence strongly suggests that significant scope does indeed exist for health improvements, because the current levels are low, because the burden of disease is largely avoidable and because policy efforts – thus far – have been sparse and weak, both domestically and internationally.

Chapter 4 holds this book's core contribution. It presents and discusses evidence on the interdependence of health and economic development, with a focus on the mechanisms by which health affects economic development. This chapter documents extensive new evidence, showing that ill health imposes a significant economic burden on societies and individuals in the Region. It also shows that expected economic benefits (in terms of gross domestic product (GDP)) from realistic, achievable health improvements would be substantial. Last but not least, this chapter assesses the economic gains in terms of a measure of social welfare or "full income", drawing on the work of Nordhaus (2003).

While the present book is the first comprehensive effort to analyse the economic impact of (in particular adult) ill health in the Region, much of the evidence about the economic implications of chronic disease is relevant beyond that geographical focus. The burden of chronic disease is growing rapidly in many low- and middle-income countries, not just in CEE-CIS (WHO 2005a; Suhrcke et al. 2006).

Showing that there is much scope for health improvement and that there are sizeable economic benefits to be reaped from health gains is not enough. Chapter 5 discusses how these countries could invest in health. A core principle underpinning this chapter and the book as a whole is that investing in health extends beyond investing in health care. The chapter begins with an economic rationale for governments to take action, not only on the health issues that governments have traditionally addressed, but also on noncommunicable disease. From a strictly economic perspective, the need for governments to address noncommunicable diseases has previously been much less obvious, which may well have prevented or deterred significant action.

If there is a case for governments (and other stakeholders) to act in order to improve population health, *how* should they act? The second part of Chapter 5 addresses this question. While a detailed, costed investment plan exceeds the scope of this book – and should anyway be the outcome of a national process of policy formulation – some principles can be established. The key message is that evidence-based methods that could overcome the greatest health challenges are available. This chapter also argues that while increasing health expenditures may be a necessary policy response in some cases, it alone is unlikely to suffice. Chapter 5 proposes two examples of areas beyond the health care sector proper that call for investment – the quality of governance and social capital – as a means of improving health in this Region.

Table 1.1 *CEE-CIS countries by World Bank Income Category*

High income (> US$ 10 725)	Upper-middle income (US$ 3466–10 725)	Lower-middle income (US$ 876–3465)	Low income (US$ < 876)
Slovenia	Croatia	Albania	Kyrgyzstan
	Czech Republic	Armenia	Tajikistan
	Estonia	Azerbaijan	Uzbekistan
	Hungary	Belarus	
	Latvia	Bosnia and Herzegovina	
	Lithuania	Bulgaria	
	Poland	Georgia	
	Romania	Kazakhstan	
	Russian Federation	Republic of Moldova	
	Slovakia	Serbia and Montenegro	
		TFYR Macedonia	
		Turkmenistan	
		Ukraine	

Source: www.worldbank.org/data/ (link to "Country Classification") (accessed 8 January 2007).

Notes: The World Bank classifies countries on the basis of gross national income (GNI) per capita. Classifications are set each year on 1 July. This classification is as of 1 July 2006.

Chapter 6 summarizes the book's aims and reviews its findings to channel the reader onto the road ahead. If the scope for improvement to both health and economies has been shown and the case has been made that investing in health both by the Region's governments and the international donor community is essential, then the reader is challenged to find the way forward. This book documents several proven cost-effective interventions in the health arena but also calls for action in the broader arenas of improving the quality of governance and fostering civic participation.

The analysis focuses on the countries of CEE and the CIS. Delineation of regions, or even of Europe itself, is always problematic. However, for the present purposes a pragmatic solution was adopted by defining the countries of interest as those that did not join the EU in 2004, with the exception of the three Baltic states, which are included as a valuable comparator with the other countries of the former Union of Soviet Socialist Republics (USSR). For a comprehensive list of the country classifications used throughout this study, see the List of abbreviations.

Chapter 2

The challenge: combating poverty and promoting economic development

The World Bank developed the commonly used international definition of absolute poverty – living on less than US$ 1 per person per day[2] – in the 1980s; the figure was the average of the poverty lines of 10 low-income countries, all wholly or in part in the tropics. This US$ 1 poverty line is also commonly used as the indicator for the MDG on poverty. However, experts widely acknowledge that a higher poverty line is appropriate in the CEE-CIS Region, as its harsh climate (falling to -40 °C in places) necessitates additional expenditure on housing, heat, warm clothing and food. To account for these necessities, the World Bank set a poverty line of US$ 2.15 per person per day in this Region; here we use this higher figure as a poverty threshold, together with the figure of US$ 4.30, also established by the World Bank, as the level above which people cease to be economically vulnerable.

A recent World Bank analysis found that the CEE-CIS Region still faces an enormous challenge in reducing poverty (Alam et al. 2005). More than 60 million people there live in absolute poverty (below the US$ 2.15 poverty line) and more than 150 million are economically vulnerable (living on US$ 2.15–4.30 per day). Figure 2.1 shows how these rates vary among the CEE-CIS countries for which data are available. As expected, the variation is wide, with those countries with a higher GDP per capita also experiencing lower absolute poverty rates.

---

2. The exact poverty line is US$ 1.08, which for the sake of simplicity is referred to here as US$ 1.

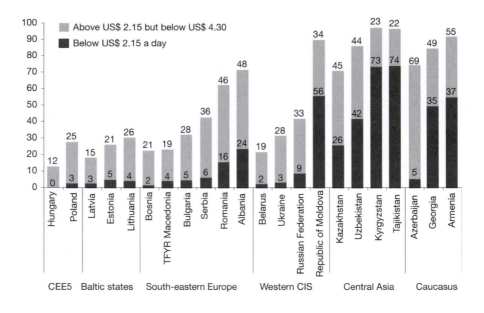

Figure 2.1 *Poverty incidence in CEE/CIS, 2002–2004 (Source: Alam et al., 2005).*

Note: For details of country categories see List of abbreviations.

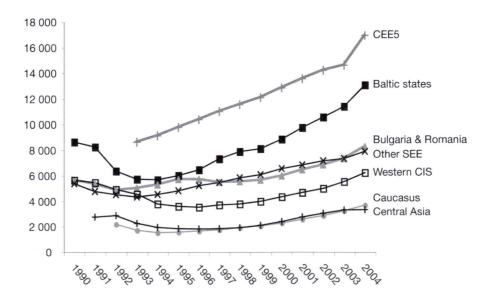

Figure 2.2 *GDP per capita (US$ PPP per year), 1990–2004 (Source: UNICEF, 2006b).*

Notes: Data for countries are unweighted averages; For details of country categories see List of abbreviations; "Other SEE": Albania, Croatia, and The former Yugoslav Republic of Macedonia; There are no relevant data for Bosnia and Herzegovina or Serbia and Montenegro.

A look at the years just before these 2002–2004 figures shows the dramatic increase in poverty that began with the onset of transition. Poverty peaked in the Region near the end of the 1990s: 100 million people lived in absolute poverty by 1998 (the number would drop by 40 million in 2003), and more than 150 million were economically vulnerable (World Bank 2000a). Both the earlier increase in poverty and the recent decline were driven to a large extent by the evolution of GDP per capita (in purchasing power parity (PPP) terms), as Figure 2.2 illustrates (by subregion).

The 2004 economic gaps between these countries are far greater than in 1990. Yet despite this increasing heterogeneity, similar trends appear in the broad pattern of economic development. The countries of primary focus here (all but central Europe) all suffered a marked fall in output in the early 1990s, followed by some degree of recovery. By 2004, most of these countries had at last caught up with their per-capita income levels of the late Soviet period.

While average national income is a major determinant of poverty, it is not the only one. Income inequality matters, too – the question how economic wealth is distributed within a given country. In CEE-CIS, during both the period of poverty increase and its subsequent reduction, the evolution of income inequality reinforced the impact of GDP on poverty. When average incomes fell sharply in the initial post-transition period, the consequences of increasing poverty were magnified by a large increase in income inequality (UNICEF 2001). Since 1998, during strong GDP growth, the narrowing of income inequality – particularly in the CIS – accelerated the reduction in poverty rates.[3]

Despite the recent recovery, the challenges ahead are great, not just for the low-income CIS countries, but also for many of the middle-income countries, where poverty rates are lower but where most of the poor live. Sustainable poverty reduction is by no means guaranteed, as shown by the World Bank analysis (Alam et al. 2005), which highlights three explanations for the lack of such a guarantee.

(1) The recent economic gains may, to a considerable extent, simply be a short-lived correction following the earlier deep falls and may soon level off. In part this is because a significant share of the recent remarkable growth performance is driven by windfalls from natural resources, and there are serious concerns as to whether the financial resources yielded by these windfalls will be reinvested to maximize long-term, sustainable growth.[4] Recent growth has also been driv-

---

3. See Mitra and Yemtsov (2006) for an in-depth examination of income inequality in CEE-CIS during transition.

4. Indeed, a large body of evidence from other countries on the interrelationship between natural resource abundance and economic growth shows that abundance of natural resources is

en by efficiency gains obtained through the (partial) reorganization of economies following the adoption of (at least partial) market-oriented reforms. Both drivers of growth tend to be of a short-run and contingent nature. More fundamental, long-term drivers of growth, in particular the quality of governance and human capital (education and health), have tended to be somewhat neglected. As has been documented elsewhere (Gros & Suhrcke 2000) and as Chapter 5 of this volume shows using more recent data, the quality of governance in many of the CEE-CIS countries is below that of other countries with similar levels of economic development. This is likely to impose a cost in terms of long-run economic growth (Acemoglu, Johnson & Robinson 2005). As for education, the CEE-CIS countries were generally characterized by a remarkably high level of educational performance at the onset of transition compared to other countries at similar levels of economic development. However, while it has been possible to maintain or even further improve key educational process indicators such as secondary school enrolment rates in some countries, the educational output and quality as reflected in the test scores of international surveys (Trends in International Mathematics and Science Study) appear to have deteriorated recently (for an in-depth analysis see Alam et al. (2005)). Part of this deterioration may be due to a decline in the resources available to the education sector.[5] The even less encouraging evolution of health, the other (often neglected) key component of human capital, is the subject of Chapter 3.

(2) The transition countries outside the fastest growing CIS countries – the countries of south-eastern Europe (SEE) and the Baltic states – have been particularly unable to create jobs at a sufficient pace to replace those lost during the period of "jobless growth" (Alam et al. 2005). This is a problem because economic growth cannot be sustained without an increase in labour supply. Employment-to-population ratios remained steady or declined almost everywhere outside the CIS. Because of the failure to stimulate sufficient job creation, the EU8 and SEE countries are well below the Lisbon Agenda targets of male and female employment rates of 70% and 60%, respectively.[6] At the

---

often counter-productive to long-term economic development (Sachs & Warner 1995a; Leite & Weidmann 1999). The European Bank for Reconstruction and Development confirmed this hypothesis in an analysis of the energy-rich CIS states of Azerbaijan, Kazakhstan, Turkmenistan and Uzbekistan, concluding that far from being a blessing that would have allowed resource-rich countries to cushion the impact of reforms and thus make faster progress, resource rents have often been wasted or appropriated by the ruling elites (Esanov, Raiser & Buiter 2001).

5. While in 1995 most CEE-CIS countries were spending more on education than the average for countries with similar levels of GDP per capita, this pattern reversed in 2002, with the majority of the CEE-CIS countries spending substantially less than the average (authors' calculations).

6. The Lisbon Agenda was agreed in March 2000 (and since updated), when the EU heads of

same time, increases in employment can play a key role in reducing poverty, since the greater number of employed people would benefit from the wage increases that would result from further productivity growth.

(3) Even if growth continues, it will not necessarily reduce poverty. Increased income inequality – which seems likely – would result in having only a few that benefit from the overall gains. Between 1998 and 2003, a narrowing of income inequality helped economic growth to reduce poverty in many countries. Income inequality was brought down to levels that are now, broadly speaking, at the low end of the international spectrum (see Figure 2.3), so that "some worsening of inequality over the medium term would not be surprising" (Alam et al. 2005, page 32).

How can the recent record be evaluated in light of the development goals that the international community has set? In 2000, heads of state and the leading international organizations committed themselves to achieving the MDGs by 2015. The principal, overarching goal is to halve by 2015 the number of people who were living in poverty in 1990. While sufficiently comparable 1990 poverty data from the CEE-CIS Region are scarce, there is no doubt that on the whole poverty rates today are higher than in 1990. Hence, literally applying the MDG yardstick to the Region would lead to the conclusion that the Region has diverged from, rather than converged toward, the ultimate goal. This would be an appalling finding, and the only other world region that has regressed rather than progressed toward this goal is sub-Saharan Africa.[7]

However, given the diverse nature of the CEE-CIS Region, it is necessary to adopt a more disaggregated, regional perspective. The World Bank has proposed subregion-specific poverty reduction goals (Alam et al. 2005):[8]

- low-income CIS countries are to reduce poverty by half relative to 1990 (at US$ 2.15 a day);

---

states and governments agreed to make the EU "the most competitive and dynamic knowledge-driven economy by 2010". Goals were also established, such as the employment targets mentioned in this chapter. For further details see, for example, ec.europa.eu/growthandjobs/ (accessed 14 July 2006).

7. In addition to Europe and central Asia, and sub-Saharan Africa, progress toward the MDGs is assessed by the United Nations across the following regions: east Asia and the Pacific, Latin America and the Caribbean, the Middle East and North Africa, and south Asia. See, for example, www.developmentgoals.org (accessed 1 January 2007).

8. According to the World Bank, the category "low-income CIS" comprises Belarus, Kazakhstan, the Russian Federation and Ukraine, while "middle-income CIS" includes Armenia, Azerbaijan, Georgia, Kyrgyzstan, Republic of Moldova, Tajikistan, Turkmenistan and Uzbekistan (Alam et al. 2005).

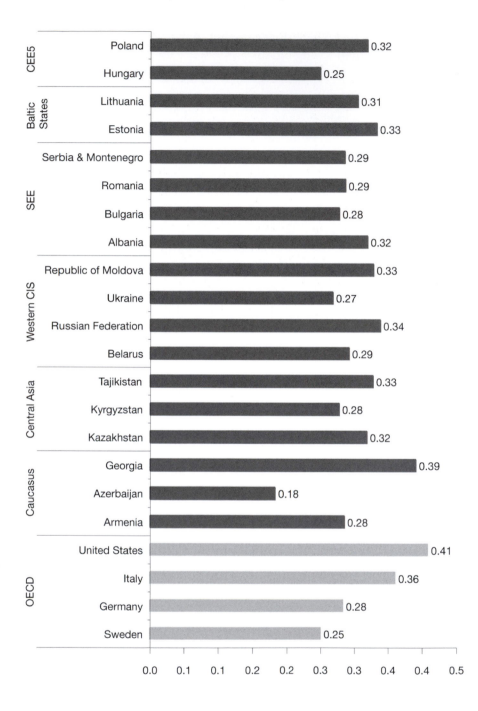

Figure 2.3 *Income inequality (Gini coefficient), latest available year (Sources: Alam et al., 2005; World Bank, 2005a).*

Note: The Gini coefficient is a standard measure of inequality (here applied to inequality of per-capita consumption): it takes values between 0 (complete equality) and 1 (extreme inequality, where all income would be appropriated by the richest person).

- middle-income CIS countries are to eliminate economic vulnerability (at US$ 4.30 a day);

- SEE countries are to eliminate economic vulnerability (at US$ 4.30 a day);

- EU8 countries are to reduce poverty by half, taking as a poverty line the lowest line in the EU15 in 2004.

In a simulation exercise, Alam and colleagues (2005) found that the growth rates required to achieve these goals by 2015 are notably higher than what is predicted based on the current determinants of growth. The long and challenging road ahead recommends a search for every possible opportunity that could help bring about more sustained economic growth and, consequently, poverty reduction. As the following chapters will argue, one such opportunity that the Region has so far largely failed to tap into is investment in health, which, along with education, is one of the two pillars of human capital. In analysing this, the present book fills a gap that, somewhat surprisingly, has been left open by virtually all recent assessments of the Region's economic growth potential.

Chapter 3

Health and health policy

Chapter 2 described the major challenge of sustaining economic growth and thereby reducing poverty in CEE-CIS. This chapter argues that there is substantial scope for investing in health to help meet this challenge. The benefits from investing in health are a function of (1) the scope for health improvement and (2) the scope for policy to stimulate those improvements, both of which are addressed in this chapter.

Health status, trends and patterns in CEE-CIS

This section covers two closely related issues: the overall health status of the CEE-CIS countries, in terms of average national figures for key health indicators as well as disease patterns, and then selected evidence on the socioeconomic distribution of health, disease and risk factors. Both the national averages and the observed socioeconomic inequalities highlight the significant scope for improvement.

Overall health

Health suffered substantially in transition when measured, for instance, by official life expectancy data. The health gap with the western European high-income countries is widening. The health situation looks even worse if some countries' data quality problems are taken into account.

The health crisis that occurred in CEE-CIS has been documented extensively elsewhere (Nolte, McKee & Gilmore 2005). Figure 3.1 illustrates the evolution

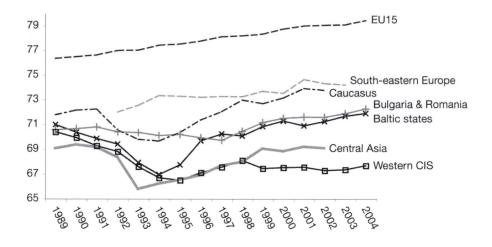

Figure 3.1 *Life expectancy at birth 1989–2003 (in years) (Source: WHO Regional Office for Europe, 2006).*

Notes: Owing to lack of data, not all subregional averages in this figure include data for every country in the subregion: South-eastern Europe includes Albania, Croatia, The former Yugoslav Republic of Macedonia and Serbia and Montenegro (excluding Bosnia and Herzegovina); "Central Asia" includes Kazakhstan, Kyrgyzstan and Uzbekistan (excluding Tajikistan and Turkmenistan); For details of other country categories, see List of abbreviations.

of life expectancy at birth since 1989 in various European subregions. While the 15 countries that made up the EU before the 2004 enlargement (EU15) did manage to improve life expectancy steadily throughout the period, the only subregions of CEE-CIS where life expectancy in 2003 (or 2004) is noticeably longer than at the start of transition – apart from the CEE5 countries (Czech Republic, Hungary, Poland, Slovakia and Slovenia) not shown here – are the south-eastern European countries (for now encompassing Albania, Croatia, The former Yugoslav Republic of Macedonia and Serbia and Montenegro) and the Caucasus – with data from the latter subject to serious doubts, as discussed later in this volume. Life expectancy has mostly been declining in the western CIS (W-CIS) since 1989, with only a small temporary reversal from 1995 to 1998, and life expectancy in 2004 is three years below the 1989 level. The picture appears only marginally more favourable in central Asia, although the reliability of data from this subregion also bears serious doubt.

In several countries, life expectancy may in fact be lower than suggested by the official figures.

Life expectancy is calculated on the basis of available mortality data. Using mortality statistics to evaluate patterns of health in a given population has two main advantages: (1) mortality data are routinely available in most countries, and (2) death is a unique, clearly defined event. Despite a comparatively advanced system of vital statistics during the Soviet period (Andersen & Silver 1997), considerable concerns have arisen since about the coverage and completeness in some of the least developed parts of central Asia (McKee & Chenet 2002); in war-afflicted regions, such as the Caucasus (Badurashvili et al. 2001); and in SEE (Bozicevic et al. 2001), where vital registration systems have been weakened and, more importantly, where the scale of migration is largely unrecorded.

Recent work by the World Health Organization (WHO) (WHO 2003) finds gaps in both the adult and the infant/child mortality registrations in part of the Region.[9] A recent, more geographically focused United Nations Children's Fund (UNICEF) study (UNICEF 2003; Aleshina & Redmond 2005) shows that in several CIS countries estimates of infant mortality rates (IMRs) calculated from survey data were considerably higher than official rates, yielding figures that are up to three times higher in Uzbekistan and up to four times higher in Azerbaijan, with notable differences also seen in Turkmenistan, Kazakhstan and Kyrgyzstan, as well as Georgia and Armenia. As detailed below, these differences persist even after accounting for possible limitations of the survey estimates and potential differences in the definition of a live birth. This is strong evidence that "true" IMRs in these countries are likely to be significantly higher than officially reported.

The imperfect adult and child mortality registration systems in some countries can be expected to give rise to a serious overestimation of overall population health measures such as life expectancy at birth. This is confirmed by Table 3.1, which compares the official life expectancy data with WHO estimates for those countries that show the biggest gaps between the two.

The discrepancies are substantial in some countries in the Caucasus and central Asia and slightly smaller in the south-eastern European countries (except for Albania). If the estimated life expectancy figures are closer to the truth than the official data, then the picture differs from what Figure 3.1 suggests. In particular, the surprisingly high life expectancy trajectories for SEE and the Caucasus would shift downward, and the already low central Asian figures would drop further. For this reason, routine data on mortality (and life expectancy) in these subregions must be interpreted with particular caution.

---

9. For instance, WHO estimated completeness of mortality data covered by the vital registration systems in 1999/2000 at 66–75% in the Caucasus (coverage: 56–73%); approximately 78% in Tajikistan (49%) and Turkmenistan (75%) and up to 85% in Kazakhstan and Kyrgyzstan (74–78%) (Nolte, McKee & Gilmore 2005). For further details see also: www.who.int/whosis/mort/en/index.html (accessed 1 January 2007) (WHO 2005b).

Table 3.1 *Life expectancy at birth: official data and WHO estimates, in years, 2002*

Country	Official reports: life expectancy	WHO: estimated life expectancy	Difference (official report minus WHO estimate)
Tajikistan	72.01	63.7	8.3
Azerbaijan	72.42	65.8	6.6
Albania	76.40	70.4	6.0
Georgia	76.09	71.7	4.4
Kyrgyzstan	67.99	64.5	3.5
Armenia	72.77	70.0	2.8
Kazakhstan	66.15	63.6	2.6
Uzbekistan	70.01	68.2	1.8
TFYR Macedonia	73.28	72.0	1.3
Ukraine	67.85	67.2	0.6
Serbia and Montenegro	72.68	72.3	0.4

Source: WHO Regional Office for Europe, 2006.

Notes: Data for Tajikistan and Georgia refer to 2001; WHO headquarters makes life expectancy estimates for its annual World Health Report; Special techniques are used to produce life tables when routine vital statistics are unavailable or incomplete, as in the case of the countries in this table; See the explanatory notes to the Statistical Annex of *The world health report 2005* (WHO, 2005c) or for more details see Salomon & Murray (2002).

Adult mortality[10] in CEE-CIS – an important health indicator of the working-age population – is much higher than in those with a similar level of economic development.

It is now widely believed that a large share of the comparatively poor and deteriorating or stagnating life expectancy in CEE-CIS is driven by high adult mortality, in particular among men (Macura & MacDonald 2005; Nolte, McKee & Gilmore 2005). In the Russian Federation, for instance, more than 75% of the decline in life expectancy during the transition was due to increased mortality at ages 25 to 64 (Leon et al. 1997; McKee 2001). Table 3.2 compares the gender-specific adult mortality rates of the CEE-CIS

---

10. Adult mortality is the probability of dying between the ages of 15 and 60, that is, the probability of a 15-year-old dying before reaching age 60, if subject to current age-specific mortality rates between ages 15 and 60.

Table 3.2 *Male and female adult mortality rates per 100 000 in CEE-CIS and selected comparator countries, 2003*

Country	Male adult mortality rate	Female adult mortality rate
Russian Federation	480	182
Kazakhstan	419	187
Ukraine	384	142
Belarus	370	130
Turkmenistan	352	171
Kyrgyzstan	339	160
Estonia	319	114
Latvia	306	120
Republic of Moldova	303	152
Lithuania	302	106
Armenia	240	108
Romania	239	107
Uzbekistan	226	142
Tajikistan	225	169
Azerbaijan	220	120
Bulgaria	216	91
TFYR Macedonia	202	86
Georgia	195	76
Bosnia and Herzegovina	190	89
Serbia and Montenegro	186	99
Croatia	173	70
Albania	167	92
Hungary	257	111
Slovakia	204	77
Poland	202	81
Czech Republic	166	74
Slovenia	165	69
Malta	49	84
Cyprus	47	99
EU15	114	59

(cont.)

Table 3.2 *(cont.)*

Country	Male adult mortality rate	Female adult mortality rate
India	283	213
Bangladesh	251	258
Egypt	242	157
Pakistan	225	199
Iran (Islamic Republic of)	201	125
Mexico	166	95
China	164	103
Morocco	159	103
Republic of Korea	155	61
Cuba	137	87
Chile	133	66
Turkey	111	176

Source: WHO, 2005d.

Note: For details of EU15 countries, see List of abbreviations.

countries to those of a larger set of other developing and developed countries. Although adult mortality rates vary a great deal within the CEE-CIS Region, rates in a large number of these countries are noticeably above those in many of the selected comparator countries.

Since adult mortality tends to fall as countries become wealthier, the appropriate benchmark countries for the CEE-CIS countries are those with about the same level of economic development. Figure 3.2 applies this criterion to assess whether a given level of mortality is comparatively high or low. The regression line represents the "expected", "normal" or "predicted" level of male adult mortality for a given level of per-capita GDP. Countries above the line have high mortality rates compared to what would be expected on the basis of GDP; they include several from W-CIS, the Baltic states and some parts of central Asia. Most notably, the Russian Federation is the furthest, among countries in the CEE-CIS Region, from where it should be: its rate of male adult mortality is 2.5 times higher than expected. Worldwide, few countries anywhere are greater outliers than the countries of the former USSR, and they are exclusively those ravaged by human immunodeficiency virus/acquired immunodeficiency syndrome (HIV/AIDS) epidemics. If the countries hardest

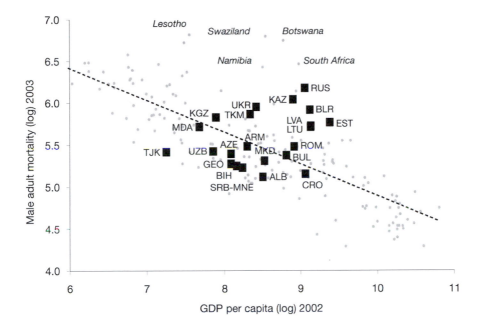

Figure 3.2 *Male adult mortality versus GDP per capita, 2003 (Source: WHO, 2005d).*

Note: For details of country name abbreviations, see List of abbreviations; GDP: gross domestic product.

hit by HIV/AIDS were excluded, the regression line would shift downwards, and even more CEE-CIS countries would display even higher levels of adult mortality compared to expectations.

The health crisis in transition countries tends to be portrayed as predominantly a male mortality crisis. More recent research has lifted the veil of the male mortality crisis to reveal a severe female morbidity crisis.

When judged on the basis of mortality statistics, women in transition countries have fared relatively well compared to their male counterparts, resulting in many countries of the former USSR having some of the largest male–female gaps in life expectancy in the world. While male life expectancy in most CIS countries is lower than in other countries at similar levels of economic development, the CIS countries do not fall markedly out of line in terms of female life expectancy. However, more recent studies show that this is an overly optimistic picture of the true health status of women, for at least two reasons.

First, while female life expectancy has been less sensitive than male life expectancy to the shocks of the past decades, women nevertheless failed to share in the improvements in life expectancy achieved in all other western and

Table 3.3 *Life expectancy at birth and healthy life expectancy for eight CIS countries, in years, 2001*

Country	Male			Female		
	Life expectancy	Healthy life expectancy	Expectancy of poor health	Life expectancy	Healthy life expectancy	Expectancy of poor health
	(1)	(2)	(1) minus (2)	(3)	(4)	(3) minus (4)
Armenia	64.6	46.4	18.2	71.5	47.4	24.1
Belarus	62.2	49.4	12.8	74.4	55.1	19.2
Georgia	66.0	56.6	9.4	72.2	51.1	21.1
Kazakhstan	58.2	48.3	9.9	68.3	47.9	20.4
Kyrgyzstan	60.2	54.1	6.2	69.0	53.3	15.7
Republic of Moldova	63.3	45.2	18.1	70.8	45.3	25.5
Russian Federation	59.6	47.8	11.7	72.4	48.0	24.4
Ukraine	62.8	46.4	16.4	73.7	43.0	30.7
Average	62.1	49.3	12.8	71.5	48.9	22.6

Source: Authors' calculations based on Living Conditions, Lifestyles and Health (LLH) survey data.

Note: These calculations use a method developed by Sullivan (1971) to combine mortality with the proportion of survivors reporting less than good health. (The LLH survey used a four-point scale to measure self-reported health whereas some other surveys use a five-point scale. Thus, while these figures can be used to compare the LLH countries, the figures should not be used for comparison with other surveys.)

northern European countries over that period. Second, and even more importantly, mortality captures only one element of population health, and it
appears to be a particularly inappropriate indicator of the health status of
women in many of the CEE-CIS countries.

The importance of looking beyond mortality statistics to assess women's health
status is illustrated in Table 3.3, which compares life expectancy and "healthy
life expectancy" (HLE) in eight countries. The recent Living Conditions,
Lifestyles, and Health (LLH) surveys[11] have made direct comparisons
possible. The HLE indicator attempts to bring together the mortality and
morbidity experience of a population. Calculated on the basis of self-reported
morbidity data, it can be interpreted as the lifespan in full health.[12] The
striking result that emerges from the table is that what was an enormous health
gap between males and females in terms of life expectancy now disappears: the
levels of HLE are virtually identical for both genders. Women face a disproportionately high burden of morbidity – almost double when viewed against
the average of the eight countries – compared to men, and this outweighs
women's far lower risk of mortality.

While the general finding that women suffer from much greater morbidity
holds for each of the eight countries, there is nevertheless some inter-country
variation. Female HLE is even substantially below male HLE in Georgia (by
5.5 years) and Ukraine (3.4 years), and Belarus shows a female HLE advantage
(the only country to do so).

Another study, using data from the Russian Longitudinal Monitoring Survey
(RLMS) and the World Values Survey, allows a comparison of the Russian
Federation's health status with that of the countries of both central and western Europe (Andreev, McKee & Shkolnikov 2003). Using this data source, the
same conclusion emerges: HLE of Russian men and women is similar because
of the very high morbidity among the latter. Looking at these data from an
interregional perspective draws a sharp contrast: a 40-year-old woman in western Europe can expect to live 30 of her remaining 36 years in good health,
whereas a Russian woman of the same age can expect only 18.5 of her remaining 31 years to be in good health.

While the likely economic impact of the disease burden in CEE-CIS is examined in detail below, for now it suffices to note that the high number of years

---

11. LLH was a series of nationally representative household surveys carried out in eight CIS
countries in 2001. For details see www.llh.at (accessed 30 December 2006).

12. HLE is increasingly used as a measure of population health, for instance by WHO (2002a),
but note that the approach does have some limitations (Law & Yip 2003).

spent in poor health among women (and men) increases the difficulty of believing that the associated economic costs would be insignificant, not least because a substantial proportion of otherwise productive years is spent in poor health.

Noncommunicable disease (especially cardiovascular disease (CVD)) and injuries explain the greatest share of both the deterioration of health and the level of mortality.

A feature that distinguishes the European transition countries from other low- and middle-income countries is the disproportionately high mortality and disease burden accounted for by noncommunicable conditions. WHO's global burden of disease estimates for the year 2002 illustrate this point. Table 3.4 shows the relative distribution of deaths by the three main disease categories: type I (communicable diseases, maternal and perinatal conditions and nutritional deficiencies), type II (noncommunicable conditions) and type III (injuries). It also shows the share of CVD mortality within total noncommunicable disease mortality. The results are disaggregated into 14 subregions. These are standard groupings of countries within the six WHO regions, aggregated on the basis of mortality level.[13] The three relevant mortality strata for the European Region, not all of which are found within each of the 14 subregions, are: A ("very low child & very low adult mortality"), B ("low child & low adult mortality") and C ("low child & high adult mortality"). This book's focus countries are all part of the European B and C categories (except for Croatia, which is in category A). A number of conclusions emerge from Table 3.4.

- Noncommunicable diseases dominate EUR-B and EUR-C (83–85%). These figures are matched only by industrialized countries of Europe (EUR-A), the Americas (AMR-A) and in the western Pacific (WPR-A). These rates are far higher than those observed in other low- and middle-income countries, in particular the traditional developing countries in south-east Asia (SEAR-D) and Africa (AFR-D and AFR-E). (These abbreviations are explained in the note to Table 3.4).

- The relative importance of injuries is particularly noteworthy in the EUR-C subregion, where they account for 13% of all deaths, the second highest share of any subregion.

- Since noncommunicable diseases and injuries account for by far the largest share of deaths, type I conditions (communicable diseases, maternal and perinatal conditions and nutritional deficiencies) account for only a minimal share (4–9%) of the overall mortality burden. Worldwide, EUR-C has the lowest share of type I conditions.

---

13. For a detailed country classification using the WHO mortality strata, see Table A3.1 in the annexes.

Table 3.4 *Distribution of deaths by cause in selected WHO regions (as a percentage of total deaths)*

Mortality stratum	*Disease category*			
	I. *Communicable diseases, maternal & perinatal conditions, nutritional deficiencies*	*II.* *Non-communicable conditions*	*Cardiovascular diseases (% of non-communicable diseases)*	*III.* *Injuries*
Europe (EUR)				
A Very low child very low adult	6.2	89.0	46.2	4.8
B Low child low adult	8.9	85.2	66.2	5.9
C Low child high adult	4.1	82.9	72.3	13.0
Africa (AFR)				
D High child high adult	69.7	22.9	46.4	7.4
E High child very high adult	73.7	19.7	45.6	6.6
The Americas (AMR)				
A Very low child very low adult	6.1	87.5	43.3	6.3
B Low child low adult	17.8	70.3	42.4	11.9
D High child high adult	42.0	49.5	34.7	8.5
South-east Asia (SEAR)				
B Low child low adult	28.5	61.2	44.7	10.3
D High child high adult	41.3	48.8	54.4	10.0
Eastern Mediterranean (EMR)				
B Low child low adult	13.1	71.0	56.6	16.0
D High child high adult	47.5	44.4	52.0	8.1
Western Pacific (WPR)				
A Very low child very low adult	10.9	81.8	40.2	7.3
B Low child low adult	14.6	74.8	42.7	10.6

Source: Mathers et al., 2003.

- Of the deaths caused by noncommunicable diseases in CEE-CIS, CVDs accounted for more than half the total – a higher share than in all other sub-regions.

A qualitatively similar picture holds true when looking at a measure of disease burden that captures both mortality and morbidity in one figure. Such estimates are available from WHO, employing the concept of disability-adjusted life years (DALYs). DALYs attributable to a disease are calculated as the sum of the years of life lost due to premature mortality in the population and the years lost due to disability for incident cases of the disease or condition. There are, however, a few small differences, although of little consequence: the relative share of noncommunicable diseases is reduced to 73% (EUR-B) and 70% (EUR-C) at the expense of an increased disease burden due to injuries (now 6% and 13%, respectively) and due to type I conditions (now 16% and 9%, respectively).

Table 3.4 provides information about only one point in time and about aggregate groupings of countries. Several other studies show that not only do noncommunicable diseases (in particular CVD) and injuries account for most of the overall disease burden in CEE-CIS but that they have also been the predominant drivers of mortality changes during transition (Nolte, McKee & Gilmore 2005; UNICEF 2001).

Of course, while the share of the disease burden that they contribute justifies giving more attention to noncommunicable diseases, this should not divert attention from the serious threats posed by other disorders that have either appeared for the first time (such as HIV/AIDS) or re-emerged (such as tuberculosis). In absolute terms the burden of disease attributable to these disorders is a concern in more than a few countries of the CEE-CIS Region, even though they remain relatively less important than noncommunicable diseases and injuries (as shown in Table 3.4). Discussion of disease patterns (below) reports that recent trends in several communicable diseases, as well as some of the causes of poor child and maternal health, point toward further increases if left unchecked.

When discussing communicable diseases, it is important to recognize that data on the current disease burden fail to capture the dangers these diseases pose if they spread rapidly. Since this chapter cannot cover all health challenges facing this Region, the discussion is limited to those issues that figure most prominently in the current discussions on MDGs: infant and child mortality, malnutrition among children and women of reproductive age, HIV/AIDS, tuberculosis and maternal health. For these health challenges, the economic effects are already rather well understood and known to be substantial.

Infant and child mortality

Infant and child mortality is most likely an underrecognized concern in several countries, as there is reason to believe that survey-based estimates paint a more accurate – and gloomier – picture of child mortality than the officially published vital registration data.

This statement notes serious concerns about the validity of infant and child mortality data, at least in some countries of central Asia and the Caucasus, where the difference between official data and survey-based estimates is particularly striking, as illustrated in Figure 3.3.[14] (For many of the other countries, survey-derived comparators are generally unavailable, making it hard to judge whether official data are biased in either direction.)

In interpreting Figure 3.3, it is important to recognize some of the limitations, both of survey-based mortality data and of vital registration-based mortality data (Aleshina & Redmond 2005).

- In many CIS countries the Soviet definition of infant mortality has been maintained. This feature decreases the IMR figure compared to the WHO definition, which is used for the survey-based estimates.

- There is also evidence of misreporting and non-registration of births and deaths, further (artificially) decreasing the IMR.

- On the other hand, the survey-based rate may be problematic in particular in the transition countries that have very low fertility rates, causing wide sampling variability and confidence intervals.[15]

- Moreover, there are several sources of nonsampling error, most of which would bias downward the survey-based estimates.[16]

- When indirect methods (such as Brass's Method) are used to estimate levels

---

14. Owing to the small sample size for births in any one year, survey-based estimates of infant mortality from the Demographic and Health Surveys (DHS) are usually given as the average of the five years preceding the survey in question. For more information on the DHS themselves, see www.measuredhs.com (accessed 17 January 2007).

15. However, as Aleshina & Redmond (2005) documents, the wide confidence intervals around the survey-based estimates in most transition countries still did not reach the much lower "official" IMR.

16. An example of a nonsampling error is related to how the respondent interprets the survey question. For instance, medical staff may sometimes misreport pregnancy outcomes, and some survey respondents report the inaccurate pregnancy outcomes given to them by medical staff. Aleshina & Redmond (2005) notes, for instance, reason to believe that the surprisingly low estimate of the IMR for Ukraine, which is based on the Reproductive Health Survey, suffers from significant reporting problems.

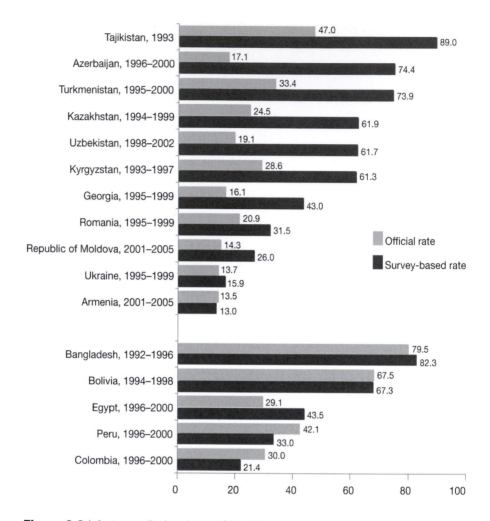

Figure 3.3 *Infant mortality in selected CEE-CIS and comparator countries (per 1000 live births). Sources: This is an updated version of Table 1 in Aleshina & Redmond (2005). More recent data were added for Armenia (National Statistical Service of the Ministry of Health & MEASURE DHS, 2006), Republic of Moldova (Republic of Moldova Ministry of Health and Social Protection, National Scientific and Applied Center for Preventive Medicine & MEASURE DHS, 2006), and Uzbekistan (Analytical and Information Centre et al., 2004).*

Note: For information on the confidence interval around the survey-based estimates, see Aleshina & Redmond (2005).

of infant mortality from survey data, the potential for error is compounded by both sampling variability and choice of model.

Despite these caveats, a strong likelihood remains that actual IMRs (and, hence, child mortality rates, which are primarily driven by infant mortality) are significantly higher than official data indicate.

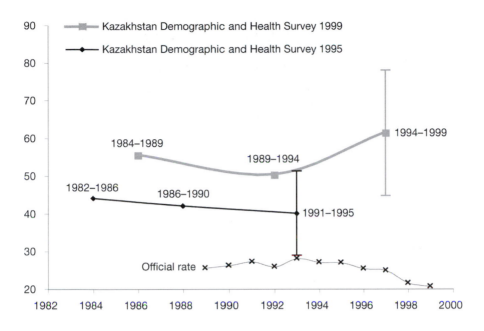

Figure 3.4 *Trends in infant mortality: official versus survey-based estimates (Kazakhstan)* *(Source: Aleshina & Redmond, 2005).*

Note: The vertical lines indicate the 95% confidence interval.

What can be said about the validity of official infant or child mortality data in transition countries that have not carried out surveys that would allow a comparison, as is the case for the south-eastern European countries, the Baltic states and the Russian Federation? Others have examined the question in different ways. Kingkade and Sawyer (2001), for instance, checked for plausibility of the relative size of the components of infant mortality, based on comparisons with presumably correctly measured western European benchmarks. Aleshina and Redmond (2005) explored the possibility that deaths of infants who had almost reached their first birthday were incorrectly recorded as having occurred after it and were thus excluded from the infant mortality count. The overall, preliminary conclusion from such work is that there are credible indications that actual IMRs are understated in SEE and many CIS countries. There is no evidence that this is the case in Croatia, central Europe and the Baltic states.

Returning to the survey-based estimates, it is important to add that, where those data are available over time, it is not only the level of infant mortality that differs markedly from official data, but also the trend. For Kazakhstan the survey-based estimates point toward an increase in mortality rates between 1984–1989 and 1994–1999, while the official data suggest a decrease over the same period (see Figure 3.4). A similar picture emerges for Uzbekistan (Figure 3.5).

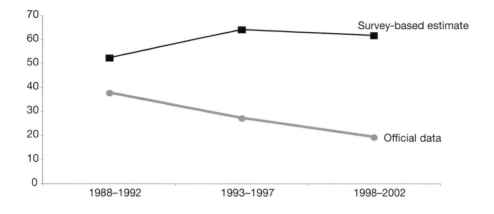

Figure 3.5 *Trends in infant mortality: official versus survey-based estimates (Uzbekistan) (Source: Analytical and Information Centre et al., 2004).*

Such basic data quality problems render an assessment of progress towards achieving the MDGs (as well as any policy evaluation) difficult, at least as far as this key indicator is concerned. Solving this critical information deficit should be high on the policy agenda. Otherwise, informed policy conclusions cannot be drawn. Improving the vital registration system is a basic prerequisite but may not be feasible in the short term. In the meantime, more use could be made of existing data through the application of advanced demographic techniques, in particular indirect estimation techniques. Such techniques are commonly used in other countries that suffer from deficiencies in their vital registration systems and enable estimation of time trends based on more than one data source (Feeney 1991).

Child malnutrition

In some countries, doubt about the low level of child mortality is at least partially substantiated by data on child malnutrition. Table 3.5 reports the most recent evidence on the prevalence of "stunting" (low weight for age) and "wasting" (low weight for height) in children under five years of age.

Stunting reflects long-term chronic malnutrition and develops over time. Wasting reflects a current nutritional crisis and can occur quickly. Both are affected by disease as well as food intake. Malnutrition reduces energy and mental concentration and increases health risks; it is thus a threat to child development and even survival.

WHO considers the severity of malnutrition as "high" when stunting prevalence reaches 30% and when wasting prevalence reaches 10%, although it stresses that these levels are arbitrary and that in a healthy, well-fed population one would expect figures of less than 3%.[17] Judged by these criteria, the levels of malnutrition among children in Albania, Tajikistan and Uzbekistan are of immediate public health concern. Kyrgyzstan, Turkmenistan and Ukraine are not far behind, with rates of stunting that are high compared to the rest of the Region and far above the 3% norm (with recent developments in Turkmenistan likely to have made the situation much worse than suggested by the available data (Rechel & McKee 2005)). Approximately one child in seven or eight is classified as stunted in Ukraine, the Russian Federation and Armenia, a higher rate than in Brazil and Turkey, but similar to that in China. The south-eastern European countries seem to fare better than the others for which data are available. Among these countries, only Croatia has managed to maintain child malnutrition at levels comparable to those in high-income countries (although the data for this country are somewhat out of date and may be slightly downward-biased as only children attending kindergarten are included).

Urban–rural differences in some countries, for example Kyrgyzstan, show how national averages can hide important problems at the subnational level, and in some cases, such as Uzbekistan, malnutrition rates were markedly lower in urban areas compared to rural ones. In contrast, progress in the reduction of malnutrition appears to have been slightly more favourable in the rural areas of Romania compared to its urban areas.

Micronutrient deficiencies

Poor intake of vitamins and minerals, collectively referred to as micronutrients, results in several poor health outcomes, all of which entail substantial economic costs over the short and long terms. For example, compromised growth and immune function is associated with vitamin A deficiency. Impaired mental development, lower educational achievement, and reduced work and reproductive capacity are among the consequences of iron and iodine deficiencies. These three micronutrients receive the most international attention at present because of their consequences for life and functioning and because programmes exist to effectively address these deficiencies at low cost. (Chapter 4, Table 4.10 describes the causes and consequences of each deficiency, highlighting the substantial costs associated with each.)

The recent global progress report on vitamin and mineral deficiency (UNICEF & The Micronutrient Initiative 2004) provides a comprehensive

---

17. A description of the WHO Global Database on Child Growth and Malnutrition is available at www.who.int/nutgrowthdb (accessed 30 December 2006).

Table 3.5 Child malnutrition: stunting and wasting (percentage of children under five years of age)

Region	Stunting (low height for age)			Wasting (low weight for height)		
	All	Urban	Rural	All	Urban	Rural
Central Asia						
Kazakhstan (1999)+	9.7	5.8	12.3	1.8	1.5	2.4
Kyrgyzstan (1997)+	24.8	14.8	27.7	3.4	4.3	3.2
Tajikistan (2003) [age 0.5–4.99]	36.2			4.7		
Turkmenistan (2000)+	22.3	19.5	24.1	5.7	6.6	5.2
Uzbekistan (2002)+	21.1	16.3	23.8	7.1	7.9	6.7
Caucasus						
Armenia (2005)+	13.0	14.0	11.5	5.1	6.0	3.7
Azerbaijan (2000)*	19.6	17.2	21.7	7.9	8.0	7.9
Azerbaijan (2001) [age 0.25–4.99]	13.3	10.6	15.9	2.4	2.7	2.0
Georgia (1999)*	11.7	9.6	13.9	2.3	2.1	2.5
Western CIS						
Republic of Moldova (2005)+	8.4	6.7	9.2	3.9	4.0	3.8
Russian Federation (1995)	12.7			3.9		
Ukraine (2000)*	15.4	14.0	18.6	6.4	6.6	5.9

South-eastern Europe

Albania (2000)*	31.7	23.8	36.7	11.1	11.9	10.6
Bosnia and Herzegovina*	9.7	10.0	9.1	6.3	6.7	6.1
Croatia (1995–1996) [age 1–5.99]	0.8			0.8		
Romania (2002)	10.1	9.5	8.7	2.3	1.8	2.0
Serbia and Montenegro (2000)*	5.1	4.2	6.3	3.7	3.6	3.9
TFYR Macedonia (1999)* [age 0.50–4.99]	6.9	5.8	8.4	3.6	3.5	3.6
World						
Brazil (1996)	10.5	7.8	19.0	5.7	4.6	9.2
Chile (2000)	14.2	2.9	20.2	2.2	1.8	2.4
China (2000)	14.2	2.9	20.2	2.2	1.8	2.4
Turkey (1998)	10.0	8.2	13.5	2.2	2.1	2.6
United States (1999–2002) [age 2–4.99]	1.1			0.4		

Sources: Data on countries marked with * are from UNICEF's (2006a) Multiple Indicator Cluster Surveys (MICS) (see www.childinfo.org/index2.htm, accessed 17 January 2007); Data from countries marked with + are from MEASURE DHS (National Statistical Service of the Ministry of Health, MEASURE DHS, 2006) and Republic of Moldova Ministry of Health and Social Protection, National Scientific and Applied Center for Preventive Medicine, MEASURE DHS (2006) (see www.measuredhs.com, accessed 11 January 2007); Data from Armenia and Republic of Moldova are based on preliminary DHS reports; Detailed sources of the remaining countries can be found in the WHO Global Child Growth and Malnutrition Database (WHO, 2006b) (see www.who.int/nutgrowthdb/, accessed 30 December 2006).

Notes: Stunting and wasting are defined as height for age and weight for height, respectively, below two standard deviations of the median in the international reference population adopted by WHO; The data for Serbia and Montenegro exclude information on the Province of Kosovo (Serbia); Data for Georgia are representative of 90% of the population; Data for Croatia refer to all children in kindergarten; Unless otherwise specified, data refer to the age group 0–4.99 years.

Table 3.6 *Prevalence of selected micronutrient deficiencies*

Country	Anaemia in children under 5 years (%)	Anaemia in women age 15–49 (%)	Number of children born mentally impaired	Total goitre rate (%)	Children under 6 with subclinical vitamin A deficiency (%)
Armenia	24	12	3 500	12	12
Azerbaijan	33	35	22 000	15	23
Georgia	33	31	11 000	21	11
Kazakhstan	49	36	54 000	21	19
Kyrgyzstan	42	31	23 500	21	18
Tajikistan	45	42	43 000	28	18
Turkmenistan	36	46	11 000	11	18
Uzbekistan	33	63	136 000	24	40
Bangladesh	55	36	750 000	18	28
Brazil	45	21	50 000	<5	15
China	8	21	940 000	5	12
Egypt	31	28	225 000	12	7
India	75	51	6 600 000	26	57
Indonesia	48	26	445 000	10	26
Iran (Islamic Republic of)	32	29	125 000	9	23
South Africa	37	26	160 000	16	33
Thailand	22	27	140 000	13	22
Turkey	23	33	335 000	23	18
Viet Nam	39	33	180 000	11	12

Source: UNICEF & The Micronutrient Initiative, 2004.

Note: Data are estimates based on latest available information.

overview of the prevalence of the effects of micronutrient deficiencies in 80 low- and middle-income countries, including some CEE-CIS countries. Table 3.6 presents data from the overview for the reviewed CEE-CIS countries, comparing them with other selected low- and middle-income countries. As the table shows, micronutrient deficiencies are affecting large numbers of the population – in particular children – of the CEE-CIS countries for which data were available. Also, estimated rates for these countries often compare unfavourably to those in several developing countries.

Malnutrition, in the form of undernutrition or micronutrient deficiencies, is thus a serious threat to the development of large numbers of children in everal parts of the Region. Yet it is important to note that this is not the only nutritional problem afflicting this Region. Overweight and obesity are also growing problems in a majority of these countries, albeit inadequately researched in most of the Region's poor countries. For example, the discussion (below) on inequality in health includes the fact that obesity already appears to be a greater problem than "thinness" in Uzbekistan. Rabin, Boehmer & Brownson (2006) shows that at least in those CEE countries for which data were available (the Czech Republic, the Baltic states, Hungary, Romania and the Russian Federation), adult obesity levels were above the western European average.

HIV/AIDS

The CEE-CIS Region is experiencing the world's fastest-growing HIV/AIDS epidemic. According to estimates by the Joint United Nations Programme on HIV/AIDS (UNAIDS), in 2006, 270 000 people in CEE-CIS became infected with HIV, bringing the number of people living with HIV/AIDS in the Region to approximately 1.7 million (UNAIDS & WHO 2006). While the rate of newly registered infections seemed to have stabilized after a steep increase in 2001, it increased again in 2005, compared to the two previous years.

Figure 3.6 illustrates how CEE-CIS as a whole "overtook" western Europe in the prevalence of people living with HIV/AIDS. The HIV/AIDS crisis in CEE-CIS has been extensively documented by others.[18]

The overwhelming majority of people living with HIV in this Region are young: 75% of the reported infections between 2000 and 2004 were in people under 30 (in western Europe the corresponding figure was 33%) (UNAIDS & WHO 2005).

The transmission patterns of the epidemics in several countries are changing, with sexually transmitted HIV cases comprising a growing share of new diagnoses. In 2004, 30% or more of all newly reported HIV infections in Kazakhstan and Ukraine, and 45% or more in Belarus and the Republic of Moldova, were due to unprotected sex. Increasing numbers of women are being infected, many of them acquiring HIV from male partners who became

---

18. See, for example, UNAIDS & WHO 2005; World Bank 2003a; World Bank 2004a; UNDP 2004; Novotny, Haazen & Adeyi 2004; Donoghoe, Lazarus & Matic 2005; Matic, Lazarus & Donoghoe 2006; Rhodes & Simic 2005; Kulis et al. 2004; Futures Group & Instituto Nacional de Salud Publica 2003; UNICEF 2001; Downs & Hamers 2003.

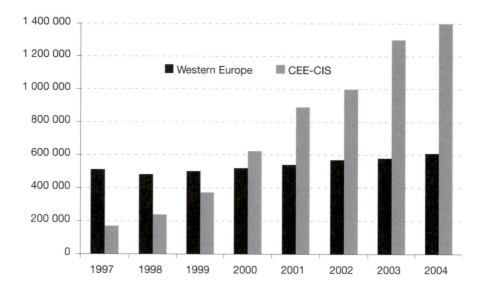

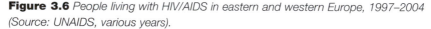

Figure 3.6 *People living with HIV/AIDS in eastern and western Europe, 1997–2004 (Source: UNAIDS, various years).*

Note: For details of country categories, see List of abbreviations; "Eastern Europe" corresponds to the CEE-CIS region; "Western Europe" comprises in this case Austria, Belgium, Denmark, Finland, France, Germany, Greece, Iceland, Ireland, Italy, Luxembourg, Malta, Netherlands, Norway, Portugal, Spain, Sweden, Switzerland and United Kingdom.

infected by injecting drugs. Until recently there was no evidence of HIV being spread to any significant extent among men who have sex with men (Downs & Hamers 2003), but recent evidence from the Russian Federation and Ukraine does document what might have simply been a hidden epidemic in this high-risk group, due to the social vulnerability of, and hence, secrecy adopted by homosexual and bisexual men (UNAIDS & WHO 2006).

The bulk of the people living with HIV in this Region are in the Russian Federation and Ukraine. Ukraine's epidemic continues to grow rapidly, while the Russian Federation has the largest epidemic of any country in Europe. Both epidemics have matured to the point where they pose massive challenges to prevention, treatment and care (Matic, Lazarus & Donoghoe 2006).

HIV has consolidated its presence in every part of the former USSR, with the seeming exception of Turkmenistan (although these data must be interpreted in the light of the secrecy maintained by the regime (Rechel & McKee 2005)); in 2004 UNAIDS estimated that the true prevalence of AIDS could be up to 0.2% of the population (UNAIDS Turkmenistan 2004). Several republics in central Asia and the Caucasus are experiencing the early stages of epidemics (Mounier et al. 2007), while in SEE relatively high levels of risky behaviour

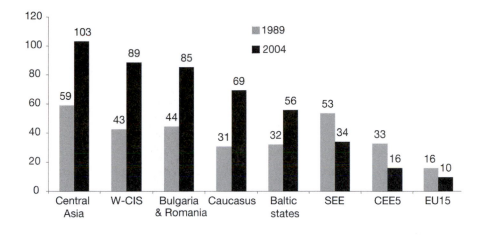

Figure 3.7 *Tuberculosis incidence 1989 and 2004 (per 100 000) (Source: WHO Regional Office for Europe, 2006).*

Note: For details of country categories, see List of abbreviations.

suggest that HIV could consolidate its presence unless prevention efforts are scaled up. Thus, while considerable uncertainty remains about the precise scale of the epidemic, on the basis of already-known levels of HIV prevalence, eastern Europe will soon be confronted with a major AIDS epidemic (UNAIDS & WHO 2005).

Tuberculosis

Tuberculosis (TB) re-emerged in the 1990s to reach alarming levels in the CEE-CIS Region after 40 years of steady decline. Figure 3.7 presents a snapshot by subregion. In five subregions, TB incidence in 2004 was approximately double that at the onset of transition. The comparatively wealthier countries (Bulgaria, Romania and the Baltic states) have not been spared. Progress has been achieved only in the south-eastern European and the five central European countries, with the latter approaching the still lower levels achieved by EU15 countries. The evolution of TB between the years 1989 and 2004 – not shown in Figure 3.7 – was one of steady increase in most countries, with only a relatively minor reversal in recent years.

TB is generally considered a "disease of the poor". It thrives in crowded conditions and thereby hits the poor hardest. People living in cramped housing, refugee camps and institutions such as prisons are most at risk. The poor also suffer more from malnutrition, which reduces resistance to disease, and they may in addition be less likely to seek prompt treatment, which increases the probability that they will infect others. A case-control study in the Russian Federation found the major contributors to the overall burden of TB to be poverty (including both a lack of assets and financial insecurity) and contact with a relative with the disease (Coker et al. 2006). TB can almost always be cured successfully by appropriate antibiotics. However, treatment takes several months, and if treatment is interrupted, the disease can become resistant to drugs in both the patients who experienced interrupted treatment and in those they infect.

"Multidrug-resistant" tuberculosis (MDR-TB) is much harder to treat, leading to many more deaths than would otherwise be the case. Treatment success rates for this type of TB fall as low as 20%, although this is in part due to the characteristics of the population affected. MDR-TB is at least 100 times more expensive to treat than non-MDR-TB. The countries of the former USSR as a whole have the world's highest burden of MDR-TB. Surveys of three oblasts in the Russian Federation found that between 5% and 9% of new cases of TB were MDR-TB. In contrast, between 1998 and 2001, multidrug resistance among new patients was under 1% in western and central Europe (14 countries) but 10% in the Baltic states (Lockman et al. 2001).

An additional reason for increased concern is the link between TB and HIV/AIDS. A person who is HIV-positive is much more likely to become ill with TB. Areas with high rates of TB in the Region tend to overlap areas with high HIV incidence, creating a dangerous interaction. Prisons in many of the newly independent states are breeding grounds for HIV-related TB and MDR-TB – a co-infection that is associated with a very high mortality rate. Thus, effective policy responses must address both these diseases simultaneously (Atun et al., in press).

Reasons for the re-emergence of TB are manifold. Economic recession, poverty, social upheaval, malnutrition, overcrowded prisons and increased homelessness have helped drive the alarming spread of TB in many parts of the Region. War and civil unrest in SEE, the Caucasus, Tajikistan and southern parts of the Russian Federation have hampered control of the disease and resulted in large numbers of internally displaced persons and refugees who are at high risk and who can carry the disease to other areas. However, the emergence of MDR-TB is more closely related to failings of health care systems. MDR-TB is primarily a consequence of inadequate or unsustained treatment. In many parts of the former USSR, TB is poorly managed, with many outdated or useless practices. This has been exacerbated by a deterioration in TB control infrastructures, a situation that parallels the re-emergence of other diseases, such as brucellosis in animals.

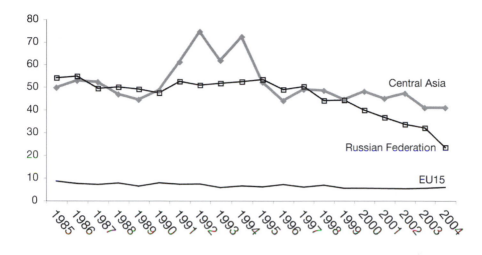

Figure 3.8 *Maternal mortality ratio per 100 000 live births, 1985–2004 (Source: WHO Regional Office for Europe, 2006).*

Reproductive health

CIS countries experienced rapid declines in natality in the 1990s. In the Russian Federation the number of births per woman fell from 2.02 in 1989 to only 1.2 in 2000, far below the replacement rate. This rate will have profound long-term consequences for many aspects of Russian society, ranging from future funding of pensions to national security, the latter due to reductions in the pool of potential recruits for the armed forces.

The most common measures for assessing a country's state of reproductive health are those that look at death rates among mothers and children. Infant mortality was discussed earlier in this chapter, so this section concentrates on maternal mortality, conventionally measured as the maternal mortality ratio – the number of maternal deaths per 100 000 live births in a given year. It includes all women who die as a result of childbearing, during pregnancy or within 42 days of delivery or termination of pregnancy, irrespective of the duration or site of the pregnancy, from any cause related to or aggravated by the pregnancy or its management, but not from accidental or incidental causes (see Figure 3.8).

Maternal mortality in the CIS countries is much lower than in developing countries although somewhat higher than in western Europe. An important issue specific to this Region arises from the widespread use of abortion as an alternative to contraception. In the Russian Federation, for example, around a quarter of maternal deaths are abortion related, and some estimates suggest that up to two thirds of abortion-related deaths there are due to procedures carried out illegally (Zhirova et al. 2004), raising questions about access to a service that is, in theory, legal and widely available. This also raises questions about the applicability in this Region of the denominator used to measure maternal mortality, which excludes abortions.

The remaining 75% of maternal deaths in the Russian Federation are a result of factors not related to abortion. Official statistics from the country suggest that about 15% of maternal deaths are due to haemorrhage and 10% to toxaemia (eclampsia), although other studies suggest that deaths from haemorrhage may account for the poor outcomes in those regions with the highest rates.

Despite the improvements that have occurred, and while the CEE-CIS Region performs relatively well compared to developing countries, recent research highlights the need for sustained action to address the many weaknesses in the area of reproductive health that go beyond the well-recognized issues of safe abortion and access to contraception. These include (1) the large differences in birth weight according to mother's socioeconomic status (Danishevski et al. 2005) – something that, if not addressed, will perpetuate inequalities into subsequent generations; and (2) the significant amount of ineffective and often harmful care, some of which results from the desire among health professionals to safeguard their incomes amid falling demand for their services (Danishevski et al. 2006).

Socioeconomic inequalities in health

While there are sufficient grounds for concern solely on the basis of the unfavourable overall health status, the unequal distribution of health and disease within countries is also worrying. As this section shows, the poor and socially disadvantaged are significantly worse off than the rich in terms of health outcomes, with the available evidence suggesting that the poor–rich gap is increasing in many places. This is relevant in the context of the overall message of this book. As is argued in more detail later, in much the same way that countries can improve their level of economic development by improving health, so can individuals better their material living standards through health improvement.

This section reviews existing evidence on socioeconomic inequalities in health and disease[19] and reports selected results from new work[20] undertaken specif-

---

19. For a more extensive review of evidence on socioeconomic inequalities in (adult) health and health care access, see Walters and Suhrcke (2005).

20. See Suhrcke et al. (2007).

ically to inform this book. Some evidence on socioeconomic inequalities in the proximate risk factors is also presented. Differences in risky lifestyles go only part of the way to explaining socioeconomic gradients in health or disease. This is partly because the evidence on the precise socioeconomic distribution of some of the risk factors more recently identified as important (obesity, for example) is less straightforward than in the case of health outcomes. Beyond this, the observed socioeconomic differences in lifestyles themselves say nothing about what is driving the different lifestyles adopted by different socioeconomic groups. In other words, it is important to recognize the often severe constraints that condition individuals to make unhealthy choices.

The poor are generally worse off in terms of health than the rich.

This conclusion is reached by most studies that have tried to disaggregate health outcomes by income (or socioeconomic status) in the CEE-CIS Region. The size of rich–poor differences varies according to the indicators selected to measure both health and socioeconomic status. Self-reported health has been the most widely used health indicator in studies of inequalities, with mortality (or life expectancy) studied far less often, primarily because of problems in accessing appropriate data.

Figure 3.9 and Figure 3.10 present information on the distribution of health and CVDs in the most and least deprived quintiles in the eight CIS countries that participated in the LLH survey. People in the richest quintile are significantly more likely to report being in "good" or "quite good" health, compared to those in the poorest quintile. The rich are also far less likely to have had CVDs compared to the most disadvantaged quintile. Although not shown in the figures, there is a fairly consistent socioeconomic gradient across all five quintiles in both cases. As the survey did not gather specific information on individual or household income (recognizing the difficulties involved in economies where transactions are monetized to varying degrees), a deprivation indicator was constructed capturing various dimensions of socioeconomic status. The quintiles are based on this indicator.

Debate is ongoing about the interpretation of self-reported health data from different socioeconomic groups. Some studies find that the poor report being in better health than the rich, which is generally attributed to both inferior knowledge among the poor about their health situation and better access to diagnosis by the rich. In Figure 3.9 and Figure 3.10, no such counterintuitive pattern appears for the eight CIS countries. This could be due to the generally high level of education and the attendant generally high capacity to judge one's health status. Other data from transition countries do, however, show counterintuitive patterns of socioeconomic distribution of chronic illness, for

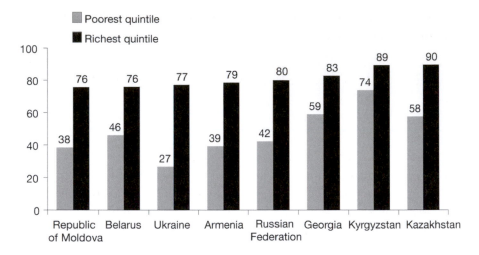

Figure 3.9 *Reported "good" or "quite good" health, 2001 (percentages) (Source: Suhrcke et al., forthcoming, 2007).*

Notes: To disaggregate the health (and other) indicators, a deprivation index was constructed, using a combination of assets and subjective assessment of the respondents (see, for example, Betti & Verma (1999) and the official adoption by EUROSTAT in 2002 (EUROSTAT, 2002)); The full set of indicators is "summarized" into a composite index, ranging from 0 (no deprivation) to 1 (maximum deprivation); Breakpoints are then identified to split the population into quintiles (five groups of equal size) running from poorest to richest. Details are in Suhrcke et al. (forthcoming, 2007).

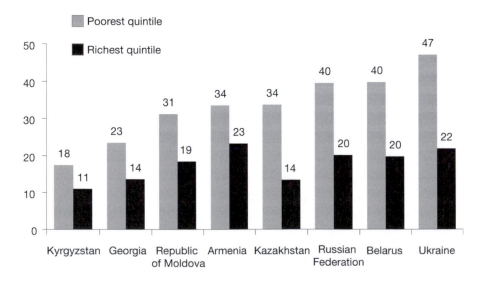

Figure 3.10 *Reported cardiovascular disease incidence (percentages), 2001 (Source: Suhrcke et al., forthcoming, 2007).*

Note: See notes to Figure 3.9.

example in Armenia in 1998/1999 and Albania in 2002 (World Bank 2002a and 2003b respectively).

What limited information is available on the socioeconomic distribution of child health indicators in CEE-CIS largely comes from the World Bank's poverty and health country reports. Figure 3.11 and Figure 3.12 show data on child mortality and stunting among children, disaggregated by wealth (or asset) quintile, in three countries from central Asia and one from the Caucasus.[21] As expected, children in the wealthiest quintile uniformly experience far lower levels of mortality and stunting. Child mortality is fairly linear, while stunting shows evidence of a threshold effect, with stunting levels comparatively similar across the three richest quintiles, but rising disproportionately in the two poorest ones. This suggests that a certain minimum level of wealth may have to be reached for individuals or households to be able to "escape" malnutrition.

Given the sharp increase in income inequality during most of the 1990s, the health gap between those at the top and at the bottom of the income ladder has likely widened. Unfortunately, longitudinal data to test this hypothesis directly remain scarce.

One exception to the above statement on data availability is a prospective cohort study of two cohorts of men in St Petersburg (Plavinski, Plavinskaya & Klimov 2003). The first cohort (from the St Petersburg component of the Russian Lipid Research Clinics Study) was followed up for 18 years from 1974 and the second for 11.2 years from 1985. A comparison of the two cohorts found that men with the lowest level of education experienced a significant increase in premature mortality risk over the period but that there was no recorded increase in mortality in university graduates.

In Estonia, Leinsalu, Vågerö & Kunst (2003) compared two census-based analyses of individual cause-specific death data from 1987–1990 and 1999–2000. Echoing the findings reported above in the Russian Federation, they noted that educational differentials in all-cause mortality increased during the 1990s, as life expectancy improved for graduates but worsened for those with the lowest educational status. By 2000 male graduates had a life expectancy 13.1 years longer than the least educated; among females the gap was 8.6 years.

The evolution of life expectancy by educational level was recently examined for Finland, the Czech Republic, the Russian Federation and Estonia for the

---

21. The World Bank uses DHS survey data. Like the LLH data presented in Figure 3.9 and Figure 3.10, the DHS data do not cover income, so a wealth proxy had to be constructed. For details see the "Poverty and Health" section of the World Bank's web site at www.world-bank.org/poverty/health/index.htm (accessed 17 January 2007).

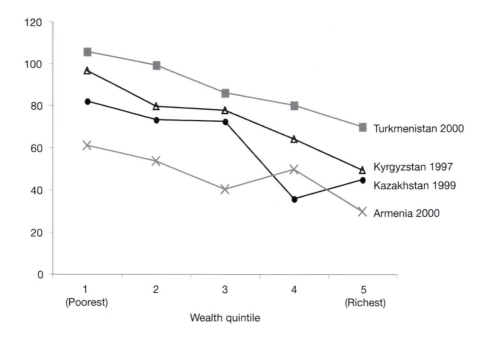

Figure 3.11 *Under-five mortality rate (per 1000 live births) by wealth quintile (Sources: World Bank, 2000b; World Bank, 2004b).*

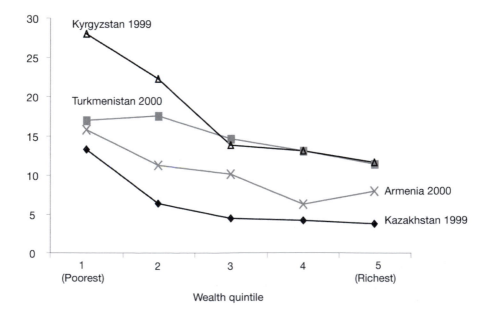

Figure 3.12 *Percentage of children moderately stunted, by wealth quintile (Sources: World Bank, 2000b; World Bank, 2004b).*

Table 3.7 *Income levels and use of vodka, cognac, liqueurs and other spirits in the Russian Federation, by consumption quintiles (percentages), 2003*

Consumption	1 (poorest quintile)	2	3	4	5 (richest quintile)
Practically every day	40	22	13	13	12
Several times a week	31	19	19	17	14

Source: National Survey of Household Welfare and Program Participation (NOBUS), in World Bank, 2004c.

years 1988/1989 and 1998/1999 (Shkolnikov et al. 2006). In the former two countries, improvements were seen in all (three) educational groups, with only a slight widening of educational differences. By contrast, in the Russian Federation and Estonia, less favourable average life expectancy trends coincided with a dramatic widening of the life expectancy gap between those with the highest education (whose life expectancy remained about constant) and those with the lowest education (whose life expectancy declined). An additional contribution of this study – one often neglected in other studies – is that the authors assessed the changes in the relative size of the different educational groups in each of the four countries. This is important, because it is not only the difference in life expectancy between educational groups that matters, but also the size of each group. Since the share of people in middle and higher education had increased more in Estonia and the Russian Federation than in Finland and the Czech Republic, the overall life expectancy decrease proved less dramatic in the former two countries than it would have been had the shares remained constant.

A combination of proximate and distal factors (that vary across countries and time) explains why the poor are in worse health than the rich.

Research in western European countries has established that social inequalities in health are driven, primarily, by a combination of socioeconomic circumstances and lifestyles, with the latter often shaped by the former. The consequences of these factors are modulated by the ability, or lack thereof, of health systems to compensate for these differences. There is much to suggest that, during the course of transition, these inequalities increased in several countries, even if data comparing inequalities between different points in time are rare. Table 3.7 provides evidence of socioeconomic differences in lifestyle-related risk factors. Inequities in the health system are discussed later.

Overall, the poor tend to display less healthy lifestyles than the rich. However, the pattern is not always clear-cut, and the existence of a relationship says little about what drives the worse health habits of the poor.

As far as smoking and heavy alcohol consumption are concerned, most (but not all) studies find an inverse relationship between unhealthy behaviour and socioeconomic status (Walters & Suhrcke 2005). Table 3.7 gives an example from the Russian Federation, showing that people in the poorest income quintile consume alcohol much more heavily than those in the richer ones.

For over- and undernutrition, the pattern seems more mixed, both in the adjusted and unadjusted comparisons. Recent studies have focused on the question of nutrition as a factor underlying socioeconomic differentials in noncommunicable disease in the Region. The RLMS administered 24-hour diet recall sheets and measured height and weight, providing a (for the CEE-CIS Region unique) longitudinal data series with which to monitor trends in nutrition since 1992. This period saw great change in dietary habits, with both a reduction in the share of the household budget on foodstuffs in the Russian Federation and a change in the food market through the impact of economic liberalization. Available evidence suggests a rising incidence of both undernutrition and obesity, with obesity being associated with both poverty and higher economic status, and trends in undernutrition especially worrying among the very young and old.[22]

In Azerbaijan the 2001 Household Budget Survey showed that there were important distinctions in the way either over- or undernutrition was linked to socioeconomic status. (Obese is defined as having a body mass index of 30 kg/m^2 or over while pre-obese/overweight is having a body mass index of 25–29.9 kg/m^2.) Figure 3.13 indicates that a higher proportion of the richest quintile (defined in terms of consumption) is classified as obese or overweight/pre-obese than in the poorer groups but that malnutrition is higher among the poorest groups (World Bank 2003b).

A cross-sectional study on the epidemiology of cardiovascular risk factors in Tirana, Albania (McKee, Shapo & Pomerleau 2004), found that while overall there was a worrying trend towards low levels of physical exercise in leisure time, this did not seem to vary by socioeconomic status as measured by either education or income.

Little attention has been paid to obesity in central Asian countries, possibly because of the (incorrect) assumption that if there is a nutritional challenge it

---

22. On obesity and malnutrition in the Russian Federation see for example Jahns, Baturin & Popkin (2003); Wang (2001); and Carlson (2001), cited in Walters & Suhrcke (2005).

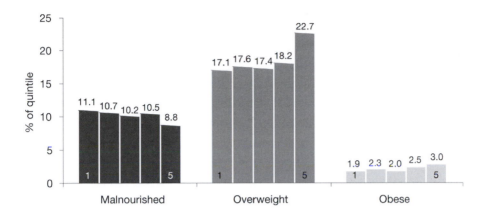

Figure 3.13 *Nutritional status among adults by consumption in Azerbaijan, from poorest to richest quintiles, 2001 (Source: Azerbaijan household budget survey 2001, as reported in World Bank, 2003b).*

concerns exclusively malnutrition. Most surveys in the Region thus far have focused on undernutrition rather than "overnutrition". The 2002 Health Examination Survey in Uzbekistan (Analytical and Information Centre et al. 2004) is an exception and demonstrates the scale of this hitherto neglected phenomenon. A staggering 31% of men and 28% of women (both aged 15–59) were found to be overweight or obese. In the case of women it is even possible to trace the recent evolution, having occurred since 1996: obesity has increased by six percentage points in a decade. Comparison of the socio-economic distribution of obesity/overweight with that of an indicator of undernutrition (having a body mass index below 18.5 kg/m2) provides an important insight (Figure 3.14).

While undernutrition follows the typical gradient in which the less educated are far more undernourished than the more educated, exactly the reverse picture is observed in the distribution of overnutrition: the higher the educational attainment, the greater the share of overweight/obese people. (While obesity/overweight prevalence increased between 1996 and 2002, the share of thin women decreased from 11% to 6%.) This picture is consistent with the experience of other countries where, during the course of economic development, "new" risk factors were first taken up predominantly by the rich and socially advantaged and then the pattern reversed (Monteiro et al. 2004; Lock et al. 2005).

The picture as it relates to obesity is therefore not straightforward, with reports of a clear positive association with wealth in some countries (the richer the more obese) and in others a U-shaped relationship with both the poor and the

Uzbek women age 15–49

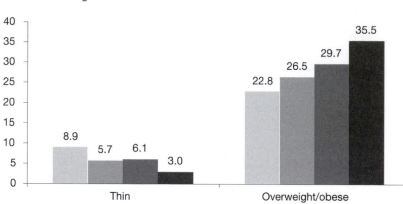

Uzbek men age 15–59

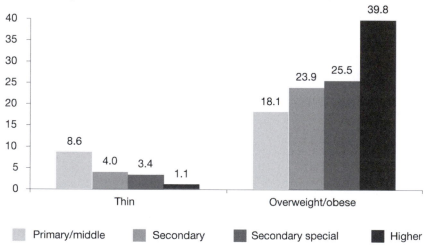

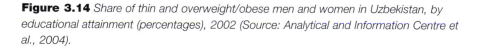

Figure 3.14 *Share of thin and overweight/obese men and women in Uzbekistan, by educational attainment (percentages), 2002 (Source: Analytical and Information Centre et al., 2004).*

rich at higher risk. The picture relating to malnutrition is linear, with poor and vulnerable groups at greater risk.

In summary, this section has shown that not only does the average level of health leave much room for improvement in the Region, but also the within-country differences in health are unduly large, with socially disadvantaged groups lagging significantly behind the wealthier ones. This characteristic applies to both adult and child health indicators. Where evidence on trends over time is available, it suggests an increase in socioeconomic inequalities in health throughout the transition period. While poor health outcomes tend to be concentrated among the poor, the socioeconomic distribution of risk factors can be more complex than is commonly assumed, especially for the emerging challenge of obesity. It appears to "enter" a population's higher socioeconomic groups first and then shift disproportionately toward the poor, a phenomenon also observed in other low- and middle-income countries.

Health policy efforts to date: domestic and international

If the health situation is as unfavourable as described above, this in itself may be an indication of insufficient health policy efforts during transition and thus far. This conclusion is particularly justified where those types of diseases that a developed health care system should be able to keep under control have spread or re-emerged, as is the case with TB, diphtheria and malaria. If these diseases cannot be prevented, the health care system should at the very least be positioned to avoid their attendant deaths. Mortality from these "avoidable causes" has stagnated or increased in some CIS countries, while steadily declining in western Europe (see Chapter 5, Subsection "Immediate causes of disability and death").

Leaving the epidemiological evidence to other parts of this book, this section focuses on more direct indicators of both domestic and international health policy efforts. The overall purpose is to illustrate the scope for improvement not only in health but also in health policy. The issue is explored on four dimensions: (1) the level and pattern of health expenditures; (2) inequities introduced through the health system; (3) the support for health from the international community via official development assistance; and (4) the roles of health and of the main health challenges in the national Poverty Reduction Strategy Papers.

Health expenditure

This section assesses the level of "effort" devoted to health by looking at recent data on national health expenditures. Taken literally, health expenditures capture only the intensity of monetary effort dedicated to the health *system*, not to health in general. In principle, governments may undertake a wide range of measures that benefit health but go unnoticed in health expenditure data. Despite these concerns, given the lack of more appropriate data, the underlying assumption in the evidence presented in this section is that health expenditures do serve as a valid proxy for the wider efforts dedicated to health.

After assessing how much countries in CEE-CIS spend on their health systems

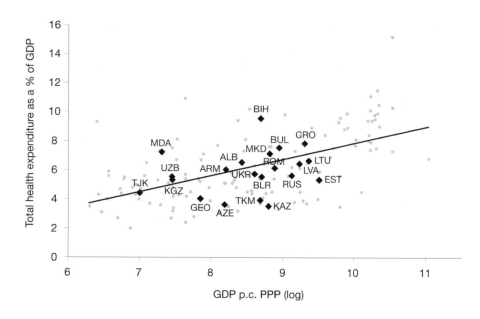

Figure 3.15 *Total health expenditure as a percentage of GDP versus GDP per capita, 2003 (Source: WHO, 2006a).*

Note: For details of country name abbreviations, see List of abbreviations.

and how they spend it, this section uses the assessment results to examine whether there are obvious indications that some countries are spending "too little" on the health system. It then discusses the scope for increasing health expenditures, especially in those countries that appear to have the greatest need to scale up resources.

CEE-CIS health expenditure from a global perspective

This section describes what the CEE-CIS countries spend on health and locates their levels and patterns of health expenditure within the global picture. Simple comparisons and linear regression analyses are used to gauge the adequacy of spending and the distribution of the financial burden between public and private sources.[23]

Several CEE-CIS countries spend less on health than would be expected given their level of economic development.

Figure 3.15 illustrates the worldwide distribution of the shares of health expenditure in GDP in relation to national GDP per capita. The linear

---

23. For an in-depth treatment of a greater range of health financing issues, see Gottret & Schieber (2006).

regression line indicates the share of total national health expenditure observed on average in a country at each level of per-capita income. Around the average trend, however, there is much variation, both in poor and rich countries. Within the CEE-CIS countries, health spending also varied substantially in 2003, from 3.5% of GDP in Kazakhstan to 9.6% in Serbia and Montenegro. Apart from a number of south-eastern European countries, the majority of the CEE-CIS countries are located below the regression line, suggesting that these countries spend less than other countries at similar levels of economic development.

From an equity perspective the ways in which total expenditures are financed are key. The cross-country evidence shows that financing occurs in a way that conflicts with equity objectives, particularly in a number of CEE-CIS countries.

Because of its consequences for financial risk, the key distinction in comparing patterns of health spending is between prepayment in all its forms and payment out of pocket at the time of service.[24] Small out-of-pocket (OOP) costs are harmless for all but the poorest users. High-cost spending, however, should be covered by prepayment to avoid the risk of either impoverishment or foregoing needed care. Since the poorer a person is, the lower the threshold for catastrophic expenses,[25] the OOP share should be lower in poorer countries. However, exactly the opposite occurs: at low incomes, the average OOP share is high and extremely variable (Figure 3.16). The average share of OOP payments in CEE-CIS equals 42.4%, varying between 79.2% in Tajikistan and 15.5% in The former Yugoslav Republic of Macedonia. Many CEE-CIS countries display a higher share of OOP payments than other countries with similar per-capita incomes. This phenomenon leaves many near-poor households highly exposed to the risk of impoverishing health expenses (Wagstaff & Claeson 2004). (The Subsection "Inequity in the health system: when the health system makes things worse" details the impoverishing impact of health expenditures in CEE-CIS and the impact of informal payments for health care on health care access.)

A comparatively high share of total health expenditure is paid privately at the point of service in the majority of CEE-CIS countries, implying that a comparatively low share of health expenditure is financed from public sources, despite the formal role of governments in providing universal access to health

---

24. In principle prepayment can also occur via private insurance. In practice, however, in particular in low- and middle-income countries, private expenditure is almost entirely made up of out-of-pocket (OOP) payments. See Musgrove, Zeramdini & Carrin (2002).

25. Catastrophic expenditures are defined as those extreme expenses that affect households' ability to maintain their consumption of basic items (Wagstaff & van Doorslaer 2001).

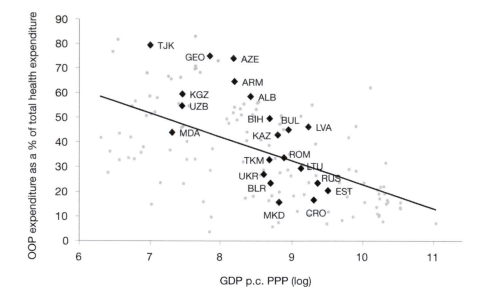

Figure 3.16 *Out-of-pocket expenditure as a percentage of total health expenditure versus GDP per capita, 2003 (Source: WHO, 2006a).*

Note: For details of country name abbreviations, see List of abbreviations; GDP: gross domestic product; PPP: purchasing power parity.

care. As with the share of total health expenditure in GDP, the share of health expenditure that is public is also increasing as countries grow richer. In this case the relationship is steeper and the overall fit of the regression much improved. Not surprisingly, most CEE-CIS countries again show lower shares of public health expenditure than other countries at similar levels of economic development (information not reported here but available on request).

Some CEE-CIS countries display absolute levels of public health expenditure that make it hard to imagine that governments can possibly provide even the basics of an essential package of preventive and curative health care services to the entire population. Low shares of GDP devoted to health by governments in comparatively poor countries translate into low per-capita US dollar amounts (see the bars in Figure 3.17).

In principle, it would be desirable to specify the minimum level of resources necessary to operate a basic health system that provides essential interventions to a population. Determining such level is, however, fraught with difficulties and subject to many assumptions. Two recent attempts to produce such an estimate were made by the CMH and WHO. Despite the difficulties involved, it is reassuring to see that both converge to a surprisingly similar dollar estimate: about US$ 80, in international dollars, per capita per year.

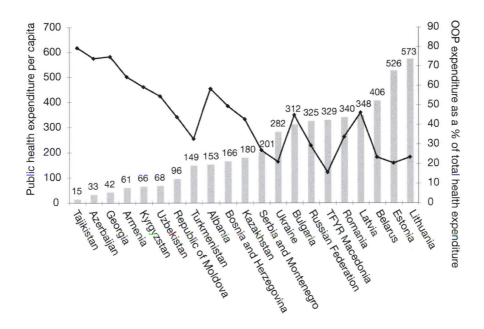

Figure 3.17 *Public health expenditure per capita and out-of-pocket expenditure as a percentage of total health expenditure, selected CEE-CIS countries, 2002 (Source: WHO, 2006a).*

Note: OOP: out-of-pocket.

The CMH calculated that a minimum total health expenditure of US$ 34 per person per year by 2007 (and US$ 38 by 2015) would be necessary to provide a package of essential health interventions. After adjusting for PPP, this equals approximately international US$ 80 per capita per year. However, this amount can only be a rough estimate, since the cost of providing a package of essential health services in a specific country will also depend on the costs of inputs, such as health care provider incomes, which will be higher in countries with higher incomes. The CMH has not applied its estimates to the specific health and socioeconomic context of the CEE-CIS Region. There is good reason to believe that an appropriate package of essential interventions would exceed the US$ 80 benchmark, given the (on average) higher development level, more complex health problems and more costly inputs.

WHO used a somewhat different approach to try to find a minimum expenditure threshold by looking for changes in the slope or shape of the relationship between health expenditure and health outcomes, as measured by disability-adjusted life expectancy (Evans et al. 2000). Countries spending less than US$ 80 per person per year appear to achieve less of their potential for health than do countries that spend more. However, it is not clear that this is due to low spending as such, rather than the effects of the AIDS epidemic and the general problems of war and poor government that afflict many of the poorest countries.

Despite the limitations of these estimates, the actual level of public expenditures observed in several CEE-CIS countries raises serious doubts as to whether a basic health system can be maintained or even exist. Judged against the US$ 80 benchmark, Tajikistan, Azerbaijan, Georgia, Armenia, Kyrgyzstan, Uzbekistan and the Republic of Moldova in particular are likely to be facing the most severe resource constraints (see Figure 3.17). Where the public system is on its knees, health care users have to rely upon informal private payment (Balabanova et al. 2004): the same set of countries also displays the highest share of OOP payments as a proportion of total health expenditures. This in turn further reinforces the demand for OOP payments. Thus, the scarcity of public resources available to the health system exposes the poor and vulnerable to a greater risk of falling deeper into poverty when they need health care services. This is the "medical poverty trap" that Whitehead, Dahlgren & Evans (2001) described.

In conclusion, at least in some cases the specific health and socioeconomic context of the CEE-CIS Region may well require more resources to be able to adequately respond to the health needs of its population. The following section takes a different approach to evaluate the appropriateness of a given level of health expenditure.

Are the CEE-CIS countries spending too little?

Despite the attempts described in the previous section, determining the minimum level of expenditures needed to maintain a basic health system, however er defined, remains highly problematic. It is also likely that the needed level increases with the country's level of economic development, as inputs become more expensive and many health challenges become more complex and costly. The production frontier methodology proposed in this section approaches the question of whether countries are spending too little from a different, complementary (albeit limited) perspective, by asking what the best performers (in terms of the health outcomes they achieve) at varying levels of development actually do spend.

The production frontier methodology has been used in various ways to assess health system efficiency at different levels.[26] Production frontiers have also been

---

26. See, for example, Anderson & Poullier, 1999; Anell & Willis, 2000; Musgrove, 1996; OECD, 1992; OECD 1994; Schieber, Poullier & Greenwald, 1991; Wagstaff, 1989.

used to assess the overall performance of a country in terms of its achievement of good health outcomes (see, for example, Wang et al. (1999)). WHO (2000) used production frontiers to rank the performance of health systems in different countries using the relationship between health expenditure and three outcome indicators: financial fairness, patient responsiveness and outcomes. The approach was also used to estimate the global expenditure gap for the CMH.

The specific approach applied here follows the work of Preker, Langenbrunner & Suzuki (2002), who calculated the global expenditure gap to achieve the health-related MDG targets. As the present exercise is meant to be more illustrative than definitive, the focus is limited to three health indicators: female adult mortality, male adult mortality and under-five mortality. The inclusion of adult mortality in the set of health indicators is a deliberate departure from common assessments of MDG resource needs and is driven by the recognition that adult health should be considered an integral health target in the Region. The present exercise also differs from Preker, Langenbrunner & Suzuki (2002) in the use of more recent data. The expenditure gap must be calculated for each of the three health outcomes. (For the methodological details see the description in the Annex to Chapter 3.)

The decision about which sample of countries to consider in identifying the "best performers" is ultimately somewhat arbitrary. It depends at least in part on what the countries concerned consider as their appropriate benchmark. Two options are pursued here, and the precise choice inevitably affects the size of the expenditure gap estimate: (1) the full set of worldwide countries (n=192) (results of which are given in Table A3.2 in the Annexes) and (2) as in Preker, Langenbrunner & Suzuki (2002), only the low- and middle-income countries (n=144). So, overall there are six (= 3 health indicators x 2 options) estimates for the expenditure gap in each country. Out of both samples a subsample of the best performing 20% of countries – that is, those with the lowest mortality rates – was chosen. The functional form that describes the relationship between per-capita income and health expenditure per capita among these best performers represents the production frontier for all remaining countries (Figure 3.18). The specific functional form used here follows the one proposed by Preker, Langenbrunner & Suzuki (2002).

As illustrated in Figure 3.18, the expenditure gap for each country is equal to the vertical distance (meaning amount per capita of public health expenditure) between the frontier and the co-ordinates of the country in question. For those countries at or above the frontier (i.e., the regression line), the expenditure gap is set equal to zero. A key assumption of the method is that although countries that are already spending much more than the best performers at similar income levels may still benefit from additional spending, there is likely to be

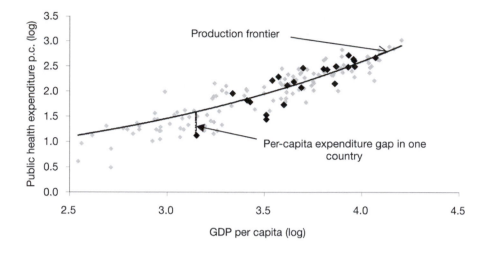

Figure 3.18 *Production frontier approach (low- and middle-income countries), based on male adult mortality, 2002 (Source: Authors' calculations).*

Notes: The production frontier is the regression line that results from a regression in a sample of 20% of the countries that are the best performers in the entire sample; Black diamonds represent CEE-CIS countries; Only countries located below the line are considered to have an expenditure gap according to the definition of the production frontier method; p.c.: per capita; GDP: gross domestic product.

considerable scope for improving the efficiency of their existing spending, since other countries are able to do much better with fewer resources.

As Figure 3.18 shows, the picture for CEE-CIS is mixed; some countries are above and some below the production frontier. Table 3.8 gives the per-capita expenditure gaps for the CEE-CIS countries as derived from Figure 3.18, that is, based on the sample of low- and middle-income countries. (Not surprisingly, if a worldwide sample of countries is used, then the production frontier shifts upwards, leaving more CEE-CIS countries below the frontier, suggesting that more CEE-CIS countries would be spending, relatively, even less. See Table A3.2 in the Annexes.)

The findings from Table 3.8 can be summarized as follows. There is an expenditure gap in 12 of the 22 CEE-CIS countries considered. (The number rises to 19 with a worldwide sample.) Within each of the 12 countries, the magnitude of the gap is broadly similar for all three health indicators. The presence and size of the gap do not appear to be linked to a country's level of economic development. Thus, there is an expenditure gap in relatively advanced countries such as the Baltic states but, for instance, no gap in the much less wealthy Republic of Moldova. As a share of actual per-capita health expenditures, the greatest level of underspending seems to occur in Tajikistan, but in Armenia,

Table 3.8 *Expenditure gap for low- and middle-income country sample (in US$)*

Region	Female adult mortality	Male adult mortality	Under-5 mortality	Public health expenditure per capita
Baltic states				
Estonia	91	28	25	461
Latvia	53	33	50	306
Lithuania	–	–	–	399
South-eastern Europe				
Albania	17	28	55	117
Bosnia and Herzegovina	–	–	–	161
Bulgaria	–	–	–	267
Croatia	–	–	–	513
Romania	–	–	–	309
Serbia and Montenegro	–	–	–	191
TFYR Macedonia	–	–	–	189
Western Commonwealth of Independent States				
Belarus	–	–	–	430
Republic of Moldova	–	–	–	88
Russian Federation	17	5	26	298
Ukraine	–	–	6	150
Caucasus				
Armenia	48	60	85	53
Azerbaijan	50	62	84	27
Georgia	–	–	–	–
Central Asia				
Kazakhstan	106	105	131	139
Kyrgyzstan	1	12	32	60
Tajikistan	17	25	39	13
Turkmenistan			15	129
Uzbekistan		4	24	65
Average (population weighted)	15.7	11.6	26.6	229

Source: Authors' calculations.

Note: While this exercise uses 2003 health data, it imploys expenditure data lagged by one year to allow at least a short time for the expenditure to have an effect on health outcomes.

Azerbaijan and Georgia, too, the gaps exceed the actual levels of public health expenditure.

Taken together, the total expenditure gap for all 22 countries varies between almost US$ 3.8 billion and US$ 8.8 billion if the low- and middle-income countries are used as the benchmark (and between approximately US$ 2 billion and US$ 30.4 billion if the worldwide sample is used). The total expenditure gap results for both versions of the exercise are shown in Table A3.3 and Table A3.4 in the Annexes.

In interpreting the results presented in this section, the limitations of the production frontier approach should be kept in mind. The approach does not provide any insights into the potential impact of additional spending, unlike work that uses elasticities of health spending and outcomes (Chapter 5 includes an exercise of this kind). The countries currently "underspending" could potentially increase their spending up to and even beyond the frontier without actually improving health outcomes. Likewise, it is plausible that countries that have no obvious expenditure gap might nevertheless benefit from extra spending, especially where a large part of the existing health infrastructure has become obsolete.

If, however, an expenditure gap does exist, as suggested by these analyses for at least a subset of these countries, the question arises as to how it can and should be filled. This question is addressed in the following subsection, "Scope for increasing CEE-CIS health spending: financing the expenditure gap".

Scope for increasing CEE-CIS health spending: financing the expenditure gap

The previous section showed that, in several but not all of the CEE-CIS countries, significant scope may exist for scaling up resources for the health system. A detailed, country-specific assessment of the "fiscal space" (discussed in Box 3.1 in general terms) is beyond the scope of this book.[27] This section examines the determinants of health expenditures in the Region, important because knowledge of the drivers of underspending helps target policy action aimed at overcoming deficits in those countries where they are present.

The proportion of public heath expenditure as a share of GDP can be low

---

27. To date there has been very little explicit analysis of fiscal space in CEE-CIS countries, be it for general expenditure purposes or specifically for health. A recent exception, with some focus on health, is the recent World Bank Public Finance Review of Ukraine, which covers health among other issues, highlighting in particular the potential for creating more fiscal space by improving allocative efficiency in the health sector (World Bank 2006a). For an application of fiscal space to infrastructure investment in SEE, see World Bank (2006b).

Box 3.1 Fiscal space

The question as to what scope exists for increasing expenditures in the CEE-CIS countries is ultimately a question about the availability of "fiscal space". In its broadest sense, fiscal space is defined as the availability of budgetary capacity that allows a government to provide resources for a desired purpose, recognizing the need for sustainability of that government's financial position. In creating fiscal space, additional resources can be made available for some form of meritorious government spending, such as, in the present case, increased health expenditure. The incentive for creating fiscal space is strengthened where the resulting fiscal outlay would boost medium-term growth and perhaps even pay for itself in terms of future fiscal revenue. If health expenditures improve health and if health in turn improves economic growth prospects, then this concept might be applicable here. In addition, considerations of fiscal sustainability recognize that with growth governments will gain additional fiscal resources. As described in Chapter 2, many CEE-CIS countries are currently realizing remarkable rates of economic growth, even if such growth may not prove sustainable.

In principle, there are different ways for a government to create fiscal space. Additional revenue can be raised through tax measures or by strengthening tax administration. Lower priority expenditures can be cut to make room for more desirable ones. Resources can be borrowed, either from domestic or external sources. Governments can use their power of seignorage (that is, having the country's central bank print money to lend to the government). Finally, governments may receive grants from external sources.

Explicit in the definition of fiscal space is the link to the concept of fiscal sustainability. This relates to the capacity of a government, at least in the future, to finance its desired expenditure programmes, to service any debt obligations (including those that may arise if the created fiscal space exists as a result of government borrowing) and to ensure its solvency. The link to fiscal sustainability has a number of implications.

First, it suggests that exploitation of fiscal space requires a judgment that the higher expenditure in the short term, and any associated future expenditures, can be financed from current and future revenues. Second, sustainability requires forcing attention on the medium-term implications of the spending programmes for which fiscal space is created in a given year. Third, as the previous point suggests, any consideration of fiscal space must be made in the context of at least a medium-term expenditure framework that involves a comprehensive perspective on the government's expenditure priorities.

Judgments on fiscal space are inherently country specific, requiring detailed assessments of a government's initial fiscal position, its revenue and expenditure structure, the characteristics of its outstanding debt obligations, the underlying structure of its economy, the prospects for enhanced external resource inflows and a perspective on the underlying external conditions facing an economy.

Sources: Heller, 2005; Gottret & Schieber, 2006; Hay, 2003.

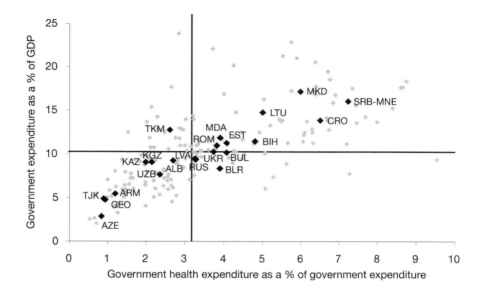

Figure 3.19 *Government health expenditure as a percentage of government expenditure versus government expenditure as a percentage of GDP, 2003 (Source: WHO, 2006a).*

Note: For details of country name abbreviations, see List of abbreviations

because total public expenditure (as a share of GDP) is low, because the share of public expenditure devoted to health (out of total public expenditures) is low, or both. In other words, there are two basic, not mutually exclusive strategies to improve the expenditure situation: increasing the overall size of government expenditures and/or increasing the share of public funds that is allocated to health.

Figure 3.19 juxtaposes the two variables for a worldwide set of countries, with the CEE-CIS countries marked in black. The vertical and horizontal lines that split the figure into four quadrants are located at the mean of both variables. Countries in the upper right quadrant are characterized by both a relatively high share of government health expenditure as a proportion of total government expenditure *and* a high overall share of government expenditure as a proportion of GDP. Countries located in the lower left quadrant are characterized by comparatively low values for both indicators. Those CEE-CIS countries that were found to be underspending according to the production frontier exercise are all located in the lower left quadrant, while most of the other CEE-CIS countries are in the upper right quadrant. Hence, perhaps surprisingly, the low share of public health expenditures in GDP is due to *both* a small "size" of government and a low prioritization for health among competing uses

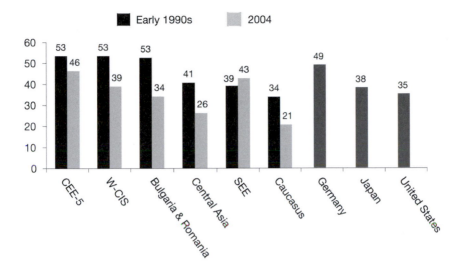

Figure 3.20 *Government expenditure as a percentage of GDP, early 1990s and 2004 (Sources: UNICEF, 2006b).*

Notes: "Early 1990s" in the legend is 1990 for the Baltic states, Bulgaria, Romania and CEE; 1991 for the Caucasus and central Asia; 1992 for western CIS; 1995 for SEE; Data for Germany, Japan and the United States refer to 2002; For details of country categories, see List of abbreviations.

of public money.

These results reflect the substantial shrinkage of government that has occurred in countries that, under socialism, were by their very nature characterized by an excessively large government sector. While in general a reduction of government activity was no doubt the natural and even desirable consequence of the transition from a centrally planned to a market-based system, in some countries this reduction has clearly gone a long way, if not too far.

The "downsizing" of the state is clear in Figure 3.20, showing that during the course of transition in essentially all subregions (except SEE), there was a decline in the size of governments, as measured by government expenditure as a percentage of GDP. The fall in government activity has been particularly marked in central Asia and the Caucasus, where the percentages in 2004 were noticeably below even that in the United States. On the positive side, the results suggest that there is scope for increasing health expenditures by increasing government expenditures in general in at least some countries. This would of course require the availability of sufficient government revenues.

There is reason to believe that in many CEE-CIS countries tax revenues can be augmented, benefiting all government programmes and not only the health

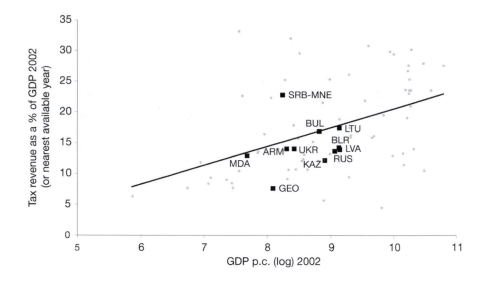

Figure 3.21 *Tax revenue as a percentage of GDP versus GDP per capita, 2002 (Source: World Bank, 2005a).*

Note: For details of country name abbreviations, see List of abbreviations; GDP: gross domestic product; p.c.: per capita.

system. Figure 3.21 gives some idea of the scope for raising tax revenue in a limited set of these countries. (There are relatively few relevant data available worldwide, so the sample is restricted.) The figure shows that the majority of the represented CEE-CIS countries appear to raise less tax revenue than countries with comparable GDP per capita, suggesting at first sight some scope for revenue enhancement.

It is, however, beyond this review to analyse in detail the tax policies in the CEE-CIS countries.[28] A low share of tax revenue can generally be due either to inefficient tax collection or low tax rates per se. In the CEE-CIS countries the former describes the actual situation more accurately. The notable size of the informal economy in several of these countries is a major constraint to efficient tax administration and collection, in particular in relation to payroll taxes.[29] Efficient tax collection may also be considered as a feature of the

---

28. For a more specific analysis of the countries' tax systems and reforms, see, for example, Stepanyan (2003) and Andrews & Shatalov (2004). For regularly updated country-specific analyses, see the World Bank's Public Expenditure Reviews (PERs).

29. For a very recent estimate of the size of the informal economy in 145 countries (including 25 transition countries), see Schneider (2006). This study found that the share of the informal economy was 40% of GDP in 2002/2003 in the average of the 25 CEE-CIS countries and varied greatly between the lowest (20.1% in the Czech Republic) and the highest figure (68% in

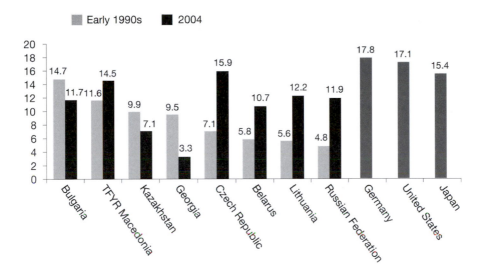

Figure 3.22 *Public health expenditure as a percentage of total public expenditure in selected countries, early 1990s and 2002 (Sources: UNICEF, 2006b for CEE-CIS countries; OECD, 2004 for Germany, the United States and Japan, which refer to the year 2000).*

quality of governance – an issue explored further in Chapter 5. The point here is that even with regard to the financing of the health system, there are important factors outside the health system proper (and outside the Ministry of Health's main areas of authority) that determine the sustainability of a health system and hence also the extent to which the health system can maintain and improve the health of its population.

While overall public resources have generally declined in almost all CEE-CIS countries, trends in the share of total government resources devoted to health are more mixed. This variable can be seen as an indicator of the extent to which government prioritizes health with regard to competing uses of public money. Figure 3.22 illustrates this for a representative set of CEE-CIS countries. In some countries the priority given to health appears to have decreased, sometimes from an already low starting level (as in Kazakhstan and Georgia). Others have been in a position to increase the share assigned to health, often

Georgia). This is somewhat lower than the Central and South American average (43.4%) and the African average (43.2%), and it is substantially higher than the Organisation for Economic Co-operation and Development (OECD) average (16.3%) and the Asian average (30.4%). For an account of the role of the unofficial economy in CEE-CIS during the first years of transition, see, for example, Barkley Rosser et al. (2000).

quite remarkably so (as in Belarus, Lithuania and the Russian Federation). Overall, the percentages of health spending tend to be well below those in advanced market economies, with the possible exception of Belarus: of all the CIS countries it stands out as not having allowed its health care system to decline as much as the others. This may, however, be at the cost of long-term sustainability, given its failure to institute necessary reforms. Moreover, while its maintenance of health expenditure may be a commendable achievement, this has not prevented an almost continuous deterioration in life expectancy since the late 1980s.

In summary, the data presented in this section indicate that, for those CEE-CIS countries with unduly low levels of current expenditure, there is scope for increasing health expenditures both by increasing the share of government expenditure measured against GDP and/or by allocating a greater share of available government expenditure to health. The extent to which one or the other option is more feasible in any country depends on the specific country context. Conducting the assessments that would inform decisions on this matter is urgently needed. Many of the measures that would improve the financial resource base of a health system (for example, establishing a system of effective tax administration) are beyond the system's immediate sphere of influence, just as many of the ways in which health can be improved are not primarily in the hands of the Ministry of Health. Unless health becomes an integral objective of government policy at large, hopes for more and better support for health may remain elusive.

Inequity in the health system: when the health system makes things worse

The amount of money spent on a health system is but one proxy for the policy efforts dedicated to health, or rather to the health system alone. This section examines the degree to which the money invested in the health system, or the operation of the health system itself, is actually "doing harm" by reinforcing, rather than mitigating, existing inequalities[30] in terms of both access to health care and health itself.

---

30. In the present section and in other sections of this book the terms "inequity" and "inequality" are used interchangeably, to reflect within-country differences between socioeconomic groups, in terms of health outcomes, health behaviours or health care access. This is in line with the common use of the terms. See Whitehead and Dahlgren (2006) for a more extensive, conceptual discussion.

*Public expenditures in the Region tend to do little to redress the inequities embod-
ied in the health system.*

One of the ways that services fail poor people is that public expenditure fails
to reach the services the poor use. So-called "benefit incidence studies"[31] offer
a methodology to assess quantitatively the extent to which public spending
does or does not reach the poor. These studies typically relate household data
on the use of public services by different income quintiles of a population to
average spending on those services from the public budget. These provide a
cross-sectional view of who benefits from public spending on services. At the
outset, it might be expected that government health spending would fail to
reach the poor in many CEE-CIS countries, where the largest share of spending goes to hospital care,[32] which is used disproportionately by the rich.

A recent global study (that included two CEE-CIS countries) found that, in
most regions, public spending on health benefits the rich more than the poor,
especially in sub-Saharan Africa (Davoodi, Tiongson & Asawanuchit 2003).
Such spending is well targeted and progressive only in the Western hemi-
sphere.[33] Table 3.9 shows regional averages. In Bulgaria and Romania, the two
countries "representing" the transition countries in the study, taken together
less than 14% of the benefits from government health spending accrue for the
poorest quintile of the population, as compared to 27% for the richest quintile. This represents a lower share for the poor and a higher share for the rich
compared to global averages. While the results from Bulgaria and Romania
cannot be taken as truly representative of the entire CEE-CIS Region, it is
important to bear in mind that these are two of the wealthier CEE-CIS countries. There is hence not much reason to expect that the incidence of public
health spending elsewhere in the Region would be any more pro-poor than in
these two countries. This is at least partly confirmed by results from Albania,
where a slightly different type of benefit incidence analysis (World Bank
2003c) shows that spending on hospitals is the most regressive form of health

---

31. In fact, rather than "benefit" incidence studies, these might more appropriately be called
"expenditure" incidence studies, because the actual benefit (or value) of spending might differ
for different people (for example, spending on urban dwellers might go much further towards
providing quality services than an equal amount spent on people in remote rural areas) (Filmer
2003).

32. Recent data indicate that, for instance in Uzbekistan, more than two thirds of the health
budget is still spent on hospitals, compared with an average of 38% in OECD countries in 2001.
The corresponding figure for Tajikistan is 79%, Kazakhstan 74%, Kyrgyzstan 65% and
Turkmenistan 63% (Walters & Suhrcke 2005).

33. The number of countries for which data were available in all world regions varied between
1 and 10 (Davoodi, Tiongson & Asawanuchit 2003).

Table 3.9 *Benefit incidence of public spending* on health in the 1990s by world region*

Region	Sample size (3)	All (1)		Primary health care (2)		Hospitals	
		Poorest quintile	Richest quintile	Poorest quintile	Richest quintile	Poorest quintile	Richest quintile
CEE-CIS (4)	4	13.6	27	14.9	21.5	11.4	29.4
Sub-Saharan Africa	9	12.9	28.6	15.3	22.7	12.2	30.9
Asia and Pacific	2	10.8	30.9	19.7	16.9	9.1	38
Western Hemisphere	10	23.1	15.2	20.4	19.1	17	22.2
Middle East and North Africa	1	16.4	23.6	–	–	–	–
TOTAL	4	16.9	23.2	17.3	20.8	13.3	28.7

Source: Davoodi, Tiongson & Asawanuchit, 2003.

Notes: * Unweighted average, as a percentage of total spending; (1): Includes more than hospitals and health centres; (2): Refers to one of the following: health centres, clinics, child health and preventive care; (3): Number of countries based on overall spending. Some countries may have more than one observation; (4): Includes Bulgaria and Romania.

spending, compared to spending on polyclinics and diagnostic centres, which tend to be more often frequented by people from lower-income categories.

Filmer (2003) confirms the hypothesis of Davoodi, Tiongson and Asawanuchit (2003) that the health system is actually increasing rather than mitigating inequities through its expenditure patterns. Filmer's synthesis of worldwide benefit incidence studies includes more CEE-CIS countries than the Davoodi, Tiongson and Asawanuchit study. The results for the countries of interest are displayed in Table 3.10.

In analysing and comparing results from benefit incidence studies, several caveats emerge. First, cross-country comparability is hampered by the fact that

Table 3.10 *Benefit incidence of public spending on health in five CEE-CIS countries*

Country, year	All health		Primary level only	
	Poorest quintile	*Richest quintile*	*Poorest quintile*	*Richest quintile*
Armenia, 1999	13	39	16	28
Bulgaria, 1995	13	25	16	21
Georgia, 2000			18	19
Republic of Moldova, 2001			17	22
Tajikistan, 1999			18	31

Source: Filmer, 2003.

studies differ in the detail to which they aggregate average spending: for example, some use a uniform estimate, some estimate separate average spending amounts for urban and rural areas, some for different provinces and so on. Second, the studies implicitly assume that the value of the expenditure is equal across all users without taking into account the means of raising funds. A quite regressive pattern of spending might still be pro-poor if financed through a progressive tax system. Third, it is hard to know what a "good" allocation is without comparing it to other types of social spending (Filmer 2003).

In many countries for which evidence was available, the poor are obtaining less access to health care than the rich, despite their greater needs.

Health care utilization increases with income in the Region, despite the fact that the health care needs (in terms of ill health, as shown above) are invariably more prevalent among the poor than the rich. For example, in Armenia, only 26% of those in the lowest consumption quintile who reported sickness received some type of health care (Figure 3.23), compared to 51% in the highest quintile (World Bank 2002a).

In the Republic of Moldova, a Public Expenditure Review (PER) by the World Bank found that the poorest 20% of the population is 70% less likely to receive ambulatory care, if in need, and 33% less likely to receive hospital services, relative to the national average (World Bank 2003d).

The effect of income on access to health care differs by age group. In Albania, inequalities in utilization are largest among children and the elderly. While

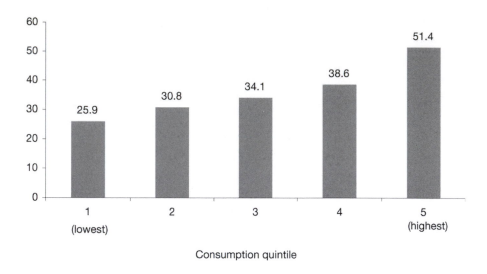

Figure 3.23 *Percentage of those sick who received care in Armenia, by consumption quintile, 1998/1999 (Source: World Bank, 2002a).*

66% of children considered to be "non-poor" seek care when ill, only 50% of poor children do. Differences in outpatient care utilization are largest among the elderly, and while about 70% of the elderly that are not poor receive out-patient care when ill, only 41% of the elderly living in poor households do (World Bank 2003c).

This lower access by the poor – despite greater health needs – occurs for several reasons, but by far the one most frequently mentioned by respondents is the unaffordability of health care (Balabanova et al. 2004).

The most comprehensive evidence on affordability of care among socio-economic groups comes from the LLH survey, which was carried out in eight CIS countries. The results in Table 3.11 show that the percentage of poor respondents citing lack of money as a reason for not seeking care is several times higher than among the rich. The size of the poor–rich differences varies widely. While some countries (Belarus and the Russian Federation[34]) appear to have managed to maintain access to some form of care for most people, in oth-ers (especially Armenia, Georgia and the Republic of Moldova) the situation is near collapse. In Belarus, a country that has undergone very little economic reform and has retained many features of the Soviet system, albeit in a situa-tion of sustained economic decline and increasing isolation, health services

---

34. For the Russian Federation see Balabanova, Falkingham & McKee (2003).

Table 3.11 *Percentage of respondents who did not visit a doctor when ill as a result of lack of money, by poorest and richest quintiles, 2001*

Country	Poorest quintile	Richest quintile	Poorest divided by richest
Armenia	92.5	36.6	2.5
Georgia	78.9	38.1	2.1
Republic of Moldova	66.7	33.3	2.0
Kazakhstan	63.0	10.3	6.1
Ukraine	54.1	3.1	17.5
Kyrgyzstan	52.0	9.5	5.5
Russian Federation	13.1	2.2	6.0
Belarus	0.0	0.0	0.0

Source: Authors' calculations based on Living Conditions, Lifestyles and Health (LLH) survey data.

Notes: Quintiles are derived from data not related to income. For details see note to Figure 3.9 or Suhrcke et al. (forthcoming, 2007).

remain affordable for virtually everyone: two thirds of households across all five quintiles stated that they never had to do without health care because of cost. In contrast, in Georgia, a country that has suffered a civil war and where the Government was not in control of some regions at the time of data collection, only 14% of households reported never having to do without care because of cost (Gamkredlidze et al. 2002). Access to care also seems to have remained generally affordable in the Russian Federation, by far the largest and wealthiest of the countries included (Balabanova et al. 2004). (The pattern of affordability of drugs is similar to that of access to care. Problems are less frequent in the Russian Federation and Belarus, but few households in Armenia, Georgia, Kyrgyzstan or the Republic of Moldova are entirely free of problems.)[35]

35. While material wealth matters a lot in the propensity to seek health care if in need, other factors were also found to matter significantly, in particular individuals' social support networks (Balabanova et al. 2004).

Table 3.12 *Financial barriers to health care in Ferghana, Uzbekistan*

	Percentage of those seeking health care in the past 30 days				
	Income quartile				
	First (poorest)	*Second*	*Third*	*Fourth (richest)*	*Total*
Did not seek health care because not enough money	31.5	26.1	15.6	13.5	21.2
Finding the money to pay for health care was difficult	77.0	79.2	63.8	57.5	68.0
Needed to borrow money to pay for health care	25.0	22.9	15.4	9.8	17.5

Source: Cashin, 2001.

In Bulgaria, more than 52% of those in the bottom two quintiles identified cost as the main reason for not seeking care despite having been ill, while the national average was 26% (World Bank 2002b). In Serbia, among those who said that they needed health care but did not receive it (other than for minor conditions that can be self-treated), 45% said this was because it is too expensive. More than twice as many of the poor households than those considered non-poor reported the expense of using services, lack of health insurance or distance from services as reasons for not using services (World Bank 2003e).

Further evidence comes from the Ferghana region of Uzbekistan, where Cashin (2001) identified extensive borrowing to fund care and delays in obtaining it due to financial barriers, although even the wealthiest group had problems (Table 3.12).

The high cost of health care is exacerbated by the widespread presence of informal payments, a health care financing mechanism that disadvantages the poor more than those who are better off. Informal payments – defined as payments to health care providers in cash or in kind and made outside official channels – were present throughout the Region during the communist period, in part as a consequence of doctors' salaries being relatively low. Direct fee-for-service payments can be thought of as introducing some accountability, but they bear important equity implications, since they constitute the most regressive form of health care financing.

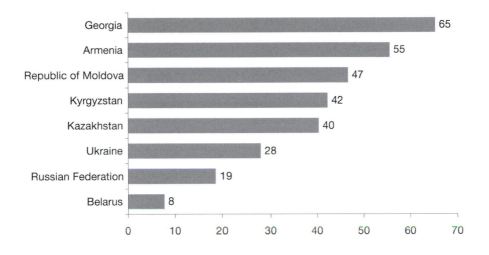

Figure 3.24 *Informal payments and gifts/donations during most recent consultations, by country (percentages), 2001 (Source: Balabanova et al., 2004).*

Informal payments effectively make access to health care conditional on the ability to pay. Since payment is not through formal channels and hence is not formally recorded, it is impossible to mitigate the consequences for individuals and families through subsidies to poor households linked to their actual expenditure. The result is that poorer households are less likely to seek medical assistance if in need. These types of payments have spread significantly throughout the Region, including the richer countries, and now account for a substantial share of health expenditures in many countries.[36] Figure 3.24 presents evidence on the scale of the problem in the eight countries that participated in the LLH survey. Not surprisingly, those countries with the highest shares of respondents reporting unaffordability of health care are the same ones that are characterized by the highest share of informal payments.

The evidence that exists suggests that the frequency and magnitude of informal payments are continuing to rise in many countries. In Azerbaijan, the share of OOP payments as a proportion of total health care expenditure is estimated to have risen from about 49% in 1999 to about 57% in 2001. In relative terms, the burden is higher among the poor, to the point where many poor households are reducing the use of services, especially preventive services, and are resorting to self-medication or traditional but less effective forms of

---

36. See, for example, UNICEF (2001). The first comprehensive review of informal payments for health care in eastern Europe and central Asia was Lewis (2000).

treatment. In 2001 about 28% of the population did not seek treatment when ill, mostly because services were too expensive. Among the poorest quintile, the fraction of individuals who did not use health services when needed was 39%. This amount of deterred care will almost inevitably have an impact on population health (World Bank 2003b).

In Bosnia and Herzegovina the need to make informal payments (over and above official co-payments and other charges) was reported by participants in the World Bank's Voices of the Poor Project study as one of the major barriers to getting decent quality medical services. In a survey of the scale and nature of corruption, one in every five people who visited a health facility in the previous two years reported making informal payments when accessing services. The major reasons for making these payments were: to provide privileges for patients, to secure good care and to ensure that physicians would not overlook them and/or would permit them to "jump the queue" (Djipa, Muzur & Franklin Lytle 2002).

Informal payments also continue as an issue in Bulgaria, despite some recent improvement. In 2001, 24% of households reported making payments for health care, a decrease from 33% in 1997. However, the share of monthly OOP expenditure on health more than doubled during the same period, from 2% to 4.5%. This increase was largely borne by the poor, as the share of expenditure by those in the poorest two quintiles is higher than for those in the richest one (World Bank 2002b).

Within countries the size of informal payments differs among health care providers – being particularly high in hospital care – and this determines to a large extent the type of health care provider the poor seek, if any.

In Albania informal payments in outpatient care (among those using such care) represent about 11% of the total per-capita household expenditure. This is still lower than the expenditure share for hospital care (among those using hospital care), which consumes nearly 25%. Among people giving "gifts" during a hospital stay (60% of all cases), 43% said the gift was requested or expected. In the case of outpatient care, about 40% of the people who went to public ambulatory facilities said that gifts were required or expected, while 25% of those who went to a nurse mentioned such a requirement. The problem of informal hospital payments seems to be considerable, despite the fact that all hospital services are supposedly free. The conditions in public hospitals are in general poor, often lacking basic services such as electricity, medicines and medical equipment. The low remuneration of personnel accentuates this problem, almost certainly contributing to the proliferation of informal payments (World Bank 2003c).

In Serbia and Montenegro, a 2003 survey confirmed that patients are paying substantially more out of pocket for accessing services in state institutions than would be suggested by the scale of small official co-payments, and those who use private services are also paying substantial amounts out of pocket (World Bank 2003e).

Official and unofficial health expenditures disproportionately negatively affect the poor in the Russian Federation. This is true both in outpatient and in-patient health care settings, although much more so in the latter. For those in the poorer three income quintiles, unofficial expenditure on inpatient care amounts to approximately 50% of average per-capita consumption expenditure. For official inpatient care expenditure, the average payment is as much as double the average consumption expenditure for the lowest income quintile. If health care costs exceed total consumption averages, this evidently puts those households at severe risk of impoverishment (that is, falling into poverty or deeper into poverty) as a result of health care needs (World Bank 2004b).

In Tajikistan, OOP expenditure on health care also accounts for a sizeable share (25%) of overall household income among those in the poorest quintile, but this is the same percentage as for those in the highest income quintile (World Bank 2000c).

Even in the more advanced countries of the Region, OOP payments represent a significant and in some cases growing concern. In Estonia, the percentage of households that face relatively high OOP payments (defined as more than 20% of their non-subsistence spending) increased from 3.4% in 1995 to 7.4% in 2002.[37]

While the burden of OOP payments is disproportionately high for the poor, recent evidence shows that many households considered to be "non-poor" in CEE-CIS are also at risk of falling into poverty as a result of substantial health expenditure following catastrophic or chronic illness (Wagstaff and van Doorslaer 2001).

Wagstaff and van Doorslaer (2001) defined catastrophic health expenditure as those extreme expenses that affect households' ability to maintain their consumption of basic items. This is different from simply examining the incidence of total health expenditures among the poor and the non-poor (discussed earlier), because the impoverishment concept involves those considered non-poor, yet vulnerable, households that may be driven below the poverty line by

---

37. Note that the standard WHO definition of "catastrophic" health expenditure sets a threshold at the point where OOP payments are equal to or above 40% of a household's capacity to pay. Applying this definition, only less than 2% of households incurred catastrophic expenditure in Estonia, which is why Habicht et al. (2005) chose the 20% threshold as their definition of "high" health expenditure.

Table 3.13 *Poverty indicators before and after incidences of catastrophic health expenditure*

Country	% in poverty before catastrophic health expenditure	% in poverty after catastrophic health expenditure	Absolute increase in % in poverty	Relative increase in % in poverty (%)
Bulgaria	4.8	6.3	1.5	31.9
Romania	9.4	10.1	0.7	7.6
Belarus	19.0	20.6	1.6	8.4
Kazakhstan	15.8	16.3	0.5	3.2
Armenia	41.2	44.6	3.4	8.4
Georgia	40.3	43.9	3.6	9.0
Kyrgyzstan	61.0	62.4	1.5	2.4
Republic of Moldova	32.5	35.4	2.9	8.8
Tajikistan	64.4	67.7	3.3	5.1
Uzbekistan	39.0	40.7	1.6	4.2

Source: Alam et al., 2005.

Notes: Data used were from the most recent available household survey; Poverty line used is US$ 2.15 purchasing power parity at 2000.

unusually large and unpredictable expenses. It is, however, important to recognize that the absence of data showing high levels of catastrophic expenditure is not a reason for complacency; in a country with low utilization of health services, it may be that catastrophic expenditure is not occurring because households simply cannot sacrifice any additional consumption. Their denial or delay of care may have fatal consequences. Hence, there are potential impoverishing effects that are not observed because households deny or postpone care.

Simulations undertaken for the recent World Bank report on poverty in eastern Europe and central Asia (Alam et al. 2005) suggest that catastrophic health care expenditure can increase the share of the population defined as poor by 3–9%. Countries with vastly different methods of funding and organizing their health systems (such as Belarus and Armenia) experience similar impacts (Table 3.13).

Table 3.14 *Percentage of people with catastrophic health expenditure, Albania*

	Poorest quintile	Richest quintile	Total
Health expenditures account for more than 10% of total income	32	14	26
Health expenditures account for more than 25% of total income	13	5	9
Health expenditures account for more than 50% of total income	5	1	3

Source: World Bank, 2003c.

Belarus, on the one hand, has a health system that has changed little from the Soviet model. Although most health status indicators show low infant and maternal mortality, adult life expectancy is declining, mainly because of rising adult male mortality (life expectancy at birth for males is 62, one of the lowest in the Region). Households spend a small fraction of their budget on health, reflecting the persistence of public funding. However, the impoverishing effect is high: most households that need health care do seek it, even if they pay only a small amount, and the impact on poverty thus occurs through the large number of people affected.

Armenia, on the other hand, presents a different picture. Although spending only 3% of GDP on health, it still has an extensive network of well-staffed health facilities. The lack of public funding of the system is being addressed temporarily by the active involvement of international donors, supplemented by payments from those in need of care (World Bank 2002a). Expenditure on health represents about 5% of average household budgets, and about half of those payments are made informally by patients who contribute a significant fraction of their incomes. The levels of utilization, however, are much lower than in Belarus. The impoverishing effect of catastrophic expenditure is high in this case because of high expenditure among the fewer households seeking care.

Table 3.14 shows the uneven ability of the Albanian health system to protect households against catastrophic health expenditure (here defined as that constituting over 10% of total income). On average 26% of people report health expenditure that is equal or above 10% of their total income, and about 9% report health expenditure representing 25% or more of their total income. People in the poorest quintiles are more than twice as likely to incur catastrophic health expenditure as their richer counterparts.

The results presented in this section demonstrate quite unambiguously the need for domestic health policies that first and foremost "do no harm", in the sense of not aggravating inequities embodied in the health system. The track record of the CEE-CIS countries appears unfavourable. Seen from a more positive angle, however, the current deficits are indicative of the considerable potential for improvement of the status quo. The following section moves from the role of domestic policies to consider the contribution of the international community.

The role of official development assistance: international efforts

International development assistance can have a significant impact on economic and social development in recipient countries. The importance of official development assistance (ODA) has been emphasized repeatedly during conferences of the United Nations. In 2000, its General Assembly adopted the MDGs as the basis for international development policies. Goal number eight commits the donor community to augment its aid efforts. In spite of renewed political commitment, actual levels of ODA have shown a declining trend since 1992 (Claeys & Wuyts 2004).

Discussion of ODA has mainly been focused on "traditional" developing countries, with particular attention to sub-Saharan Africa. Hardly any attention has been paid to the CEE-CIS Region. A recent study prepared as background work to this analysis starts to fill this gap by analysing development assistance for health (DAH) (Suhrcke, Rechel & Michaud 2005). Its main findings are summarized here.

The central question that it sought to answer was: *"Is international DAH to the CEE-CIS Region too low, given existing health needs and domestically available financial resources?"*

The results strongly suggest that while the overall level of development assistance going to the Region is within or even at the higher end of the norm of what other regions have been receiving, the level and share of development assistance channelled into health is well below what might be expected. Definitions and data sources are described in Box 3.2. Before turning to the issue of DAH specifically, the distribution and development of overall ODA will be described, both in CEE-CIS and worldwide.

Box 3.2 Data and methods

Official development assistance (ODA) is defined by the Organisation for Economic Co-operation and Development (OECD) as financial flows to a defined set of "developing countries" (including some countries from CEE-CIS) provided by official agencies, including state and local governments, or by their executive agencies, which are: (1) administered with the promotion of economic development and welfare of developing countries as their main objective; and (2) concessional in character and conveying a grant element of at least 25%.

Official aid, in contrast, is defined by the OECD as development assistance meeting the above criteria, but allocated to the remaining non-"developing country" recipients (most of which are from CEE-CIS). Since the countries in this Region are the main focus of this analysis, the term "official development assistance" is used for both types of assistance.

A second relevant distinction relating to development assistance concerns commitments and disbursements. Commitments are funds set aside to cover the costs of projects, which can span several years. Disbursements are the actual amounts made available by donor countries each year. The ODA data used for the present analysis is based on commitments, which are more widely reported by donors than disbursements and tend to capture donor decisions more directly (McGillivray & White 1993). Donors have more control on commitments than disbursements, which depend in part on the recipients' willingness and administrative capacity to manage the money (McGillivray & White 1993). To compensate for the often sizeable annual fluctuations in commitments, three-year averages were calculated.

The analysis is based on two main data sources: the OECD International Development Statistics database (OECD 2003) and the database on development assistance for health, which was specifically compiled for the Commission on Macroeconomics and Health (CMH). The OECD database provides information on receipts of total ODA and on sector-specific commitments to ODA by bilateral donors. While this sector-specific material contains valuable information about assistance to the health sector, the CMH database, which covers the period 1997–1999, has more complete data on development assistance for health, including transfers from major nongovernmental foundations (Michaud 2001). As a result, the database is not confined to official development assistance for health from the public sector, but covers development assistance for health more generally.

Table 3.15 *Official development assistance per capita by world region (1999–2001, average in US$)*

Official development assistance	US$
Oceania	208
CEE-CIS	27
Sub-Saharan Africa	23
North Africa	22
Central America	22
Middle East	14
South America	10
Far East	6
South Asia	4

Source: Suhrcke, Rechel & Michaud, 2005.

Note: Data refer to commitments, including those that are unallocated.

Total development assistance to CEE-CIS

Table 3.15 presents the per-capita distribution of ODA by region for the average of the years 1999–2001. Perhaps the most striking finding concerning regional distribution is the high level of per-capita allocations to Oceania (largely explained by its small population size), while regions most commonly viewed as in need of development assistance, such as the Far East, south Asia and sub-Saharan Africa receive comparatively limited ODA in per-capita terms. The CEE-CIS Region ranks second after Oceania of all regions in terms of ODA per capita.

Clearly, as far as total ODA is concerned, the CEE-CIS Region as a whole does not seem to have been neglected compared to other recipient regions. (This, however, does not necessarily mean that the CEE-CIS Region or any other region represented receives "enough" general development assistance.)

The result is confirmed by a more disaggregated analysis of the distribution of total development assistance across all recipient countries worldwide. As documented by Suhrcke, Rechel & Michaud (2005), when controlling for the level of economic development (proxied by per-capita gross national income (GNI)), most of the CEE-CIS countries are located above the regression line.

Table 3.16 *Development assistance for health to different world regions*
(1997–1999 average)

Region	Development assistance for health per capita (US$)	Development assistance for health as a % of official development assistance
Oceania	9.98	4.7
Central America	4.22	19.8
Sub-Saharan Africa	2.06	8.6
South America	1.64	16.5
North Africa	1.24	4.4
South Asia	0.84	16.8
Middle East	0.52	3.4
Far East	0.50	7.8
CEE-CIS	0.34	1.7
Average	1.00	8.9

Source: Suhrcke, Rechel & Michaud, 2005.

This implies that they tend to receive more ODA than other countries with similar per-capita incomes.[38]

Development assistance for health to CEE-CIS

A different picture emerges in the analysis of DAH. Both DAH and the share of DAH as a proportion of total ODA turn out to be very low for the CEE-CIS Region (see Table 3.16).

In per-capita terms, only US$ 0.34 in development assistance was given for health in CEE-CIS in 1997–1999, corresponding to 1.7% of total ODA.

---

38. This is not to imply that per-capita income was the only relevant determinant of ODA that should be accounted for in the evaluation of whether any given level of ODA to a country is low or high. The policy performance of recipient countries or the self-interest of donors are two other and not necessarily mutually exclusive explanations that have been put forward in the literature (e.g., McGillivray & White, 1993; Berthélemy & Tichit, 2002; Alesina & Weder, 2002; Burnside & Dollar, 2004).

These values are significantly lower than the US$ 1.00 that was, on average, spent globally on DAH and the almost 9% of ODA going to health in all recipient countries worldwide.

A look at the share of DAH in total ODA on the country level shows that, in many CEE-CIS countries, development assistance to the health sector is virtually non-existent. In 15 of the Region's 27 countries, average DAH in the years 1997–1999 was less than 0.1% of total ODA. Even in the countries that receive the highest share of DAH and the highest per-capita amounts (Albania, Armenia, Georgia, Tajikistan and Uzbekistan), the levels typically remain below worldwide averages.

The data discussed so far suggest that the donor community has generally given a low priority to health in the allocation of aid to CEE-CIS, but this comparison of the amount of DAH may be over-simplistic. One might hypothesize that the CEE-CIS countries appropriately obtain so little, simply on the grounds that they have a better health status than most other recipient countries, thereby needing less.

One challenge in testing this hypothesis is that "health status" is not an unambiguously defined or easily measurable concept. What could the health indicators that guide donors' allocations be? Child mortality rates and life expectancy at birth are two of the most widely used indicators of population health, but important differences distinguish the two measures. In general, child mortality is more reliably measured. In many countries where there is almost no information on adult mortality, data on child mortality are collected, either through routine collection systems or surveys, in particular the series of Demographic and Health Surveys (DHS) and the UNICEF Multiple Indicator Cluster Surveys (MICS). *The world health report 2000* used child mortality to assess the performance of health care systems because these data were much more widely available than data on adult mortality (WHO 2000). In contrast, life expectancy is not reliably measured in a large number of developing countries, and many of the figures reported in official sources are not based on actual data, but are extrapolations from child mortality using standard life tables. This explains why child mortality rather than life expectancy is a widely used indicator of development progress and one key indicator of the MDGs (Rechel, Shapo & McKee 2004). It could therefore be expected that child mortality will explain the allocation of DAH better than life expectancy. Figure 3.25 confirms a positive relationship between the child mortality rate and DAH per capita across recipient countries worldwide. In an analysis including all countries worldwide, a 10% increase in the child mortality rate is on average associated with an almost identical percentage increase (10.6%) in per-capita DAH. Among the countries of CEE-CIS, this relationship is even more pronounced.

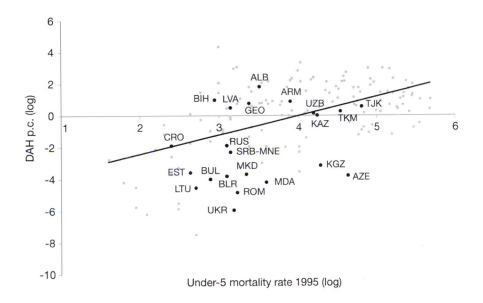

Figure 3.25 *Development assistance for health per capita (1997–1999 average) and under-five mortality rate (1995), worldwide (Source: Suhrcke, Rechel & Michaud, 2005).*

Notes: DAH: development assistance for health; p.c.: per capita; For details of country name abbreviations, see List of abbreviations.

Bivariate regressions of the kind reproduced in Figure 3.25 (and in Figure 3.26), while having the benefit of displaying relationships visually, should only be used if it can be shown that these relationships persist in empirical models that simultaneously control for a wider set of explanatory factors. As Table 3.17 on page 84 shows, this does seem to be the case here.

These results suggest that donors may take into account differences in child mortality in their decisions on the allocation of DAH. However, most of the CEE-CIS countries lie below the global regression line, indicating that they receive less DAH per capita than other countries with similar levels of child mortality. Interestingly, variations in child mortality appear to influence donor decisions even more strongly within the CEE-CIS Region.

A second potential determinant of DAH is life expectancy at birth. Figure 3.26 suggests that this indicator does not greatly influence allocation decisions for DAH. Although a negative relationship exists between the two variables, the explanatory power of the global regression equation is substantially inferior ($r^2=0.11$) to the corresponding one in Figure 3.25 ($r^2=0.24$) for child mortality. DAH allocations on a global level do not seem to be guided strongly by differences in life expectancy.

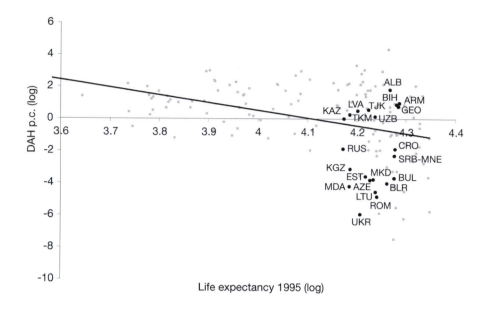

Figure 3.26 *Development assistance for health per capita (1997–1999 average) and life expectancy (1995), worldwide (Source: Suhrcke, Rechel & Michaud, 2005).*

Notes: DAH: development assistance for health; p.c.: per capita.

The location of most of the CEE-CIS countries in Figure 3.26 is again below the global regression line, indicating that they receive less DAH than other countries with similar levels of life expectancy. Looking at the association among CEE-CIS countries alone, the explanatory power of the equation is reduced virtually to zero (r^2=0.01), with no statistically significant relationship between life expectancy and DAH per capita.

Hence, across all countries worldwide, DAH seems to be associated much more closely with child mortality than with more general population health indicators. Such a pattern of aid allocation fails to capture the serious adult health concerns in CEE-CIS. Yet, the results also show that even if donor allocations were guided by the distribution of life expectancy across countries, CEE-CIS would still be receiving less health-related development assistance than other countries with similar levels of life expectancy.

Apart from the health status of the population, it is also reasonable to expect that the higher the levels of national health expenditure per capita are, the lower the external assistance for health will be. Is it that the CEE-CIS countries receive less international DAH because they are already spending sufficient amounts themselves? The data do not confirm this. Again, in most of these countries, DAH is on average lower than for other countries with similar levels of national health expenditure.

How does the picture of a seemingly neglected region change if a number of potential explanatory variables are simultaneously controlled for? So far only univariate explanations of the level of DAH were considered, which may have biased the results. When controlling for a set of relevant explanatory factors that reflect both the needs and the policy performance of the recipient countries, the initial results are actually reinforced. To assess whether, after controlling for all these factors, the CEE-CIS Region on average obtains more or less than "expected", a dummy variable was introduced for the entire Region. Table 3.17 presents the main results of the regression analysis.

In Table 3.17 the sign, the significance and the size of the CEE-CIS dummy are of primary interest. In all the models the results are consistent, showing that even after controlling for an extensive set of relevant determinants of DAH, the CEE-CIS Region receives significantly less than "expected". On the other hand, while the overall fit of the regressions – r^2 between 0.52 and 0.58 – is satisfactory, it is also true that there are likely to be other important determinants that could not be taken into account.[39]

In drawing policy conclusions from these findings, the limitations of the analysis need to be borne in mind. One in particular is the lack of appropriate data, which meant that it was not possible to analyse trends in DAH over time. Doing so would enable identification of likely causal relationships between the variables. More data collection, such as that undertaken to support the one-off initiative for the CMH, is needed. Furthermore, the way that money is spent is likely to matter more for health outcomes than the absolute amount of public expenditure, although it is hard to imagine that the extremely low expenditures in parts of the Caucasus and central Asia have no negative impact on health.

Also, donor aid is unlikely to be a solution by itself but may be important if targeted effectively towards the poor, especially where it contributes to

---

39. Apart from the dummy variable, a few other results in Table 3.17 are worth noting. The under-five mortality rate variable always enters significantly and with the expected sign (a higher rate brings more aid). Overall, countries with a lower income per capita receive more health assistance. Both results appear to support the hypothesis of the "needs-based" distribution of aid. Interestingly, the other two health needs indicators appear to either have no independent explanatory power (adult mortality) or have the "wrong" sign (life expectancy)! The control of corruption variable is used as a proxy for the policy performance of the recipient country. Its relationship to DAH is far from robust and shows only very limited levels of significance, if any. Its negative sign suggests that countries with more corruption tend to receive more aid (see Alesina & Weder (2002) for a similar result in relation to overall ODA). The population size also enters significantly: smaller countries receive more aid in per-capita terms (see also Berthélemy & Tichit (2002)).

Table 3.17 *Multivariate analysis of determinants of development assistance for health*

	-1	-2	-3	-4	-5	-6	-7	-8
GNI per capita (US$)	-0.779 (2.09)**	-0.187 (0.84)		-0.858 (2.40)**	-0.285 (1.27)		-0.81 (2.16)**	-0.188 (0.83)
Control of corruption	-0.692 (1.93)*	-0.708 (2.04)**	-0.513 (1.70)*	-0.379 (1.08)	-0.392 (1.15)	-0.271 (0.92)	-0.619 (1.70)*	-0.644 (1.83)*
Health expenditure per capita (current US$)	0.575 (1.68)*		-0.072 (0.42)	0.557 (1.75)*		-0.162 (0.96)	0.603 (1.77)*	
CEE-CIS	-2.506 (5.00)***	-2.541 (5.00)***	-2.279 (4.60)***	-2.505 (5.07)***	-2.54 (5.06)***	-2.309 (4.77)***	-2.41 (4.70)***	-2.458 (4.73)***
Total population	-0.401 (5.71)***	-0.405 (5.89)***	-0.396 (5.95)***	-0.42 (5.84)***	-0.424 (6.00)***	-0.407 (5.96)***	-0.41 (5.75)***	-0.413 (5.91)***
Under-5 mortality rate	0.729 (2.47)**	0.657 (2.19)**	0.82 (3.08)***	1.468 (3.93)***	1.406 (3.68)***	1.511 (4.37)***	0.997 (2.64)***	0.892 (2.40)**
Life expectancy at birth				4.632 (3.37)***	4.674 (3.30)***	4.495 (3.20)***		
Adult mortality rate							-0.505 (1.04)	-0.449 (0.93)
Observations	139	139	151	138	138	150	139	139
R-squared	0.56	0.55	0.52	0.58	0.58	0.55	0.56	0.55

Source: Authors' calculations. The control of corruption variable is from World Bank (2005c).

*Notes: All variables are in log, except for the control of corruption variable, which is in standardized format; The CEE-CIS dummy variable assumes a value of 1 if the country is in CEE-CIS and 0 otherwise; Robust statistics in parentheses; * significant at 10%; ** significant at 5%; *** significant at 1%.*

systemic reforms. This suggests that any analysis should not assume away the problem of governments' inability to allocate resources and deliver services effectively. Indeed, it implies that donor support should take full account of government performance in resource allocation and monitoring of outcomes.

Despite these caveats, a clear conclusion emerges: the health needs of the CEE-CIS Region are not sufficiently recognized in the process of negotiating development assistance and play no significant role in the allocation of development assistance to this Region. The reasons for such neglect are a matter for speculation. A partial explanation is that, as shown above, DAH seems to be allocated on the basis of child mortality rather than other indicators of population health. Given the disproportionately serious adult health concerns in many CEE-CIS countries, this results in an underrecognition of the Region's overall health needs. The neglect of health in the Region is not helped by the focus of the health-related MDGs on child and maternal mortality, which disregard more general population health indicators (Rechel, Shapo & McKee 2004).

The role of health in Poverty Reduction Strategy Papers: qualitative evidence

The previous three sections support the hypothesis that health policy efforts — both domestic and international — have been less than they might have been, given the resources that are in place. The focus of those sections was on quantitative indicators. As not all policies can be evaluated effectively on the basis of quantitative indicators alone, this subsection complements the approach with a more qualitative perspective. In particular, this subsection assesses the extent to which health has been recognized explicitly as a key factor in the promotion of economic development and poverty reduction in CEE-CIS. While the perception of health by national governments can never be gauged with great precision, some insights could be gained from taking a closer look at the national Poverty Reduction Strategy Papers (PRSPs), as well as their related annual progress reports. If health is found not to feature as a major issue in these documents, this finding may indeed reflect a low appreciation of health as a key policy area. This may, in turn, explain why some of the quantitative indicators presented in the preceding sections appear comparatively unfavourable. In addition, it may provide a further rationale for the focus of this book: the economic argument for investing in health.

As of 30 December 2006, the following nine countries from the CEE-CIS Region had prepared PRSPs: Albania, Armenia, Azerbaijan, Bosnia and Herzegovina, Georgia, Kyrgyzstan, Republic of Moldova, Serbia and Montenegro, and Tajikistan. (The former Yugoslav Republic of Macedonia

---

Box 3.3 Poverty Reduction Strategy Papers (PRSPs)

The stated aim of a PRSP is to present a coherent strategy that helps countries to experience faster sustainable growth and achieve a substantial reduction in poverty. As such, the extent to which health is reflected in these strategies might be a credible indication of the importance attributed to health in promoting economic development. Countries are obliged to produce a PRSP to qualify for concessional assistance from the World Bank (through its International Development Association (IDA)) and the International Monetary Fund (IMF; through the Poverty Reduction and Growth Facility (PRGF)). In addition, PRSPs were the basis for the provision of multi-lateral debt relief under the Highly Indebted Poor Countries (HIPC) initiative. Countries prepare PRSPs through a participatory process involving domestic stakeholders and external development partners, including the World Bank and the IMF. Regularly updated with progress reports, PRSPs describe the country's macroeconomic, structural and social policies and programmes over a three-year (or longer) horizon to promote broad-based growth and to reduce poverty, as well as identifying associated external financing needs and major sources of financing. So-called "interim" PRSPs (I-PRSPs) are often prepared prior to the full PRSPs. They summarize the current knowledge and analysis of a country's poverty situation, describe the existing poverty reduction strategy and lay out the process for producing a fully developed PRSP in a participatory fashion.

While the World Bank and the IMF provide consultation to a country, both assess the strengths and weaknesses of the poverty reduction strategy and identify priority areas for strengthening the strategy during implementation in so-called Joint Staff Advisory Notes (JSANs), formerly "Joint Staff Assessments". The JSANs are submitted with a member country's PRSP or I-PRSP.

Sources: Background information as well as the original PRSP documents are available on both the International Monetary Fund (IMF) and World Bank web sites (www.imf.org/exter-nal/np/prsp/prsp.asp and www.worldbank.org/prsp, respectively, accessed 1 December 2006). For more information on JSANs see www.imf.org/external/np/jsa/index.asp, accessed 1 December 2006.

---

and Uzbekistan have presented so-called "Interim-PRSPs" (I-PRSP)).[40] Box 3.3 briefly describes the purpose and contents of PRSPs (and related outputs).

---

40. There is a need to distinguish the extent to which the listed CEE-CIS countries have been involved in the PRSP process. Bosnia and Herzegovina, Serbia and Montenegro and The former Yugoslav Republic of Macedonia were granted concessional lending through the International Development Association (IDA) on the grounds of their post-conflict status. They were never considered as candidates for the Highly Indebted Poor Countries (HIPC) initiative, and the International Monetary Fund (IMF) never provided any Poverty Reduction and Growth Facility

Table 3.18 *Poverty Reduction Strategy Paper documents reviewed by WHO*

Country	Type of document	Year
Albania	GPRS	2001
Armenia	PRSP	2003
Azerbaijan	SPRED	2003
Bosnia and Herzegovina	PRSP	2004
Georgia	PRSP	2003
Kyrgyzstan	PRSP	2002
Republic of Moldova	PRSP	2004
Serbia and Montenegro	PRSP	2004
Tajikistan	PRSP	2002

Source: WHO, 2006c.

Notes: PRSP: Poverty Reduction Strategy Paper; GPRS: Growth and Poverty Reduction Strategy; SPRED: State Program on Poverty Reduction and Economic Development.

WHO continuously evaluates the PRSPs from a health perspective. As of 20 December 2006, an evaluation of the nine existing PRSPs had been carried out. Detailed results of these evaluations are available at www.who.int/hdp/database/ (WHO 2006c).[41] Table 3.18 lists the documents that have been reviewed to date.

The review of these nine national documents confirms that there is indeed scope for incorporating health more significantly and in more effective ways into the national poverty reduction strategies.

• In four of the nine countries (Albania, Armenia, Kyrgyzstan, Serbia and Montenegro), there was no explicit recognition of health as a means to achieve poverty reduction and sustainable economic growth.

(PRGF) funds to them. On the other hand, while Uzbekistan has prepared an I-PRSP, it has thus far successfully resisted any serious reform-focused lending from the IDA meant to be based on PRSP (personal communication, R. Yemtsov, World Bank).

41. See Dodd & Hinshelwood (2004) for a broader, worldwide review of the significance of PRSPs for health.

- The health situation is generally described fairly comprehensively, at least as far as population averages are concerned.

- The health goals formulated do not reflect the full spectrum of the major disease challenges. In particular, noncommunicable diseases are generally not included in the set of health goals (with the partial exception of Serbia and Montenegro and Tajikistan), despite the fact that in most cases they are described as the biggest disease burden.

- While in all nine documents the poor are acknowledged to be in worse health than the rich, this acknowledgement is only weakly supported with data.

- The health goals are not disaggregated by socioeconomic group. Hence, the monitoring of those goals will not allow an assessment of whether progress has actually benefited the poor.

- The health strategy is often described in quite some detail. However, most PRSPs suggest an expansion of health care provision with neither a discussion of whether this is the best course of action nor an assessment of past failures or successes.

- All PRSPs include a section that acknowledges the importance of cross-sectoral action for health. However, there is much scope for widening the range of cross-sectoral action. While the areas of water and sanitation usually are referred to, the important area of nutrition gets little mention. No mention is made of potential fiscal policy measures (such as tobacco taxation).

In sum, there appear to be significant opportunities for strengthening the place of health in the PRSPs – in particular in light of the evidence on the contribution of health to economic outcomes, the focus of Chapter 4. While it is encouraging to see some health issues explicitly mentioned in the PRSPs, exclusion of any significant consideration of noncommunicable disease neglects the largest part of the health challenges that these countries face, whether measured in terms of mortality or morbidity.

Why this neglect of noncommunicable disease? Understandably, the global development agenda has been geared towards communicable disease and child and maternal health, as those elements represent the major burdens in the poorest countries. As discussed in the preceding section, these goals have also made their way into the MDGs, further cementing their place as the foci of international development efforts. Increasingly, the PRSPs are being linked to the MDGs, and the PRSPs may even tend to become the key vehicle for expressing countries' strategies to reach the MDGs. In the case of the CEE-

CIS countries – and in fact also in many other developing countries – this makes sense only if the health-related MDGs are interpreted more broadly to include chronic disease challenges as well.

Part of the neglect might also be explained by the prevailing view that non-communicable diseases do not matter for poverty reduction and/or economic development. In addition, noncommunicable diseases continue to be considered as diseases of affluence, despite abundant counter-evidence (Ezzati et al. 2005). Their economic implications are underresearched (Suhrcke et al. 2006); this issue is explored in detail in Chapter 4, using data directly from the CEE-CIS countries

Chapter 4

Health and economic development

Chapter 2 explained that, in terms of achieving sustained economic growth, as well as CEE-CIS Region-specific, appropriate poverty goals, the road ahead for many CEE-CIS countries remains challenging. Chapter 3 demonstrated that there is: (1) substantial scope for health improvements in the CEE-CIS countries; and (2) ample room for expanding and improving health policy efforts in these countries, partly with the hitherto limited support of the international community.

Although the chapter provided some new information, it was primarily a review of what was already known, even if some of the latter was presented in a new way. This chapter adds evidence on the close link between health and the economy in the CEE-CIS Region. Most of the evidence, synthesized below, was specifically produced for this book or related studies the authors have recently undertaken.[42] From among the possible linkages, this chapter focuses in particular on the ways that ill health negatively affects economic outcomes in the Region and less on the reverse pathway, whereby higher economic status contributes to health, which has received substantial attention elsewhere (Wilkinson & Marmot 2003).

The present chapter argues that the comparatively unfavourable health status – in part a consequence of weak policy efforts – has imposed a substantial economic cost on the people and countries of the Region. Or, in more positive, forward-looking terms, if the health situation can be improved by appropriate

---

42. See in particular Suhrcke, Võrk & Mazzuco (2006) on Estonia; Favaro & Suhrcke (2006) on SEE; Suhrcke et al. (2007) on the Russian Federation; and Suhrcke et al. (2006).

health (and health-related) policies, then a direct positive contribution to sustained economic growth could be expected.

Before turning to the impact of health on economic outcomes in CEE-CIS, this chapter briefly summarizes the reverse link, that is, from economic outcomes or development to health. As this is the more traditional view – that health is a by-product of economic development – and as it is widely documented elsewhere, it is unnecessary to add to that literature here, but a brief summary is likely to be helpful for some readers.

Again, it is not the purpose here to argue that the link from health to economic development is any more important than the converse, traditionally accepted link. The key point is that the relationship runs both ways and that a bidirectional relationship of this kind means that one problem cannot be solved without simultaneously tackling the other. Accordingly, governments will benefit from investing a given amount of resources in both the health and economic sectors, rather than in just one, as appears to have been the case thus far in the CEE-CIS Region.

Economic development determines health

It has long been the predominant view that good health is a consequence of favourable economic status, for an individual as well as for a country as a whole. The fact that this is not the primary focus of this book does not, of course, imply that such is not the case in the CEE-CIS countries. On the contrary, in particular in the early years of transition, the economic collapse played an important role in the sharp deterioration of health status (Cornia & Paniccià, 2000). The list below gives but a few examples of the ways in which poor economic status contributes to poor health in general (Sala-i-Martin 2005).

- Poor people and poor countries do not have adequate material resources to obtain the money necessary to buy health care, or to buy enough and good quality food.

- Since poor people are more likely to be malnourished, immunodeficient and thus vulnerable to infectious diseases, they are more likely to be unhealthy.

- The poor are more likely to live in massively overcrowded areas without clean water and sanitation. As a result they have a greater propensity to suffer from otherwise readily avoidable diseases.

- Some poor people live far from doctors and hospitals, making it expensive and difficult to seek help when problems arise. They are more likely to go untreated and, therefore, to suffer from worse health.

- Poor people are more likely to have less education; education, in turn, is an important determinant of health (for example, by way of better coping mechanisms, improved understanding of health risks, faster adoption of new health technologies).

- Economic status affects health through a social network effect that has "material" and psychological dimensions. Poor people tend to have less intense social support networks, a subject discussed in Chapter 5 in relation to social capital in the CEE-CIS context.

Health determines economic development

This section starts by introducing the framework used to understand the several potential ways in which health could affect economic outcomes, while also presenting selected evidence from outside CEE-CIS in order to substantiate empirically each of the mechanisms discussed in the conceptual model. The section is split into two broad parts: the first presents new evidence on the economic impact of (ill) health in CEE-CIS. As mentioned earlier, this evidence is mainly about adult health issues and hence focuses predominantly on noncommunicable disease. In addition, the section draws together other existing evidence to highlight the economic impact of the more conventional topics in health and development literature, which focuses on communicable disease and maternal and child health issues. The second part of this section looks ahead by estimating the expected benefit (in terms of higher future per-capita incomes and higher future economic welfare), if certain plausible scenarios for adult mortality reduction were achieved.

Conceptual framework and empirical evidence from beyond CEE-CIS

Studies abound confirming the robust link between life expectancy (or adult mortality) and economic growth, even when controlling for other relevant determinants of economic growth. In a recent empirical study of the determinants of economic growth, Sala-i-Martin, Doppelhofer & Miller (2004) incorporate dozens of potential factors into their econometric analysis of robust estimators, spanning technology, openness, macroeconomic stability, the rule of law, democracy and religion. Although intuitive at first sight and proposed by researchers from different disciplines, many of these factors turn out not to be robustly correlated with growth. An exception is life expectancy at birth, which was one of the few variables whose significance and size was not markedly affected by the combination of other determinants included in the model. Countries that had a higher life expectancy in the 1960s are those that grew the fastest over the following four decades. Quite surprisingly, in some cases life expectancy was found to be a more reliable determinant of growth than the education proxies employed.

As these studies used a worldwide sample of countries, they also provide empirical results that are potentially directly relevant for the CEE-CIS countries. (In a later section of this chapter, one version of these worldwide empirical regularities is used as an approximate benchmark to forecast the impact of mortality reduction on economic growth in the CEE-CIS countries.) However, those findings say nothing about the ways in which health affects economic outcomes, on either the micro or macro level.

A simple conceptual framework to organize the different mechanisms (and the associated evidence) is to use an aggregate production function of the type generally used by economists:[43]

$$Y = A\ F(K,\ hL)$$

where Y is output or product, A is the "total factor productivity (TFP)"[44], $F(\ )$ is a production function, K is physical capital, L is labour, and h is the "quality of labour", or human capital.

Based on this simple model, GDP growth can occur only if there are increases in the *level of TFP, A*; in the aggregate *level of physical capital, K*; or the *quality or quantity of labour, hL*. In what follows, each of these mechanisms will be described, and selected relevant empirical evidence from outside CEE-CIS will be presented. This provides a larger set of *potential* mechanisms that can in principle be used to develop further empirical hypotheses to be tested in the CEE-CIS context in future work. The subsequent section then provides direct evidence from CEE-CIS, the majority of which was prepared specifically for this book or for closely related work (see studies cited in footnote 42). Given the limits of existing data sources, the focus of the CEE-CIS evidence produced is mainly on the mechanisms that run via the improvement of the quantity and quality of labour.

---

43. The presentation of the conceptual framework here is borrowed in part from Sala-i-Martin (2005).

44. Growth in TFP represents output growth not accounted for by the growth in the other relevant inputs (here labour and physical capital). TFP is a measure of how efficiently all inputs combined are utilized in a production process. As such it is not necessarily only a measure of technology: it could be a function of other things, such as monetary shocks or the political system in place. It is also called the "Solow residual".

Quality and quantity of labour: labour productivity and labour supply effects

Labour productivity, labour supply and education jointly affect the quality and quantity of labour, which in turn determine economic output. Health affects labour productivity, labour supply and education in different ways.

Labour productivity. Healthier individuals could reasonably be expected to produce more output per hour worked. On the one hand, productivity could be increased directly by enhanced physical and mental activity. On the other hand, more physically and mentally active individuals could make better and more efficient use of technology, machinery and equipment (Currie & Madrian 1999).

Labour supply. Somewhat counterintuitively, economic theory predicts a more ambiguous impact of health on labour supply. The ambiguity results from two effects working to offset each other. If the effect of poor health is to reduce wages through lower productivity, a substitution effect would lead to more leisure and therefore lower labour supply as the economic return from work diminishes. On the other hand, an income effect would predict that as lifetime earnings are reduced through lower productivity, the individual would seek to compensate by increasing his or her labour supply. The income effect is likely to gain importance if the social benefit system fails to cushion the effect of reduced productivity on lifetime earnings. The net impact of the substitution and income effects thereby ultimately becomes an empirical question (Currie & Madrian 1999).

Education. Human capital theory suggests that more educated individuals are more productive (and obtain higher earnings). If children with better health (and nutrition) attain higher educational status, suffer less from school absenteeism, and are less likely to drop out of school early, then improved health in youth would contribute to future productivity. Moreover, if good health is also linked to longer life, healthier individuals would have more incentive to invest in education and training, as the rate of depreciation of the gains in skills would be lower (Strauss & Thomas 1998).

What is the evidence from high-income countries concerning each of the three hypothesized mechanisms?

A significant amount of research from the United States demonstrates a negative impact of ill health both on labour productivity and on labour supply. Mitchell & Burkhauser (1990) used the Survey of Disability and Work in 1978 to find that arthritis reduced wages by 27.7% for men and 42.0% for women. Moreover, it reduced the number of hours worked by 42.1% and 36.7%, respectively, for men and women. Stern (1996), using the Panel Study on Income Dynamics of 1981, shows that limited ability to work due to illness reduced wages by 11.7% and 23.8% for men and women, respectively, when a selection correction for participation in the labour force is introduced. In addition, the probability of staying outside the labour force increased by an estimated 13%. Using the same data, Haveman et al. (1994) estimates that (lagged) ill health decreased worked hours by 7.4%. Berkovec & Stern (1991), using data from the National Longitudinal Survey of Older Men (1966–1983), found that poor health status reduced wages by 16.7%. Baldwin, Zeager & Flacco (1994), using data from the 1984 Survey on Income Program and Participation, found that health limits reduced wages by 6.1% for men and 5.4% for women. While the varying percentages from these studies lead to theoretical ambiguity, at least in high-income countries there is overall more evidence of a significant negative impact of ill health on labour supply than on productivity (wage rates).

In a recent review of the existing evidence on the impact of health on the economy in the EU, Suhrcke et al. (2005) summarized a large number of studies that assessed the impact of health on various labour market outcomes in high-income countries according to the conceptual model set out above. Although this evidence does not come from CEE-CIS countries, it can nevertheless be considered as more directly relevant than the work of the CMH with its focus on developing countries.[45]

As for the effect of health on education, a considerable amount of empirical evidence exists from developing countries (see, for example, the literature review by Strauss & Thomas (1998)). In high-income countries, there has been a considerable volume of work on the association between health and education (Freedman & Martin 1999). Most studies attribute this association to the impact that education has on health outcomes, without in most cases providing empirical justification for this interpretation of causality. Case, Fertig & Paxson (2005) and Gregg & Machin (1998) provide highly suggestive evidence to support the view that at least part of the widely observed association between health and education is because better health leads to better education. Using

---

45. The report cites European evidence of an effect of ill health on labour force participation. Examples come from Ireland (Gannon & Nolan 2003); Spain (Pagán & Marchante 2004); Sweden (Lindholm, Burström & Diderichsen 2001); Germany (Riphahn 1998; Lechner & Vazquez-Alvarez 2004); and the Netherlands (van de Mheen et al. 1999). The role of ill health in anticipating retirement in several EU countries is described by Jiménez-Martín, Labeaga & Martínez Granado (1999); in Germany by Siddiqui (1997) and in the United Kingdom by Disney, Emmerson & Wakefield (2003). Adverse effects on earnings or wages are shown, for instance, by Contoyannis & Rice (2001) and Gambin (2004) in the United Kingdom. Brunello & d'Hombres (2005) demonstrates a wage-depressing effect of obesity on several EU countries, especially so for women.

a longitudinal United Kingdom survey, both studies find evidence that child health (in early childhood and infancy) affects educational attainment and cognitive development during later childhood. Broadly similar results were found by Del Gaudio Weiss & Fantuzzo (2001) in a United States setting.

Physical capital

Savings and investment. The health of an individual or population is likely to affect not only the level but also the way that income is distributed among consumption, savings and investment. Individuals in good health are likely to have a longer time horizon, as they can reasonably expect to live longer, so their propensity to save may be higher than that of individuals in poor health. Consequently, a population experiencing a rapid increase in life expectancy may be expected – other things being equal – to save more. This should also contribute to the propensity to invest in physical capital (Bloom, Canning & Graham 2003).

Complementarity between human and physical capital. If human capital is complementary to physical capital, then there is little incentive to invest in physical capital when human capital is low. Firms are hesitant to invest in countries where the labour force is unhealthy. This has been shown to apply for countries that are facing widespread communicable disease epidemics (Alsan, Bloom & Canning 2004), but it might also plausibly play a role in countries facing a disproportionate chronic disease burden, such as in the CEE-CIS Region.

Crowding-out of public investment in physical capital. There could also be an effect on public investment; governments of countries with large-scale epidemics experience sizeable demands on their budgets for health outlays that prevent them from investing in physical infrastructures. Public capital slowly deteriorates, reducing the rate of return of complementary private physical capital (Sala-i-Martin 2005).

Impoverishment through health care expenditure. In countries where there is no or limited health insurance and widespread OOP payments for health care, people are often forced to spend their life savings and liquidate physical assets in an attempt to cure an ill family member. This may force children out of school and prematurely into the labour force. Consequently, the health problem reduces the family's assets and earning potential (Whitehead, Dahlgren & Evans 2001).

Total factor productivity

Health can have a direct effect on total TFP. The aggregate productivity of an economy depends on the business and research activities that citizens undertake, among other factors. There is some evidence that health status can negatively affect these decisions, although more empirical work is needed to strengthen the evidence on this specific channel.

Creativity. Good health, and in particular good child and maternal health, make a person more creative (McCain & Mustard 1999). Just as a healthier person will be more efficient in producing goods and services, so will that person be more efficient in producing new ideas. One would thus expect an increase in a country's ability to generate innovation should it effectively invest in health.

Coping skills. Better child and maternal health helps young people develop a greater ability to cope with stress and hence to adapt to the frequently disruptive and stressful effects of rapid technological, economic and other change. A healthier labour force could also be expected to be more flexible and adaptable to changes (such as changes in task profiles and the organization of labour), reducing job turnover and its associated costs (McCain & Mustard 1999).

Indeed, a growing volume of research provides empirical evidence to substantiate the purported mechanisms that may lead from health to economic outcomes at the micro- and macroeconomic levels. However, most of that work was undertaken in developing countries and is of uncertain relevance to the CEE-CIS context. As the previous chapters explain, both the economic and health situations are very different in this Region compared to traditional developing countries. A perhaps cynical, but widely held view is that the specific pattern of health in CEE-CIS, with its dominant share of noncommunicable diseases, does not impose a significant economic burden, simply because noncommunicable diseases tend to occur toward the end of work life. This view holds that any efforts to reduce noncommunicable disease-related mortality would simply lengthen the lives of those who had already delivered their lifetime contribution to the national economy. Costs of social and health care would soar without a commensurate increase in productivity, simply because pensioners are not "productive", by definition, resulting in a net economic loss. This argument continues to be accepted not least because there has been hardly any serious evidence to the contrary (Marquez & Suhrcke 2005).

The hypothesis that the noncommunicable disease problem is "only" a matter of pensioners dying was rejected in the review of epidemiological evidence in Chapter 3. Mortality rates among the working-age population were shown to be particularly high in the CEE-CIS countries. In addition, it has been shown that high levels of adult mortality are associated with (and preceded by) high levels of morbidity. (And even if noncommunicable diseases affected only pensioners, they would have an impact on everyone's life-cycle decisions on savings and human capital accumulation, as discussed above, with potentially negative consequences for national economic development.) In what follows, a series of analyses shows that adult ill health does impose a significant cost to both individuals and countries in the CEE-CIS Region.

While the main focus here is on adult chronic diseases, it is important to recall that many of the CEE-CIS countries are also facing serious challenges in relation to some communicable diseases as well as in child and maternal health (see Chapter 3). The economic effects of these threats are far better understood than those of noncommunicable diseases, with much that can be drawn on from previous research, even if only a fraction of it specifically relates to CEE-CIS countries. Where relevant, some of this work is cited below.

Empirical evidence from CEE-CIS

This section uses the simple production function framework given above to assemble evidence on the economic impact of health in CEE-CIS countries. Exclusively micro data are used to assess the recent impact of (ill) health on various economic outcomes. There would be little point in even attempting to detect a macroeconomic impact of health in the period since the breakdown of the communist regimes, a period of unprecedented political and economic change that was surely *not* determined by health to a significant extent. There is little doubt that the first decade of transition ranks as one of the more extreme examples of what was described in the previous section – the impact of socioeconomic conditions on health (Cornia & Paniccià 2000). As the countries in this Region are emerging from transition at different speeds, health will increasingly act as a determinant and not only a consequence of economic development.

The fact that this section focuses on the situation in recent years does not imply that health had no impact on economic outcomes prior to transition. Indeed the contrary may be true. As one background paper to this report documents, while the role of health in economic development in the Soviet era has not been an international research topic, a significant amount of domestic research highlighted various ways in which health left its mark on economic outcomes (Davis 2004).

The work on the post-Second World War period offers particularly interesting insights: substantial economic returns were attributed to a number of large-scale medical programmes to tackle infectious diseases, such as TB, polio, malaria and diphtheria. In light of this evidence it is tempting to hypothesize that the substantial population health gains experienced by the countries of the former USSR between 1950 and the early 1960s might indeed have contributed to its remarkable economic development during that period.

Likewise, the fact that the subsequent economic decline was associated with a commensurate stagnation and even deterioration in many noncommunicable disease indicators could reflect at least in part the impact of health on economic development. While there had been considerable Soviet research documenting the costs of infectious disease, there were no studies examining the economic benefits of tackling noncommunicable disease. Such benefits would also have been rather difficult to demonstrate, because no major successes in curtailing the noncommunicable disease burden had been realized (Davis 2004).

Microeconomic impact

This section presents findings of analyses of the impact of (ill) health at the individual or household level in 14 CEE-CIS countries. While it does not include all the countries that this book focuses on, it does include a sufficiently representative set of them. An extension beyond this number was not feasible simply because additional household surveys were not accessible to the authors at the time of writing.

The evidence presented below focuses on the labour market impact of (ill) health, that is, the impact on labour market participation, labour supply, labour productivity (proxied by the wage rate), earnings and early retirement.[46] The chosen focus does not imply that this is the only important economic effect. On the contrary, it may well be that a large economic impact can arise through the effect of health on education. It is rather that the labour market impact was of the type that could most easily be assessed given the nature of the available survey data. More work is clearly needed to shed light on the extent to which some of the other economic consequences of ill health that have been described in other regional contexts apply in the CEE-CIS countries.

The identification of a causal impact of health on these outcomes is not as straightforward a procedure as one might hope. The technical challenges involved in this estimation and how they have been overcome in the actual

---

46. It is important to keep separate the impact on labour supply and productivity at least on the conceptual level, even if in practice the data at hand often do not allow disentangling one from the other. In the tautological equation $Y = L (Y/L)$, output equals the product of labour supply and labour productivity. As argued above, the effect of health on labour supply is theoretically ambiguous, while the one on productivity is not. How to measure the different impacts? While it is straightforward to measure labour supply – for example, by the hours worked per day or per week – labour productivity is harder to measure in economies where the output does not derive from manual work, as is the case for the largest share of labour in developed countries. Since, however, in a competitive market the wage rate equals the marginal productivity, the wage rate is typically used as the proxy for productivity.

Based on the New Keynesian theory of downward rigid or "sticky" wages, the wage rate correctly proxies productivity only above a minimum level. Below that threshold wages are unrelated to actual productivity. For details of this theory see Mankiw & Romer (1991).

analysis are described in general terms in Box 4.1. As a general rule, the methods applied are based entirely on approaches that have been widely used in the scientific literature. More details of the methodology employed and the empirical results of each exercise are described either in related papers by the authors or, where the work has not yet been published, in the Annex to Chapter 4.

Box 4.1 General methodological issues in the estimation of the labour market impact of ill health

The choice of methodologies is largely determined by data availability and by an informed evaluation of the importance of the endogeneity problem, which tends to negatively affect many, if not all, efforts to establish a causal relationship in empirical economic and social research. An endogeneity problem arises in three cases: first, when there is a simultaneous relationship between the chosen health proxy and labour market outcomes that would bias the statistical relationship measured by the most common econometric technique (ordinary least squares (OLS) estimation); second, in the case of non-random measurement error in the health indicator used because, especially in the case of self-assessed health outcomes, the reliability of the measure depends on unobservable respondent characteristics; and third, when some crucial variables are omitted because they are not contained in the dataset at hand or are unobservable (such as individual preferences on time and risk).

Consistent estimations of the impact of health on alternative economic outcomes are achievable through two-stage techniques. For the present purpose the two-stage method has been implemented either as a single-equation "instrumental variables" (IVs) estimator or through "simultaneous equations" models. In both cases the endogenous variables are replaced by their predicted values, coming from their own regression over a set of IVs, plus all the exogenous variables that are part of the model. The researcher must choose as instruments one or more variables that are correlated with the endogenous variable but uncorrelated with the error term. A necessary condition for the identification of the coefficients is that the instruments included in the first stage do not explain the second-stage dependent variable. The "Sargan test of overidentification" (Sargan 1958) enables a judgment about whether the chosen instruments are "good" in a statistical sense. This procedure allows purification of the health variable from its correlation with the error term, that is, from its sources of endogeneity.

Given the available data, in most cases the analysis was carried out for a cross-section of individuals at one point in time. Only in the case of the Russian Longitudinal Monitoring Survey (RLMS) was it possible to analyse the relationship between health and labour market outcomes for the same individuals at more than one point in time.

(cont.)

Box 4.1 *(cont.)*

The RLMS offers additional possibilities of finding good instruments: following empirical strategies of the kind suggested by Hausman and Taylor (1981), the researcher does not need to find valid instruments outside the model, because he or she uses the already-included exogenous variables to instrument the relevant endogenous variable. The only requirement is the inclusion of both time-varying and time-invariant variables among both the exogenous and endogenous ones.

The technical details of the specific exercises vary somewhat depending on the survey data available.[47] The surveys used for the analysis are listed in Table 4.1.

Table 4.1 *Datasets used for original data analysis*

Survey	Year	Web site for more information
Living Conditions, Lifestyles and Health (LLH) survey: Armenia, Belarus, Georgia, Kazakhstan, Kyrgyzstan, Republic of Moldova, Russian Federation, Ukraine	2001	www.llh.at/
Russian Longitudinal Monitoring Survey (RLMS)	1994–2002	www.cpc.unc.edu/rlms/
National Survey of Household Welfare and Program Participation (NOBUS): Russian Federation	2003	siteresources.worldbank.org/ INTRUSSIANFEDERATION/ Resources/NOBUS.pdf (in Russian only)
Albanian Living Standard Measurement Survey (LSMS)	2000	www.worldbank.org/lsms/
Bosnia and Herzegovina LSMS	2001	www.worldbank.org/lsms/
Bulgarian Integrated Household Survey	2001	www.worldbank.org/lsms/
The Province of Kosovo (Serbia) LSMS	2000	www.worldbank.org/lsms/
Tajikistan Living Standard Survey	2003	–
Estonia Labour Force Survey	2002	–

Source: Authors' compilation.

47. In one exercise presented in this chapter, a different methodology is applied to assess causality, the so-called propensity score matching technique. This technique is used in the context of assessing the impact of chronic illness on household incomes in the Russian Federation. The basic idea of this methodology is described in that text, and more detail is available in Suhrcke et al. (2007). In Chapter 5 this technique is used in part of the analysis of the effect of social capital on health.

Eight CIS countries (LLH survey)

This section presents results on the effect of health on labour force participation (LFP) from a 2001 survey covering eight CIS countries.[48] As mentioned above, due to the bidirectional relationship between LFP and health, one cannot assess the causal relationship from health to participation – which would be the prime interest here – through a simple regression analysis. To overcome the problem, the method applied here and in several other applications below follows that developed by Stern (1989). He devised a two-stage procedure in order to elicit the impact of general health conditions and of the presence of limits in performing usual working activities on LFP. This approach can be adapted to the LLH dataset, which also contains questions on self-reported health, medically diagnosed chronic diseases, and disabilities. (For more details and for the full set of results see the Annexes, Table A4.1 to Table A4.5.)

Table 4.2 describes the impact of general health condition on LFP. The health measure takes four levels: "good", "quite good", "rather bad" and "bad". In all eight countries, moving from "bad" to "quite good" health increases the probability of participation in the labour market by a certain percentage, ranging

Table 4.2 *The impact of general health condition on labour market participation in eight CIS countries (marginal effects), 2001*

Country	Good	Quite good	Rather bad
Armenia	-0.014	0.160***	0.076*
Belarus	–	0.341***	0.192***
Georgia	0.186***	0.126***	0.066
Kazakhstan	-0.076	0.235*	0.099
Kyrgyzstan	0.081	0.191	-0.001
Republic of Moldova	–	0.290***	0.159***
Russian Federation	0.225	0.372***	0.173***
Ukraine	–	0.136**	0.079

Source: Authors' calculations.

Notes: * significant at 10%; ** significant at 5%; *** significant at 1%.
Benchmark: "bad health".

---

48. See www.llh.at for background information on the survey (accessed 1 January 2007).

Table 4.3 *The impact of activity limitations on labour market participation in eight CIS countries, 2001*

Country	Presence of activity limitations
Armenia	-0.163***
Belarus	-0.251***
Georgia	-0.069**
Kazakhstan	-0.304***
Kyrgyzstan	-0.188***
Republic of Moldova	-0.223***
Russian Federation	-0.230***
Ukraine	-0.167***

Source: Authors' calculations.

Notes: * significant at 10%; ** significant at 5%; *** significant at 1%.

from 12.6% in Georgia to 37.2% in the Russian Federation.[49] The results in Table 4.2 were obtained in relation to the benchmark represented by the level "bad".

Table 4.3 presents the impact of limitations to daily activities on labour market participation. The variable is dichotomous: limitations on activity are either present or absent. Again, the expected negative impact of ill health (here proxied by activity limitations) on economic outcomes is confirmed for all countries in the survey. In Georgia the probability that individuals with limitations on their activities will participate in the labour market is at least 6.9% lower than for individuals without such limitations. This probability rises as high as 30.4% across the countries (Kazakhstan). This is the impact of health on LFP after accounting for potential impacts of LFP on health (for example, due to stress or unhealthy working conditions).

Ill health heavily affects LFP in all the countries surveyed, especially the more industrialized ones, such as the Russian Federation and Belarus. Further investigation would seek to explain the observed cross-country differences in the scale of this impact.

---

49. Due to the very small number of respondents who reported good health, the results corresponding to that level have limited use.

◆ Russian Federation

The authors recently documented the impact of ill health on economic outcomes in the Russian Federation; this section draws extensively on this work (Suhrcke et al. 2007).[50] The labour market outcome indicators assessed are: labour supply and productivity, the probability of retirement, the probability of losing one's job and household income (which goes beyond the labour market).

Impact of health on labour supply and labour productivity

Various methodologies and two different Russian surveys were used to develop a robust and reliable picture of the impact of adult health on labour productivity with each methodology addressing in different ways the econometric challenges described in Box 4.1. Using RLMS data, it appears that women reporting good health enjoy wages that are 22% higher and men 18% higher than those reporting poor health (when any measurement bias related to self-reported health is addressed by standard econometric techniques). Similar results were obtained using National Survey of Household Welfare and Program Participation (NOBUS) data: males in good health earn about 30% more and females 18% more. Finally, a panel analysis based on the RLMS rounds for 2000–2003 confirms that good health status increases the wage rate for males while it does not significantly affect the number of hours worked weekly. These results align with those of the cross-sectional estimates, although now the effect of good health is reduced: being in good health increases the wage rate by only about 7.5%. Generally speaking, these analyses mean that ill health appears to have had a significant and sizeable impact on labour productivity, an impact that seems to be more pronounced among males than females.

Impact of chronic illness on retirement

Two different, complementary approaches were followed to measure the impact of chronic illness on both age of retirement and on the probability of retiring in the subsequent year, both indicators of labour supply. The approaches were a Cox regression and a panel logit regression. Controlling for other relevant determinants of the decision to retire (such as age, gender, income), both approaches confirm that chronic illness increases the probability of retiring early. The former approach assesses the effect of chronic illness on the probability that an individual will retire in a given year after the first year of employment. However, the direction of the causality is uncertain: Does ill health predict retirement or vice versa? The second approach to some extent addresses this limitation by examining the effect of chronic illness on the

---

50. Suhrcke et al. (2007) fed primarily into the recent World Bank report on adult health in the Russian Federation, in particular chapters 6 and 11 (World Bank 2005b).

probability of retiring in the subsequent year.

While the technical details of the Cox regression results can be difficult to interpret, they are more intuitively understandable if applied hypothetically. A hypothetical male aged 55 on median income and being at the average in terms of certain other characteristics[51] would be expected to retire at age 59, while a chronic illness would lower his expected retirement age by two years. Similar results are obtained for females. However, only evidence of an existing association between chronic illness and earlier retirement is shown, since it is not possible to determine the time of onset of an individual's chronic disease with the available data. Indeed, even whether the illness occurred before or after retirement is unknown. This analysis does not indicate whether the statistical association reflects the effect of chronic illness on retirement or vice versa. It is, however, possible to address this issue by using a panel logit regression.

The panel logit regression leverages the fact that some of the RLMS respondents have been followed over several survey years.[52] This allows the use of a panel logit regression to assess the impact of chronic illness in one year on the probability of retirement in the next: the effects of chronic illness on the probability of entering retirement in the next year are assessed, not the effect on the probability of retiring at a given year after first employment. Otherwise, the set of explanatory variables to be controlled for is identical to the Cox model. Results show that an individual who suffers from chronic illness has a significantly higher probability of retiring in the subsequent year than the same individual free of chronic illness (see Figure 4.1). This pattern is similar to those based on the Cox regressions, with only minor differences. Chronic illness emerges as a highly significant predictor of subsequent retirement. Given the different methodology, this result provides a more reliable basis for claiming causality between chronic illness and the probability of retirement. The magnitude of its effect is sizeable compared to other variables in the model.

With either approach, the effect of chronic illness is found to vary with income: the lower the income the more chronic illness affects the decision to retire. This implies that less affluent people carry a double burden of ill health: first, they are more likely to suffer from chronic illness, and second, once ill, they suffer worse economic consequences than rich people, a feature that tends

---

51. The other characteristics are that he is married, has one child, has a high school diploma, was born in the Russian Federation and is living in an urban area.

52. This is the "panel" component of the RLMS, which in principle offers important opportunities for testing hypotheses that involve causality. One shortcoming of this panel dimension is that the survey is not a true panel design, as both entire households and individual members of households are not followed if they move from their dwelling. Nevertheless, the effect of attrition is relatively modest.

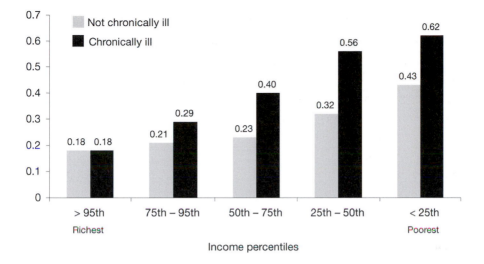

Figure 4.1 *Average predicted probability of retiring in the subsequent period, based on panel logit results (Source: Authors' calculations based on RLMS rounds 9–11, based on panel logit results).*

Note: Results refer to an individual with the same hypothetical characteristics as the one mentioned in the Cox regression (including Footnote 51).

to perpetuate socioeconomic disadvantage (see Figure 4.1).[53] Technically speaking, this result is reflected in the statistically significant interaction term between income and chronic illness in the regression models.

Impact of alcohol consumption on the probability of being fired

Several studies in other developed countries have shown that heavy alcohol consumption has a negative impact on earnings, incomes and wages, because it reduces individual productivity and may impair working arrangements (Mullahy 1991; Cercone 1994). In this section the idea is applied to the available Russian data by exploring whether alcohol consumption in one year (2001, round 11 of RLMS) increased the risk of job loss in the subsequent year (2002, round 12). The rationale is that job loss would be a natural consequence of an appreciable reduction in individual productivity. (Details are in Suhrcke et al. 2007.)

This assessment shows that one negative economic impact of severe alcohol consumption, arguably the most important (proximate) contributor to

---

53. Note that this approach does not allow exploration of a similar variation of the effect of ill health across the income scale in the wage and earnings regressions presented above. This would require a different approach, for instance a quantile regression. (See, for example, Rivera & Currais (1999) for an application of such regressions to Brazil.)

premature mortality in the Russian Federation, is that it significantly increases the probability of job loss. Using a panel probit model and controlling for gender, age, education, work experience, wage rate and the form of ownership of the employing organization, alcohol was found to have a positive and statistically significant, although relatively small, effect on the probability of being fired. For every additional 100 grams of pure alcohol consumed per week, the probability of losing one's job increased by about 3%. This fairly contained effect may reflect the simplified structure of the estimated model: further research would disentangle the complex but no doubt important effects of alcohol on the Russian labour market.

Impact of chronic illness on household income
In order to deal with some technical constraints facing estimates of the causal effect of health on household income – mainly the issue of endogeneity of the health proxy used – a strategy was applied that differs from that used in most of the other analyses.[54] A difference-in-differences estimator was used in combination with a propensity score matching technique and applied to the RLMS surveys from 1994 to 2002. This technique allowed comparison of pairs of households that were identical except for the presence of health problems. Details of the methodology and results are in Suhrcke et al. (2007). See also Chapter 5, Subsection "Social capital and health" for further explanation of this methodology.

This two-step procedure found chronic illness to contribute an annual loss of 5.6% of median per-capita income for a hypothetical household with average characteristics.[55] The first step confirmed a negative effect of poor health (in general) on household income. This effect is greater in 1998–2002 than before the Russian financial crisis. A more detailed logit model was then used to assess the extent to which chronic illness increases the likelihood of experiencing adverse health events. These steps showed that chronic illness increased the risk of health problems. Combining the effect of chronic illness and poor health on income then gives the overall indirect impact of chronic illness on household income. This contributes to the conclusion that chronic illness had a negative impact on household incomes in the Russian Federation, particularly in the period 1998–2002.

---

54. In the previous sections, the endogeneity problem was addressed either by exploring the lagged effect of ill health on a specific economic outcome using panel regressions or by applying an instrumental variable estimation in the cross-section regressions. (In one case the instrumental variable estimation was also used in the panel context.)

55. The characteristics are: in urban areas, with no smokers and no ex-smokers, no people aged over 60 or below 14, with at least two workers and at least one person who has a high school diploma.

◆ Tajikistan

The previous empirical exercises looked at the impact of health on various indicators of *either* labour supply *or* labour productivity, trying to "purify" the effect by isolating it from the potential reverse impact of these labour market outcomes on the health indicator in question. The slightly more involved empirical framework adopted in this section allows *simultaneous* assessment of the effect of health on both labour supply and labour productivity, while also taking into account the reverse causality from labour supply to health.[56] The analysis used data from the 2003 Tajikistan Living Standard Measurement Survey (LSMS).

The model allows simultaneous consideration of the following reciprocal relationships between self-reported health, labour supply and labour productivity (proxied by the wage rate).

- Labour supply influences self-reported health and vice versa: on the one hand, too much work may harm health through prolonged physiological and psychological stress or through prolonged exposure to unhealthy substances or unhealthy places; on the other hand, respondents may claim ill health to data collectors to justify their low participation in work.

- Health affects both labour supply and productivity, as shown in previous sections.

- The wage rate is the main determinant of labour supply.

Health may therefore affect labour supply, both directly and indirectly, by way of its effect on the wage rate. The reciprocities noted above imply that self-reported health, labour supply and wages all act as determinants and outcomes at the same time. Therefore, as in the previous exercises, estimating the pure effect of health on labour supply and productivity requires some caution.

The simultaneous equation approach proposed by Haveman et al. (1994), adopted here, represents one way of taking the interdependencies directly into account in the empirical analysis. The approach jointly estimates three equations, each with a different dependent variable: self-reported health, labour supply and wages.

This framework also permits assessment of the response of a household member to ill health affecting other household members. The underlying hypothesis is that individuals might compensate for illness in their family by increasing

---

56. The drawback of this approach compared to Stern (1989) is that it does not take into account the subjective nature of self-reported health, nor does it correct for individual-specific measurement errors (or voluntary misreporting). On the other hand, it does take into account the impact of health on wage rates and further improves the model specification.

Table 4.4 *Results of the simultaneous equation model for Tajikistan, 2003*

	Self-reported health	Labour supply (hours per week)	Log monthly wage
Labour supply (hours per week)	0.044***	–	–
Log wage	–	-1.89***	–
Self-reported health (very good=1 very bad=5)	–	-2.82	-0.081***
Mean health of other household members	–	11.52***	–

Source: Authors' calculations.

Notes: Absolute value of z statistics in parentheses; * significant at 10%; ** significant at 5%; *** significant at 1%.

their own labour supply. In doing so, they may attempt to mitigate the potential earnings loss or the increased health care expenditure incurred by the ill household member(s). The health status of the other household members is measured by the mean value of the self-reported health indicator. The key results are reported in Table 4.4. (The Annex to Chapter 4 and Table A4.6 give a more detailed methodological description and complete empirical results.)

The empirical results support many of the above hypotheses. Ill health does reduce wages (that is, labour productivity) to a sizeable degree, and individuals respond to the ill health of other family members by increasing their own labour supply. However, although the labour supply effect has the expected sign, it is insignificant. The second column shows that self-reported health (coded from 1 "very good" to 5 "very bad") depends significantly on labour supply: the longer the hours spent at work, the lower the self-reported health status. The third column shows that labour supply varies negatively with the wage rate (transformed to a logarithm) but not with self-reported health. Finally, the fourth column shows that health significantly reduces wages: a worker in good health earns, on average, an hourly wage that is approximately 16% higher than a worker in poor health. However, the total health impact (direct and indirect through wages) on labour supply remains ambiguous.

As for coping behaviour in response to ill health among other household members, the results indicate that workers, on average, increase their own labour supply by 11.5 hours per week if the mean health status of the other family members worsens by one level (for instance, from average to bad). It is plausible that such coping responses may well represent a welfare loss, in particular in a dynamic sense. This is, however, ultimately an empirical question that future research must answer.

◆ **South-eastern Europe (Albania, Bosnia and Herzegovina, Bulgaria and the Province of Kosovo (Serbia))**

This section provides an overview of the impact of ill health on labour market outcomes in selected south-eastern European countries or entities. The findings are based on work carried out by the authors on a related project (Favaro and Suhrcke 2006). Countries were included if appropriate microdata were available and accessible, which was the case for Albania, Bosnia and Herzegovina, Bulgaria and the Province of Kosovo (Serbia). (As a result of differences between surveys, not all could be used for every empirical application.) The results of the analysis are presented for all the countries, for each labour market outcome indicator considered. These were the probability of being employed, labour productivity (measured by hourly wages), earnings, labour supply (measured by weekly hours of work) and the probability of early retirement. Although the results are typically presented for more than one country in the same table, the comparability of the estimates among countries is severely limited, not least given differences in the survey methodologies. Nevertheless, the results overall confirm, in a fairly robust manner, the negative impact of ill health on various labour market outcomes.

Probability of being employed
Table 4.5 presents estimates of the impact of self-reported health on the probability of being employed, whereby health was instrumented by different objective measures of disability. The three self-reported health categories are used as explanatory variables, and the fourth – "very poor health" – as the benchmark category. Each row evaluates the percentage increase in the probability of being employed as health improves compared to the "very poor" state of health.

As Table 4.5 shows, the biggest effect in terms of increased employment probability occurs when moving from "very poor" to "poor" health (although some caution is needed to avoid too literally comparing the results from the two surveys). Further improvements in health from this level add comparatively little value.

An example explains how to interpret these results. An Albanian individual with average characteristics and reporting "poor health" has a 22.6% higher probability of being employed than an individual reporting "very poor" health.

A similar two-stage analysis was carried out using the variable "number of missed days of working activity due to disability", which has often been used instead of self-reported health as a proxy for health.[60] This analysis could be carried out for all four countries. The Albanian analyses suggest that one additional day of work missed due to disability reduces annual earnings by 1.7%. In Bosnia and Herzegovina, one missed day due to disability reduces annual earnings by 0.6%. The effects of health were not significant in Bulgaria or the Province of Kosovo (Serbia).

However, the effect of ill health on labour supply – measured by the number of hours worked – is statistically significant in Bulgaria and the Province of Kosovo (Serbia), with health again proxied by the number of days missed due to disability and the use of a two-stage procedure. An additional day of inactivity due to disability induces a 0.6% reduction in hours worked in Bosnia and Herzegovina and 0.9% in the Province of Kosovo (Serbia).

Based on the limited number of countries in SEE for which it could be assessed, ill health appears to have less impact on labour productivity, proxied by the wage rate. A statistically significant impact was found only in Albania and in Bosnia and Herzegovina: a missed day (in a month) due to disability in Albania leads to a 5.2% reduction in hourly wages, that is, in productivity. For Bosnia and Herzegovina the effect is statistically significant, but relatively small: one day missed because of illness reduces productivity by 0.1%.

No significant effect was detected in either Bulgaria or the Province of Kosovo (Serbia), using the same measure of health. An analysis based on the method used by Lee (1982) that used self-reported health in a two-stage model found no significant effect in Albania or the Province of Kosovo (Serbia).

Impact of ill health on retirement
Ill health – here measured by the presence of a chronic illness – also affects the decision to retire, an additional dimension of labour supply. Individuals affected by chronic disease are significantly more likely to retire compared to other workers, irrespective of age, in the countries where this could be examined: Albania, Bosnia and Herzegovina and Bulgaria. Table 4.6 shows that the effect appears particularly strong in Albania, although precise cross-country

---

59. The evidence presented in the section on the Russian Federation also contained a modest exercise that assessed the impact of alcohol consumption on one labour market outcome, the probability of losing one's job.

60. A two-stage estimation methodology is used, estimating a tobit model in the first step for predicting the "number of days of inactivity due to disability" and adding the prediction of this estimate in the second stage (as a regressor of the equation explaining the labour market outcome in question).

Table 4.6 *Results of Cox regression model on age to retirement, Albania, Bosnia and Herzegovina, and Bulgaria*

	Coefficients		
	Albania	*Bosnia and Herzegovina*	*Bulgaria*
Age	1.112**	-0.044**	-0.135**
Age squared	-0.009**	0.001***	0.001**
Female	8.152**	0.137	0.328
Age* female	-0.105**	-0.001	0.006
Married	0.302	0	-0.029
Chronic disease	0.359**	0.03**	0.142**
Observations	3757	95888	6126

Source: Favaro & Suhrcke, 2006.

Notes: * significant at 10%; ** significant at 5%; *** significant at 1%.

comparisons cannot be made because of differences in the data.

To derive these results, a different methodology was used: a Cox regression model, similar to the exercise described above for the Russian Federation.[61] Controlling for other relevant determinants of the decision to retire (such as age, gender and income), an assessment was made of the impact of chronic illness on the probability that an individual will retire in a given year after the first year of employment.[62] A limitation of this methodology is that one cannot be entirely sure about the direction of causality.

In summary, even if the evidence is mixed across the different outcome indicators, considerable evidence exists demonstrating the negative labour market impact of ill health. Among the various effects observed, there appears to be more evidence supporting an impact on labour supply than on labour productivity. A possible explanation for this difference is that wages are often

61. The Cox regression is a hazard regression model where the log hazard function of retirement is assumed to be a linear function of a baseline hazard function and some covariates. The coefficients estimated represent a proportional shift of the baseline hazard function due to the covariates. This methodology is usually employed in survival analysis, where the outcome considered is death.

62. Given the lack of information on the LSMS datasets, the age of 18 is assumed as the entry age in employment.

difficult to reduce,[63] so the labour market cannot equilibrate easily by reducing the wages of employees in bad health.

◆ Estonia

The results presented in this subsection are based on work published in a recent study on macroeconomics and health in Estonia (Suhrcke, Võrk & Mazzuco 2006). Using the Estonian Labour Force Survey, it was possible to examine the impact of ill health on three outcomes: labour force participation, labour supply and salaries, based on the two-stage procedure commonly used in this section. Using a less complex estimation procedure, an additional assessment was made of the impact of ill health on retirement (similar to the approaches used for the Russian and SEE data).

Labour force participation, labour supply and salaries
In all model specifications, the same general result is obtained: ill health is consistently bad for all three labour market outcomes. Individuals with a predicted "fair" health status are less likely to participate and are more likely to work fewer hours and achieve lower salaries than those with good health status. Those with a "poor" health status are even worse off for all three outcomes.

The size of the impact can again be illustrated by the marginal impact on LFP (Table 4.7). Men in "poor health" are almost 40% more likely not to participate in the labour force compared to those in "good health". For women the corresponding number is almost 30%.

The negative impact of ill health is confirmed for the two other labour market outcomes that were examined: weekly working hours (Table 4.8) and monthly salaries (Table 4.9). Being in poor health compared to good health reduces weekly working hours by more than 12 hours for men and by approximately 8 for women. Poor health also reduced men's monthly salaries by almost 1300 Estonian Kroon (€83, approximately 30% of the mean male salary) and women's by about 621 Kroon (€40, approximately 20% of the mean female salary). These are substantial effects, at the higher end of what the actual effects will be, because the sample also includes those respondents who were not working at the time of the survey.

Early retirement
Ill health emerges as an important factor in anticipating the decision to retire

---

63. Indeed, they correctly proxy productivity only above a minimum level, as explained in Footnote 46.

Table 4.7 *Reduction in the probability of participating in the labour force, compared to self-reported "good health" (marginal effects), Estonia*

	Male (%)	Female (%)
Fair health	-10***	-15***
Poor health	-39***	-29***

Source: Suhrcke, Võrk & Mazzuco, 2006.

Note: *** significant at the 1% level.

Table 4.8 *Reduction in weekly working hours compared to self-reported "good health", Estonia*

	Male	Female
Fair health	-2.7***	-3.0***
Poor health	-12.4***	-8.1***

Source: Suhrcke, Võrk & Mazzuco, 2006.

Notes: Numbers are derived from a transformation of the model coefficient as explained in Wooldridge (2002); *** significant at the 1% level.

Table 4.9 *Reduction in monthly salaries in response to "fair" and "poor" health compared to self-reported "good health", Estonia*

	Male		Female	
	Estonian Kroons	% of mean salary of working men	Estonian Kroons	% of mean salary of working women
Fair health	-205*	-4.8	-130*	-4.2
Poor health	-1 290***	-30.2	-621***	-20.0

Source: Suhrcke, Võrk & Mazzuco, 2006.

Notes: Numbers are derived from a transformation of the model coefficient as explained in Wooldridge (2002); * significant at the 10% level; ** significant at the 5% level; *** significant at the 1% level; Mean annual salary for working men is Estonian Kroon 25 420 and for women Estonian Kroon 20 750.

in Estonia. Both men and women reporting a chronic illness or disability[64] are more likely to have retired in the two years prior to the survey. The effect is statistically highly significant. For men, ill health increased the probability of retiring in the following year by 6.4% compared to those who do not report a chronic illness or disability. For women the corresponding figure is 5.6%.

Further explanatory variables in addition to health status were included, such as age, the amount of hours usually worked in a week, the number of members in the respondent's household, ethnicity, marital status, educational attainment and certain job characteristics (whether the subject is an employee and whether the contract is permanent or fixed term).

Data from the 2002 round of the Estonian Labour Force Survey were used to generate these estimates. The survey captures the population from age 15 to 74, living in Estonia. In order to exclude the possibility that the relationship between health and retirement is subject to reverse causality, the effect of health on retirement was assessed only for individuals who were working before 2000. The dependent variable was then constructed to take the value 1 if the individual left a job between 2000 and the survey year (2002) and 0 otherwise. The microeconomic results presented in this section paint a remarkably robust picture: ill health negatively affects labour market outcomes in Estonia.

◆ Ukraine[65]

A recent study found health status to have sizeable effects on earnings in Ukraine (Ivaschenko 2002), using the 1995 LSMS. It suggests that a 10% improvement in an individual's health status generally increases income from labour by 10.9% for men and 10.3% for women. The methodology used in the study is broadly similar to the one employed for the analysis of the Tajikistan data described above. The estimations address possible sample selection bias that arises from using a sample of working individuals, treats self-reported health status as an endogenous variable and uses an instrumental variable estimation method to obtain unbiased estimates of the effects of health on labour incomes.

The author looked at the effects of health across the income distribution using quantile regressions. The result showed that, for men, the impact of health on earnings is significant only at the bottom of the distribution, corroborating the

---

64. Ill health is here defined as an affirmative answer to the question, "Do you suffer from a lasting disease or disability which has lasted or is likely to last for 6 months or longer?"

65. The results from Ukraine reported here were not produced for this report but stem from Ivaschenko (2002), which used the Ukraine 1995 LSMS.

hypothesis that for jobs requiring much physical effort (presumably low-paid jobs) health is a particularly important determinant of returns in the labour market.

The type of job also affects the relationship between health and labour incomes, as the inclusion of an interaction term between health and the types of job reveals. For unskilled male workers (defined by a grade of job and the level of education that a job requires), health status has a substantial impact on earnings.

Further evidence on the economic impact of ill health in CEE-CIS

The evidence presented in the case studies above focuses on the impact of adult health on the labour market for a reasonably representative selection of countries from the CEE-CIS Region. The main reason for assembling this evidence is to provide hitherto non-existing evidence to test the hypothesis that adult health *does* matter for economic outcomes – in this case for a set of labour market outcomes. Since the greatest share of adult ill health is accounted for by noncommunicable disease (and injuries), and since some of the health proxies employed directly measure chronic illness, the findings can at the same time be interpreted as evidence in support of the economic importance of noncommunicable (or chronic) disease.

This does not, however, mean that labour market outcomes are the only relevant economic outcomes to consider; nor does it mean that other health challenges do not impose any notable economic costs. On the contrary, one reason why the focus here is on adult health (including noncommunicable diseases) and not on other health concerns is precisely that it is already widely accepted that communicable disease and child and maternal health issues do impose a major economic burden.[66] As mentioned earlier, the CMH made this point particularly clear (CMH 2001). A few studies also exist that demonstrate the economic costs of some of these issues for the CEE-CIS Region, although there continues to be scope for more work on this topic. Some of this existing work is summarized briefly below, focusing on the issues of mal- and undernutrition as well as on HIV/AIDS.

Micronutrient deficiencies

Inadequate intake of vitamins and minerals, usually referred to as micronutrients, results in a number of poor health outcomes, all of which entail sub-

---

66. On the economic benefits of investing in children's health, see, for example, Belli, Bustreo & Preker (2005).

Table 4.10 *The causes and consequences of iron, iodine and vitamin A deficiencies*

Nutrient	Causes	Consequences
Iron	Poor intake increased physiological requirements (such as pregnancy, growth), parasitic infections (such as malaria, hookworm), blood loss (such as from IUDs, postpartum haemorrhage)	Prematurity, low birth weight, increased risk of morbidity and mortality, decreased capacity to work and cognitive function
Iodine	Poor intake due to iodine-deficient soils	Severe mental retardation (cretinism), average reduction of IQ by 11 points with all iodine deficiency, prematurity, stillbirths, spontaneous miscarriages
Vitamin A	Poor intake of foods with vitamin A activity	Partial or complete loss of eyesight, suppressed immune system activity, increased morbidity and mortality in children and possibly women, stunted growth and retarded development in general

Source: Levin et al., 1993.
Note: IUD: intrauterine device.

stantial economic costs over the short and longer term. As noted previously, vitamin A deficiency is associated with compromised growth and immune function, while iron and iodine deficiencies are associated with impaired educational achievement, labour productivity and reproductive capacity (Table 4.10). All three deficiencies can be overcome by programmes that are easily implemented at low cost.

Several World Bank reports elaborate on the economic importance of mal- or undernutrition worldwide (World Bank 2006c; Gillespie, McLachlan & Shrimpton 2003) and in the CEE-CIS Region (Rokx, Galloway & Brown 2002), although typically there are no direct cost estimates for the CEE-CIS countries. The recent Global Progress Report on Vitamin & Mineral Deficiency (UNICEF & The Micronutrient Initiative 2004) gives some quantitative idea of the economic costs associated with micronutrient deficiencies in 80 low- and middle-income countries, including a selection of CEE-CIS countries, all from central Asia and the Caucasus. The prevalence data from this report are in Chapter 3. Table 4.11 focuses on estimates of the economic costs associated with the known prevalence of micronutrient deficiencies for the CEE-CIS countries that were reviewed. Costs vary from 0.3% of GDP in Armenia to 1.2% in Tajikistan and Uzbekistan.

Table 4.11 *Nutritional deficiencies and estimated economic costs, selected countries*

Country	Economic cost due to all forms* of vitamin and nutritional deficiency (% of GDP)
Armenia	0.3
Azerbaijan	0.7
Georgia	0.5
Kazakhstan	0.6
Kyrgyzstan	0.9
Tajikistan	1.2
Turkmenistan	0.7
Uzbekistan	1.2

Source: UNICEF & The Micronutrient Initiative, 2004.

Notes: * "All forms" of vitamin and micronutrient deficiency includes folate deficiency in addition to those mentioned in this table; Data are estimates.

Undernutrition

The evidence for the impact of severe malnutrition on cognitive function is particularly convincing in infants and preschool children. Early childhood malnutrition can lead to cognitive impairments that last into the school-age years. Even short-term hunger (e.g., missing breakfast) leads to impaired cognitive performance in school-age children. The relationships between malnutrition and mortality, morbidity, educational performance and work performance are widely documented (McGuire 1996). Stunting in childhood continues into adulthood, resulting in adults of short stature (Ruel, Rivera & Habicht 1995). One study in the Philippines found a linear relationship between physical stature and productivity in adult workers and calculated that a 1% decrease in height is associated with a 1.4% decrease in productivity (Haddad and Bouis 1991). Studies assessing the cost of undernutrition in the CEE-CIS context appear to be largely absent, although there is at least one exception, in Uzbekistan (Rokx, Galloway & Brown 2002).

In Uzbekistan, a simple calculation showed that stunting will cause enormous losses of future productivity. Of the pre-school children included, 31% were found to be stunted by the age of three years. Of those stunted, 14% were severely stunted. After the age of about 22 months, severely stunted children were about 10 centimetres shorter than normal children, and moderately stunted children 7 centimetres shorter. Stunting during childhood develops into height deficits of the same magnitude in adulthood. Assuming an average height of 1.60 metres, 7–10 centimetres corresponds to a 4.38–6.25% reduction in height due to impaired growth during childhood, which is estimated to yield losses in labour productivity of 6.0% for the moderately stunted and 8.6% for the severely stunted. Assuming an annual current wage of US$ 870, the loss of productivity in these children will result in economic losses of about US$ 33 million (Rokx, Galloway & Brown 2002).

HIV/AIDS

As discussed in Chapter 3, the CEE-CIS Region is experiencing the world's fastest-growing HIV/AIDS epidemic. Numerous recent studies demonstrated the huge economic burden imposed by HIV/AIDS on individuals, households and countries (CMH 2001; Haacker 2004; Bell, Devarajan & Gersbach 2003), particularly in developing countries. In the CEE-CIS Region, two World Bank studies assessed the economic consequences of HIV/AIDS in the Russian Federation (Ladnaia, Pokrovsky & Rühl 2003) and more recently in Ukraine (International HIV/AIDS Alliance in Ukraine and World Bank 2006).[67]

It is unsurprising that the human suffering and devastation caused by HIV/AIDS imposes serious economic costs worldwide, far beyond the costs of prevention and treatment. They arise because the prevalence of HIV and AIDS affects the factors of production of national wealth: labour and human and physical capital.

The disease has a two-fold effect on labour supply: a decline in absolute numbers of workers as the death rate increases and a decline in the productivity of workers made ill by the virus or forced to leave the workforce to care for a family member(s). Beyond the immediate impact on the labour market, HIV/AIDS can erode a country's human capital as it disproportionately affects young people. Without the disease, young people would be more likely to stay in the labour force for a longer time, building up human capital and expertise.

Investment and real capital formation are affected through two primary channels. The first relates to the diversion of resources necessary to combat the disease and prevent HIV-positive individuals from developing full-blown AIDS. The second channel concerns the impact of HIV on private savings.

---

67. For a continuing update of economic studies of HIV/AIDS in CEE-CIS as well as related material, see eca.iaen.org/ (accessed 7 January 2007). This subsite of the International AIDS Economics Network focuses on the economics of HIV/AIDS prevention and treatment in the CEE-CIS Region. It provides data, tools and analysis for researchers and policy-makers working to define and implement effective AIDS policy in CEE-CIS.

The savings rate of HIV-positive individuals declines as they have to shift resources into health care and preventive treatment, and as their time horizon (and their preference for future consumption) diminishes. The diminished availability of savings increases the costs of investment and hence will adversely affect the rate of real capital formation over time.

What were the findings of the Russian study in terms of the economic cost of HIV/AIDS? Rather than assessing the past or current impact of the disease (as was performed for adult health in the exercises described above), a simulation model was used to predict the potential macroeconomic effects of different future HIV/AIDS scenarios. Results for an unchecked epidemic suggested that under some scenarios the following outcomes would occur.

- GDP in 2010 would be 4.15% lower than in the successful intervention scenario and 10.5% lower by 2020. Perhaps more significantly for long-term development, the uninhibited spread of HIV would diminish the economy's long-term growth rate, reducing growth by half a percentage point annually by 2010 and a full percentage point annually by 2020.

- Investment would decline by more than production. Without intervention, investment would decline by 5.5% by 2010 and 14.5% by 2020, indicating an increasing impediment to economic growth.

The economic costs of HIV and its impact on an economy's rate of growth therefore exceed the narrow fiscal dimension commonly discussed. To assess just the fiscal consequences of the budgetary costs of treatment and prevention, the adverse effect on budgetary expenditures for other programmes and the devastating long-term effects on the stability of health and pension systems is to ignore the larger economic consequences of HIV.

The recent study on HIV/AIDS in Ukraine is interesting in that it also highlights some of the broader social repercussions over the short and medium terms (2004–2014). The phenomenon of children being orphaned to HIV/AIDS is already taking a toll on both society and households there. According to the medium scenario (out of three), Ukraine will have 42 000 dual orphans due to AIDS-related deaths of both parents by 2014. Those children (and at least twice as many children who will have lost at least one parent) are at risk of impeded access to quality education, health care, and even basic needs, which in turn puts them at higher risk of unemployment, diseases, and poverty.

In pure epidemiological terms, AIDS is projected to reduce male life expectancy by 2–4 years: from 65.6 in the hypothetical scenario of no AIDS, to 63.4 (optimistic) or 61.6 years (pessimistic scenario). (Effects for women are of similar magnitude.) Turning to the more narrow economic effects, the study predicts that based on various plausible AIDS scenarios during 2004–2014, an expected 1–2% reduction in the labour force would be attributable to the epidemic. In addition, since the younger groups are most affected, the labour force losses will be felt for a long time. Using a rather detailed computable general equilibrium model, the study was also able to specify sectors of the economy that will be hit hardest: those producing non-energy materials and processing metallurgy and metal. Output in those sectors is predicted to fall by up to a third in the most pessimistic scenario (compared to the no-AIDS benchmark).

The study also highlights the detrimental effects in the business realm, for the health sector as well as the public sector (International HIV/AIDS Alliance in Ukraine and World Bank 2006).

Macroeconomic impact

If the excessive burden of adult ill health in CEE-CIS were reduced, what economic benefits might result? This section presents two ways of assessing the potential macroeconomic impact of future health improvements for a selected, representative set of CEE-CIS countries. The first subsection takes a commonly employed economic growth framework to project the future path of per-capita incomes, conditional on different adult mortality trajectories. The second goes beyond the use of GDP and proposes a broader – welfare-based – measure of economic benefits. Irrespective of how economic benefits are measured, the overall economic gains that can be reaped from improving health appear substantial.

Impact on economic growth

Recent worldwide empirical evidence strongly suggests that health is a robust determinant of economic growth. This impact is driven by effects on savings (Bloom, Canning & Graham 2003), on human capital investment (Kalemli-Ozcan, Ryder & Weil 2000), on labour market participation (Thomas 2001), on foreign direct investment (Alsan, Bloom & Canning 2004), and on productivity growth (Bloom, Canning & Sevilla 2003). The combined effects of health on economic growth are confirmed in theoretic and empirical work by Barro (1997); Bhargava et al. (2001); Bloom, Canning & Sevilla (2001); and Jamison, Lau & Wang (2004), among many others.

Studies examining the impact of health on income levels or income growth differ substantially in terms of the country samples, time frames, control variables, functional forms, data definitions and estimation techniques they use. Nevertheless, parameter estimates of the effects of life expectancy on economic growth have been remarkably comparable and robust across studies, notwithstanding the observation that the empirical growth regression results are generally not particularly robust, given the high degree of multicollinearity between many of the explanatory variables used (Levine and Renelt 1992; Sala-i-Martin, Doppelhofer & Miller 2004). In some studies, initial health status, typically proxied by life expectancy or adult mortality, proved to be a more significant and more important predictor of subsequent growth than the education indicators employed (Barro 1997).

Bhargava et al. (2001), for instance, shows in the context of a panel regression that the five-year growth rate of GDP per capita depends on a country's adult mortality rate, among other factors. The work also shows that the direction of causality runs unambiguously from adult mortality to growth. This section applies an empirical relationship of this kind to five selected CEE-CIS countries and then employs the empirical results to project different future trajectories of GDP per capita, conditional on three different scenarios for future adult mortality. In doing so, an assumption is made that the empirical regularities that exist in a representative world sample of countries also exist for the countries examined (see Box 4.3 for details). The three simple future scenarios for adult mortality are shown here.

- Scenario 1 (benchmark): adult mortality rate remains at the same rate as in 2000;

- Scenario 2 (intermediate): adult mortality rate declines at 2% p.a. (per annum);

- Scenario 3 (optimistic): adult mortality rate declines at 3% p.a.

Box 4.3 Technical details and results of economic growth impact estimates

A standard pooled ordinary least squares (OLS) growth regression was run for the period 1960–2000. The dependent variable is the contemporaneous real gross domestic product (GDP) per capita in logs. The other explanatory variables are the five-year lagged GDP per capita, the lagged fertility rate, the lagged working-age mortality rate[68] and the Warner-Sachs index[69] of openness. The fertility rate is from the World Development Indicators (World Bank 2005a), and the adult mortality rate is constructed from the World Health Organization (WHO) mortality database.

Since OLS panel growth regressions yield downward-biased estimates of the

---

68. Working age is assumed to extend from 15 to 64.

69. This variable is a time-invariant dummy variable with value 1 if an economy has been considered as open during 1965–1990. See Sachs & Warner (1995b) and Gallup, Sachs & Mellinger (1999).

(cont.)

Box 4.3 *(cont.)*

predicted real GDP per capita (Trognon 1978), a fixed-effect (FE) estimator is also applied on the same regression equation estimated with OLS. The FE regression is known to yield upward-biased estimates of the predicted real GDP per capita (Nickel 1981). Hence, the unbiased real GDP path is bounded by the OLS and FE estimates. Estimates from OLS and FE regressions are reported in Table 4.12.

The growth projections from the OLS estimations show an average growth rate of 14% per five-year period, roughly 3% p.a. Accordingly, the growth projections based on the FE estimations even suggest an annual growth rate of approximately 7%. The results, in Table 4.12, show a convergence rate of 14% with OLS, or even 35% with FE estimator, well above the 2% that is established in the empirical growth literature. However, as Islam (1995) noted, convergence rates increase dramatically in a panel data context. The long-run convergence rate is then mixed with business cycle

Table 4.12 *Growth regression results, five countries*

OLS – dependent variable: current log real GDP per capita	OLS	FE
Lagged log real GDP p.c.	0.862***	0.642***
	-39.69	-13.45
Openness index: 1965–1990	0.157***	–
	-6.76	–
Lagged log fertility rate	-0.048	-0.190***
	-1.6	-3.34
Lagged log adult mortality: 15–64	-0.077**	-0.155**
	-1.97	-2.46
Constant	1.908***	4.714***
	-4.79	-6
Observations	302	302
R-squared	0.965	0.873

Sources: GDP data are from Penn World Data 6.1 (Heston, Summers & Aten, 2002) (available at pwt.econ.upenn.edu/, accessed 1 December 2006); "Openness index" is a time-invariant dummy variable between 1965 and 1990 from Gallup, Sachs & Mellinger (1999) (available at www.cid.harvard.edu/ciddata/ciddata.html, accessed 1 December 2006); The fertility rate is from World Bank (2005a).

Notes: Heteroscedasticity-consistent standard errors in parenthesis (robust t statistics) *, **, *** denote significance at the 10%, 5% and 1% levels, respectively; Country dummies and fixed effects are not reported; OLS: ordinary least squares; FE: fixed effects.

Box 4.3 *(cont.)*

effects. Concerning the variable of interest in this study, the lagged adult mortality rate is found to be highly significant for both estimators, with a negative sign as expected. Hence, the larger the mortality rate, the lower the GDP per capita growth.

Next, these alternative growth regressions are used to predict GDP per capita up to the year 2025. This requires an assumption about the future path of the fertility rate: in order to attribute the entire gain in future GDP to adult mortality reduction, it is assumed that fertility rates remain constant. Similarly, the openness status of the five countries considered (the Russian Federation, Romania, Georgia, Kazakhstan and Lithuania) is assumed to remain constant over the next 20 years.

As described above, three different annual rates of reduction in future adult mortality are assumed: 0%, 2% and 3%. Based on these scenarios, a projection is carried out separately on the OLS and FE estimates, shown in **Figure 4.2**.

As Figure 4.2 illustrates, the predicted per-capita GDP path is highly dependent on the choice of estimation methodology. As expected, the FE estimates produce a steeper per-capita GDP gradient than the OLS estimates; the "true" effect will lie somewhere in between. Either estimate clearly shows, however, that reducing mortality rates would have a sizeable impact on future incomes, and the size of that impact would grow over time. Table A4.7 in the Annexes presents GDP per capita forecasts for five selected CEE-CIS countries.

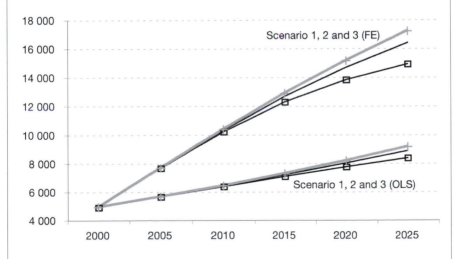

Figure 4.2 *GDP (in US$ PPP) per capita forecasts based on OLS and FE regression (Source: Authors' calculations based on model presented in Table 4.12, using results for Georgia).*

Notes: OLS: ordinary least squares; FE: fixed effects.

Table 4.13 illustrates the expected gains in a conservative way: it looks exclusively at the gains predicted on the basis of the OLS estimates, and only in the intermediate scenario. The benefits are presented in two ways. The fifth column gives the annual percentage gain for each year in the table. (Given the model specification, which includes five-year lagged mortality rates, reducing mortality from 2000 onwards affects GDP only from 2005 on; this reinforces the conservative nature of the estimates.) As there is an impact on economic growth, the percentage differences grow over time. The sixth column gives the total discounted value of the differences between the benchmark scenario and the intermediate scenario in each single year from 2000 to 2025. (This corresponds to the present value of the area between the benchmark predicted GDP per capita and the one in Scenario 2.) Table 4.14 summarizes the total discounted benefits of the intermediate and optimistic scenarios with respect to the benchmark scenario, based on both OLS and FE estimates.[70]

Table 4.14 shows that the total discounted benefit of the relatively modest Scenario 2, measured by the more conservative estimation methodology (OLS), already indicates substantial benefits, when expressed in terms of 2000 GDP. The benefits vary between 26% for the Russian Federation and Kazakhstan and 40% for Georgia and Romania. Such differences are essentially a result of the so-called catching-up effect: the fact that countries starting from lower levels of per-capita GDP tend to grow faster than those starting from higher levels. In this context, improving health (or decreasing mortality) speeds up growth much more effectively in the poorest countries.

The benefits estimated on the basis of the OLS results are already sizeable, but are dwarfed by the benefits estimated on the basis of the FE regression and even more so should the most optimistic scenario be realized. Put simply, it could be argued that any effective health investment plan launched in 2000 would realize a net economic gain, if it would: (1) achieve the 2% p.a. adult mortality reduction with respect to a benchmark case; and (2) cost less than the estimated benefits of, say, 26% of GDP (in the case of Kazakhstan).

These numbers should be seen primarily as indicative of the magnitude of the economic gains that can be reaped from better population health. Yet, while such superficial calculations as those in the previous paragraph can seem attractive, some caution is required. Ideally, the costs of any health investment programme must be taken into account and cannot be subtracted from the benefits ex post, simply because the programme itself and the way it is financed may affect economic growth. While the development of such a model would

70. See Table A4.7 in the Annexes for the complete forecast series, based on both OLS and FE regression, for all three scenarios.

Table 4.13 *Predicted GDP (US$) per capita for benchmark and intermediate scenarios at five-year intervals for five countries*

Year	Scenario 1: benchmark (constant AMR)	Scenario 2: intermediate (2% p.a. reduction in AMR)	% gain of Scenario 2 vs Scenario 1 in the same year	Total discounted benefits as a % of 2000 GDP p.c.
Russian Federation				
2000	8 013	8 013	–	26
2005	8 038	8 038	–	
2010	8 059	8 097	0.5	
2015	8 078	8 212	1.7	
2020	8 094	8 378	3.5	
2025	8 108	8 590	5.9	
Romania				
2000	4 287	4 287	–	40
2005	4 920	4 920	–	
2010	5 540	5 566	0.5	
2015	6 137	6 239	1.7	
2020	6 703	6 938	3.5	
2025	7 233	7 663	5.9	
Lithuania				
2000	7 242	7 242	–	30
2005	7 618	7 618	–	
2010	7 959	7 996	0.5	
2015	8 264	8 402	1.7	
2020	8 537	8 837	3.5	
2025	8 780	9 302	5.9	
Kazakhstan				
2000	7 394	7 394	–	26
2005	7 448	7 448	–	
2010	7 495	7 529	0.5	
2015	7 535	7 660	1.7	
2020	7 570	7 836	3.5	
2025	7 601	8 053	5.9	
Georgia				
2000	4 904	4 904	–	40
2005	5 645	5 645	–	
2010	6 373	6 403	0.5	
2015	7 076	7 193	1.7	
2020	7 744	8 015	3.5	
2025	8 369	8 867	5.9	

Source: Authors' calculations.

Notes: See Box 4.3 for further details; The discount rate used is 3%; AMR: adult mortality rate/10 000; GDP: gross domestic product; p.a.: per annum; p.c.: per capita.

Table 4.14 *Summary of discounted benefits as a share of 2000 GDP per capita in five countries*

	2% p.a. reduction of adult mortality rate (%)		3% p.a. reduction of adult mortality rate (%)		GDP p.c. (US$)
	OLS	FE	OLS	FE	(2000)
Russian Federation	26	62	39	95	8013
Romania	40	129	61	198	4287
Lithuania	30	77	46	118	7242
Kazakhstan	26	58	40	88	7394
Georgia	40	126	62	194	4904

Source: Authors' calculations.

Notes: Discounted (at 3% per year) gain from reducing adult mortality, keeping fertility rate constant at 2000 level; Measured with respect to the 2000 GDP per capita in percentage terms; GDP: gross domestic product; p.a.: per annum; OLS: ordinary least squares; FE: fixed effects; p.c.: per capita.

be desirable, it is far beyond the scope of the present book – and in fact beyond the current "state of the art" in the literature.

Impact on economic welfare

Several prominent economists, as well as international financial organizations such as the International Monetary Fund (IMF) and the World Bank recently began measuring the economic cost of mortality using a broader concept than GDP per capita. The new approach starts from the uncontroversial recognition that GDP is an imperfect measure of social welfare: it fails to incorporate the value of health. This new approach recognizes that the true purpose of economic activity is to maximize social welfare, not solely to produce goods.

Health is highly valued – more than most market or other non-market goods. It is not incorporated in the measurement of GDP because as a non-market good it has no quoted market price.[71] Yet obviously health has value. When asked, people are willing to pay substantially for better and longer health, so

71. The health care inputs included in the measurement of GDP represent only a small share of the true value of health, as argued here.

there must be an implicit value that people attribute to health. While this value is high, it is not infinite, since people are not willing to give up everything in exchange for better health.[72]

One way to make the high value attributed to health more explicit is by measuring the extent to which one is willing to trade off health with specific market activities for which a price exists. Willingness-to-pay (WTP) studies undertake this measurement. WTP can be inferred from risk premiums in the job market: jobs that entail health risks, such as mining, pay more in the form of a risk premium. Numerous WTP studies now make it possible to calculate a "value of a statistical life" (VSL), which can be used to value changes in mortality. Usher (1973) first introduced the value of mortality reductions into national income accounting. This was carried out by generating estimates of the growth in "full income" (or "wealth"), a concept that captures changes in life expectancy by including them in an assessment of economic welfare, for six political entities (Canada, Chile, France, Japan, Sri Lanka and Taiwan, China) during the middle decades of the 20th century. For the higher-income countries, about 30% of the growth in full income resulted from declines in mortality. Estimates of changes in full income are typically generated by adding the value of changes in annual mortality rates (calculated using VSL figures) to changes in annual GDP per capita. Even these full-income estimates are conservative, including only the value of changes in mortality while excluding the total value of changes in morbidity.

For the United States, Nordhaus (2003) rediscovered Usher's pioneering work and found that the economic value of increases in longevity in the last hundred years roughly equals the value of measured growth in non-health goods and services. Nordhaus tested the hypothesis that improvements in health status have made a major contribution to economic wealth (defined as full income) over the 20th century. A more detailed assessment reveals that "health income" probably contributed somewhat more to changes in full income than did non-health goods and services before 1950 and marginally less than non-health goods and services afterwards. If the results of this and other related analyses (e.g. Viscusi & Aldy (2003); Crafts (2003); Miller (2000); Cutler & Richardson (1997); Costa & Kahn (2003)) are confirmed, then the role of health should be reconsidered: the social productivity of spending on health (via the health system and other sectors that impact on health) may be many times greater than that of other forms of investment.

---

72. Referred to here are situations where people face marginal trade-offs between health and other goods, not the far less representative situation where people face immediate death, the prospect of which would increase readiness to pay.

Following the procedure Nordhaus proposed, the total value of reducing adult mortality by 2% or 3% per year from 2000 to 2025 (non-adult mortality rates remaining constant) was calculated for the same five CEE-CIS countries (Georgia, Kazakhstan, Lithuania, Romania and the Russian Federation) as in the economic growth estimates in the previous section. The benchmark against which these two scenarios are evaluated is again one in which total (adult and non-adult) mortality rates remain constant at the 2000 level.

The Nordhaus procedure essentially involves the multiplication of the VSL by the number of avoided deaths for each year between 2000 and 2025. The critical input is the VSL. Determining a reliable estimate of the VSL for each of the five countries is, however, beyond the scope of this book. The evaluation is carried out using two different, but simple estimates for the VSL.

For the first set of evaluations, a conservative estimate of US$ 500 000 is assumed for all five countries (Table 4.15). This is the same conservative value used for a VSL for the Russian Federation in World Bank (2005b) and Suhrcke et al. (2007).

The second set of evaluations take account of a widely accepted finding that one important way in which the VSL differs across countries is in relation to differences in per-capita incomes in the countries. The Miller review (2000) adjusted the VSL according to GDP per capita, based on the following relationship: VSL = 132 x GDP per capita.[73] For the present illustrative purposes this rule of thumb will be used to estimate the VSL for the five countries of interest. The results are shown in Table 4.16.

The welfare impacts in Table 4.15 are always below those in Table 4.16, simply because the resulting VSL for each country is consistently higher in the second set of estimates compared to the first. The discounted (at 3% per year) and undiscounted sums of these values were then calculated and compared to the total real GDP over the same period.

The chosen approach differs slightly from Nordhaus' original procedure by adopting real GDP rather than real consumption as its term of comparison for the value of reduced mortality. Hence, the following results should be interpreted as the proportion of income that a representative individual (as well as the country as a whole) is ready to pay each year in order to reduce the mortality rate. Table 4.15 presents the results when the VSL is set at US$ 500 000

---

73. This specification implies an income elasticity of 1, which is in line with the range of income elasticities of the VSL that Miller finds to vary between 0.95 and 1.00. In perhaps the most comprehensive study to date, Viscusi & Aldy (2003) finds income elasticities of 0.51 to 0.53. The lower the elasticities the higher the VSL for the five countries would be. This further strengthens the conservativeness of the selected estimates.

Table 4.15 *Value of reduced mortality with VSL at US$ 500 000 (as a percentage of 2000 real GDP)*

Case	Georgia	Kazakhstan	Lithuania	Romania	Russian Federation
Scenario: 2% p.a. reduction of adult mortality					
Undiscounted	8.3	13.3	9.2	14.6	15.0
Discounted	6.0	9.5	6.7	10.6	10.8
Scenario: 3% p.a. reduction of adult mortality					
Undiscounted	11.2	17.8	12.4	19.7	20.2
Discounted	8.3	13.0	9.1	14.5	14.8
2000 real GDP (Billion US$)	25	110	27	96	1 166
2000 real GDP p.c. (US$)	4 904	7 393	7 242	4 287	8 012

Source: Authors' calculations.

Notes: VSL: value of a statistical life; p.a.: per annum; p.c.: per capita.

Table 4.16 Value of reduced mortality with VSL at 132 x GDP per capita (as a percentage of 2000 real GDP)

Case	Georgia	Kazakhstan	Lithuania	Romania	Russian Federation
Scenario: 2% p.a. reduction of adult mortality					
Undiscounted	10.8	25.9	17.7	16.6	31.6
Discounted	7.8	18.6	12.8	12.0	22.9
Scenario: 3% p.a. reduction of adult mortality					
Undiscounted	14.6	34.8	23.8	22.3	42.7
Discounted	10.7	25.3	17.4	16.4	31.4
2000 real GDP (Billion US$)	25	110	27	96	1 166
2000 real GDP p.c. (US$)	4 904	7 393	7 242	4 287	8 012

Source: Authors' calculations.

Notes: VSL: value of a statistical life; p.a.: per annum; p.c.: per capita.

and Table 4.16 shows the results when the VSL is 132 times the value of the 2000 real GDP per capita.

The figures in Table 4.15 and Table 4.16 also indicate the high economic "welfare" benefits associated with the reduction in adult mortality according to the 2% and 3% scenarios. The expected benefits – expressed as a share of 2000 GDP – vary markedly across the five countries, with the variation being driven to a large extent by the initial level of adult mortality rates: a 2% (or 3%) reduction starting from a high level of mortality such as in the Russian Federation translates into greater gains than from lower initial mortality levels. It is important to reiterate that these are conservative estimates and they are not directly comparable with the economic growth-based estimates from the previous subsection. This is because: (1) in the present case the future GDP per capita is not assumed to respond to a reduction in mortality; and (2) the VSL is assumed to be constant over the entire period. The use of future increases in GDP per capita would significantly increase the estimated benefits, since the VSL increases in per-capita GDP.

Conclusions

It is widely accepted that economic status contributes to health: this chapter shows that health status contributes to economic outcomes, at the micro- and macroeconomic levels, in narrow as well as in broad economic terms. It follows that if health can be improved, a whole range of economic benefits would result.

The prime area of interest was noncommunicable disease and, hence, the empirical research presented focused on adult health. At the same time some of the already-existing evidence on the economic relevance of communicable disease and child health is synthesized.

After reviewing findings from outside CEE-CIS that would illuminate the research undertaken by the authors, the chapter examines the effects of ill health in the CEE-CIS Region at the individual and household levels. Wherever feasible, empirical methodologies were applied to come close to an assessment of *causality* and not merely of *association* in the relationship between health and the economic indicator of interest. For the most part this was achieved by using a two-stage regression model.

The bulk of the micro-economic evidence documents how ill health detracts from individuals' labour market productivity and supply, key vehicles affecting household incomes and – in the aggregate – economic growth. The research effort exploited micro-level survey data from eight CIS countries, and in addition single-country evidence for the Russian Federation, Tajikistan, SEE, Estonia and Ukraine. The variability of findings makes them hard to characterize briefly, but the overall message of the negative economic impact of ill health holds true throughout.

The fact that all the other ways in which ill health may hamper economic development (e.g. by eroding savings and restricting educational attainment) were not directly captured in the empirical analysis suggests that the full effects might even be greater. Future research should clearly fill this gap.

The second part of this chapter moves forward to ask the question, if poor health is shown to negatively affect economic growth, then what promise for growth could reasonable health improvements provide? To assess the possibilities, projections were run for three scenarios (adult mortality was chosen as the health indicator as it has been shown to be a reliable predictor of economic growth, among other non-health factors): a stable adult mortality rate (AMR), an AMR reduced by 2% annually and an AMR reduced by 3% annually. Results found the impact of reduced adult mortality would (1) be sizeable and (2) grow over time, with variations that depend on a country's GDP at the starting point of the projections. The poorer the country at the start, the bigger the growth effect that will result from a reduced AMR. Caution is appropriate in interpreting the precise magnitude of the calculated gain, but sizeable gains would result from even a 2% drop in the AMR.

Using a different approach to measure the effect that a similar drop in an AMR would have on welfare with two separate values for a statistical life, these calculations also show reliable economic gain from improved mortality.

It is important to re-emphasize that it has not been the purpose of this chapter to argue that the mechanism running from health to economic development is any more important than the converse, well-known impact of economic development on health. What the chapter does try to underline is the fact that the relationship does indeed run both ways – not exclusively from economic wealth to health. A bidirectional relationship of this kind means that one problem cannot be solved without simultaneously addressing the other. This also means that governments are better off investing a given amount of resources in both, rather than in just one, as explained earlier.

While this is a crucial policy implication, it remains a general one and says nothing about the contents of any policies that ought to be put in place to achieve the desired health improvement. While it is not the aim of this book to give a detailed investment plan for the countries in CEE-CIS, Chapter 5 nonetheless addresses selected key issues regarding the rationale for, and the contents of, public policies to improve health.

Chapter 5
Investing in health

The preceding chapters assembled wide-ranging evidence showing that much is to be gained from investing in health in the CEE-CIS Region, not only in terms of actual health gains but also in terms of the economic benefits. None of what has gone before, however, specified *who* should invest or *how* to invest in health. Both issues are addressed in this chapter. Since a comprehensive assessment of these questions would easily justify a book of its own, the focus is on certain key points that may not have figured sufficiently in the policy debate so far.

Turning first to the question of "who should invest" reveals many potential players who can and should make important contributions to the health of a given population. The start of this chapter emphasizes that governments do have an essential and hitherto underestimated role to play in order to "do something" about the excessive burden of noncommunicable disease that accounts for the greatest share of the Region's ill health. While this role may be self-evident from a public health point of view, it is much less so from an economic perspective, so this section explores the economic rationale for public policy interventions to address the main health challenges in CEE-CIS. A focus on the role of government is not meant to downplay the role of other players, in particular civil society and the private sector.

The following section turns to the question of "how to invest", focusing on selected key issues. Clearly it is impossible to provide an exhaustive account here, but some of the main policy questions, especially in relation to health system reform, are available elsewhere (see, for example, Figueras et al. (2004)).

Any discussion of what should be done must inevitably start from an assessment of the determinants of the unfavourable health status in the CEE-CIS Region. This is followed by a synthesis of the main policy implications arising from these determinants, arguing that while the health system has a key role in effectively tackling the problems in the Region, a major response across governments is also required. The subsequent section explores why increasing health expenditure will often be necessary but will likely be insufficient on its own; that section highlights two factors that will be important in converting existing or increased resources into effective action: the quality of governance and the strength of social capital. It is argued that these are two areas where there are considerable weaknesses, with adverse consequences for population health. Significant gains in health could be achieved by addressing these weaknesses.

Who should invest?

An awareness of the potential investors in the Region finds three entities of greatest interest to our purposes here: civil society, the private sector and government. Each of these parties has a role to play in contributing to achieving better health and supporting growing economies in the CEE-CIS Region. After a review of those roles and some of the particularly challenging issues governments face, this chapter analyses how all three parties could begin with examinations of the determinants of poor health in the Region and cost-effective interventions, as well as the promising value of factors outside the health sector proper, such as good governance and social capital.

Civil society organizations already make a substantial contribution in the Region, especially in activities directed at vulnerable and marginalized populations, such as the Roma minority in central Europe (EERC 2006), prisoners, commercial sex workers, intravenous drug users (OSI 2006), people suffering from mental disability and children in institutions (OSI 2005). With all these populations, which are often hardest to reach with health-promoting messages, governments face major challenges and are least able to respond effectively. This is especially true for many people infected with HIV, in particular intravenous drug users and commercial sex workers, many of whom live on the margins of society with little contact with official agencies. Indeed, the scope for contact between government and these populations may be reduced because of distrust and fear of the consequences of engaging with what these populations may view as instruments of the state. In many places the only effective responses – harm-reduction activities that promote needle exchange, using methadone as a heroin substitute in addiction treatment and the distribution of condoms – are undertaken by nongovernmental organizations (OSI 2005; OSI 2006; McKee et al. 2000). It will be important for governments to work with a wide variety of agencies, respecting their particular expertise and skills.

However, the organizations working in these areas face great challenges in the policy arena. First, the populations they seek to help are often subject to discrimination and are seen as undeserving by majority populations, views that are sometimes echoed by politicians pursuing populist approval. Second, in parallel with the situation relating to ODA described in Chapter 3, there is little financial support for civil society organizations working in this Region compared to those in other parts of the world. High-profile global campaigns, such as Live Aid, are focused almost exclusively on the needs of Africa. The only major nongovernmental funder to play a substantial role in this Region is the Open Society Institute (OSI) and, while it and the many national organizations it has created have achieved a great deal with limited funds, a great deal more is needed.

In other parts of the world, the *private sector* has played an active role in supporting health initiatives. In some cases this has involved activities by employers, directed at the health of employees and their families; other activities have been more wide ranging, such as pharmaceutical manufacturers' efforts to expand access to essential drugs. Perhaps the most notable example is the Bill & Melinda Gates Foundation, which was established by the founder of Microsoft and his wife and which has been a major force behind the Global Fund to Fight AIDS, Tuberculosis and Malaria. In contrast, despite the emergence of a substantial number of billionaires in CEE-CIS since transition, private or commercial philanthropy in the area of health is yet to develop. It is noteworthy, however, that in some countries of the Region awareness of the importance of employee health for sheer business profits is spreading, as exemplified by the recent initiative "Business for a Healthy Society" by the International Business Leaders Forum in the Russian Federation.[74]

This Region is thus multiply disadvantaged, as it not only receives a suboptimal level of international development assistance but is also poorly served by private and commercial contributions. In these circumstances it is especially important that governments take the lead in promoting the health of their populations. By leading, governments may attract inputs from other sources.

The role of government

This section adopts an exclusively economic perspective to argue that government does have a role, in combination with civil society and the private

---

74. For more information, see http://eng.iblf.ru/projects/ill-health/health.html (accessed 1 March 2007).

sector, in dealing with the leading health challenges that afflict the Region.[75] Some might ask whether this case needs to be made. As has been discussed earlier, when the priorities of governments (and international donors) are assessed not by their words but by their expenditures and actions, it is apparent that poor health and, in particular, the burden imposed by noncommunicable disease do not feature strongly.

As already noted, it is a priori far from clear that an economic rationale exists for government intervention in noncommunicable disease or in health in general. Accepted economic reasoning holds that government intervention is merely an afterthought – market forces are usually considered to work best (or at least better than governments) in achieving, from a social perspective, the optimal allocation of resources. Liberal societies hold that government should not interfere with what seems, at least at first glance, to belong to the private sphere where people decide how to live their lives: the issue is "freedom of choice". There are, however, conditions under which the market, if left alone, fails to achieve optimal outcomes. In these cases, economists recommend policy interventions to correct market failure. This section examines if and when such conditions apply in the case of the risk factors that give rise to noncommunicable diseases. In addition, Box 5.1 describes the widely accepted economic rationale for government intervention in such areas as the provision of health services and control of communicable disease.

The economic rationale for intervention in health can be formulated on both efficiency and equity grounds.[76] "Efficiency" grounds justify public intervention when the social objectives of equity of access or outcomes are unlikely to be attained given existing income and resource distributions ("equity" grounds). This section focuses on the former, recognizing that the promotion of efficiency is less contentious than that of equity, especially in this Region where considerations of equity have, at times, incorrectly been seen as a reversion to the policies of the Soviet era. This is, however, not to imply that considerations of equity do not apply to noncommunicable diseases. Given the evidence presented earlier of the negative economic effects of such diseases, coupled with the observation that the poor bear a disproportionate share of the

---

75. See Suhrcke et al. (2006) for a more elaborate discussion of the arguments in this section.

76. More precisely, public policy intervention is justified from an economic perspective if two conditions are met: a market failure exists, and interventions exist that would correct the market failure without imposing costs on society that exceed the benefits. This section focuses on the evidence of the first condition and postpones discussion of the second to subsequent work. Evidence on the cost–effectiveness of interventions is presented below. Neither is the possibility of government failure discussed at length here, despite its also being an important and empirically relevant issue.

Box 5.1 The economic rationale for government intervention in health care and communicable disease

Arrow (1963) set out a theoretical foundation for public policy intervention in the health sector that is now widely accepted. In outlining this case, Arrow subdivides the health sector into the *provision of health services* and *health insurance*. Both sub-sectors warrant strong concerns about market failure. The arguments presented here are directly applicable to chronic disease treatment and insurance, as well as other health issues. In many low- and middle-income countries, the government health services treating chronic disease are minimal at best, and formal health insurance is not well developed in the CEE-CIS countries.

Health service provision

The main problem in health service provision is that buyers have insufficient informa-tion to (1) know which service they require and (2) assess its quality. If health services were traded on a free market, buyers would have to trust the sellers (e.g. the hospi-tals or doctors), whose interest (i.e., including profit maximization) is unlikely to align perfectly with that of patients. In such conditions, leaving health service provision to the market without any public intervention would result in large inefficiencies. To address the issue, the buyers should be placed in a position where they can decide appropriately which service to purchase.

Another source of market failure in health care provision is the existence of positive externalities associated with the consumption of health services. The situation of externalities is clear with communicable diseases, where health services produce positive externalities as they stop the spread of contagion, e.g. treating an individual for tuberculosis provides the external benefit of protecting the health of those in the population who might be exposed through the individual. Since individuals, if left alone, take account of only their own private costs and benefits, the market by itself will generate insufficient consumption (or use) of services. Public intervention (through subsidies for instance) then becomes necessary to promote consumption, for instance through immunization campaigns or networks of medical facilities to provide coverage for those in need.

Health insurance

The problems of health insurance are essentially related to the presence of asymme-try in the information available to insurers and those they insure (Rothschild & Stiglitz 2006; Wilson 1980). When insurance programmes hedge against risks related to individual behaviour and decisions, a concern arises about the phenomenon of moral hazard, in which the redistribution of risks changes people's behaviour. It has been argued that, as the possession of insurance will neutralize any income loss that might result from illness, insured individuals have less incentive to protect their health. On the contrary, they might take risks they would avoid if uninsured. *(cont.)*

Box 5.1 *(cont.)*

Another acute concern related to asymmetric information is adverse selection, which arises because people in poor health are more likely to enrol in health insurance than those in good health. People in poor health often know they have an above-average need for insurance, while the insurance company lacks that information. In the absence of public intervention, it is believed that adverse selection would make the insurance market unsustainable. Too few healthy people would enter the market, making coverage of the insured pool more expensive to insurers. To meet the expense, the insurers would increase rates, driving away healthier customers. Eventually, so many healthy people would leave the market that insurers would follow suit for lack of profit, leaving the marketplace empty.

Government action can be effective in this area, either by offering universal health insurance financed through taxation or by imposing compulsory, universal health insurance and by obliging insurance companies to accept everyone. To make this work, the government must of course be able to enforce such regulation effectively.

burden of these diseases, the equity rationale is also highly relevant to the argument for intervening to reduce them in CEE-CIS.[77]

Considering only those issues that are of the highest direct relevance to non-communicable diseases, there are at least four conditions under which the market, left alone, fails to maximize efficiency, requiring policy interventions to correct the market failure:

- production or consumption externalities
- departures from rationality
- insufficient and asymmetric information
- time-inconsistent preferences/internalities.

Are any of these causes of market failures likely to apply in cases of noncommunicable disease and the lifestyle risk factors that are their prime proximate causes? To provide an answer, two issues must be separated: (1) the case for intervention in the health sector to provide access to treatment for chronic disease (see Box 5.1); and (2) the case for intervention in the domain of broader (outside the health sector) government policy to influence the lifestyle choices that lead to chronic disease. This section focuses on the latter, since, as men-

---

77. Although this book does not specifically address the equity justifications for public policy, the authors recognize that the traditional economics textbook division between efficiency and equity is at least partly misplaced, and may even be counterproductive, in the light of more recent evidence on potential complementarities between the two (World Bank 2004c). This issue should be developed in further research.

tioned above, the case for the former is already largely accepted.

The above four potential causes of market failure that policy-makers should consider during decision-making are discussed in the following subsections.

Externalities

Externalities are costs or benefits that are associated with the consumption of a good or service by an individual and that do not accrue to that individual (who alone bears the "private" costs/benefits) but which accrue to someone else or to society in general. Tobacco smoking is a classic example of behaviour with negative externalities, the harmful effects of second-hand smoke (US DHHS 2006) and the failure of health insurance to account for the higher use of medical services by smokers than nonsmokers (Jha & Chaloupka 1999). As externalities are not borne by individuals, costs or benefits are not automatically factored into consumption decisions, so levels of consumption (e.g. of tobacco, alcohol or unhealthy foods) can be higher than is beneficial to society as a whole. The size of the external costs and benefits is a challenging conceptual and empirical question, and is dependent on the institutional context, the cost-valuation method employed and where the line is drawn between private and external costs.

The accumulation of knowledge on the adverse health consequences of smoking, second-hand smoke and transmission of poor health by mothers to their unborn children (US DHHS 2006) has increased estimates of the external costs of tobacco use. Vigorous debate continues over the significance of the external effects of smoking-related diseases on health care costs. Smokers undoubtedly accrue above-average health care costs per year – but overall lifetime costs may be the same or even less than for nonsmokers in the developed world, as smokers die at a younger age (Viscusi & Aldy 2003). However, this argument loses much of its force where most smokers die while in working ages, as is the case in many CEE-CIS countries.

The effects of second-hand smoke and transmission of poor health to unborn children by smoking include an increased risk of various diseases and low birth weight of children born to smoking mothers (Charlton 1996).[78] Several studies have assessed the magnitude of the external effects of second-hand

---

78. See Andreeva et al. (2005) for recent evidence on the consequences of parental smoking on birth and child health outcomes in Ukraine. The study finds that while smoking during pregnancy was low (below 5% of pregnant women) in the sample of nearly 700 women examined, it was, for instance, associated with placental insufficiency and low birth weight. A father's smoking was associated with decreased fertility, late toxicosis and lower infant functional status, among other negative outcomes.

smoke – Gruber (2002) puts the costs at US$ 0.70 per pack in the United States, and the negative effects on infant health due to smoking mothers have been estimated to equal that amount.

Arguments derived from the effects of second-hand smoke may be of particular relevance for low- and middle-income countries (including CEE-CIS countries), where many people lack health insurance and where informal social networks, mainly extended families, provide "social security". A recent study showed that smokers or people living in a household where someone smokes were more than a third more likely to have to borrow money or liquidate household assets during a period of hospitalization compared with those in nonsmoking households (Bonu et al. 2005). Also, it is easy to see how the loss of income following a breadwinner's illness or disability might have substantial repercussions for children dependent on intrafamily transfers and who might be required to abandon their education in order to supply income, with negative consequences for the accumulation of their human capital.

The example of smoking may also illustrate one critical conceptual issue in the assessment of external costs that is likely to make a substantial difference in terms of the overall cost assessment. Traditionally, economists have considered the costs borne by the household as private. Implicitly, each member of the family was assumed to have identical preferences, or, alternatively, a smoker was assumed to have incorporated all preferences of other family members into his or her decisions about whether and how much to smoke. The traditional paradigm is changing, however, toward a view that considers the costs borne by household members other than the smoker as external. As a large share of the costs of smoking occurs within households (through second-hand smoke or intergenerational transmission), adding these costs to external cost estimates would greatly increase their size and thereby reinforce the rationale for government intervention (Sloan et al. 2004).

The external costs of heavy alcohol consumption are also substantial, manifesting primarily as traffic fatalities and violence. Manning et al. (1991) estimated that in the United States the total property damage from alcohol-related motor vehicle accidents was approximately US$ 3.6 billion in 1983 and that US$ 3.1 billion was spent that year on alcohol-related criminal trials. Kenkel (1993) found the total value of death and injuries resulting from drunk-driving in the United States in 1986 to be US$ 17.6 billion.

Unhealthy diet has not been shown to have any immediate external health consequences (except certain intergenerational effects that are transmitted either socially[79] or physiologically), but the insurance-induced external costs

---

79. Certain risky behaviours, such as smoking, alcohol consumption and perhaps dietary

can be substantial. The 1991 Manning study directly compared the external costs of obesity and smoking in the insurance context and found those for obesity to be greater.

Departures from rationality

The assumption that people act rationally (in other words, they maximize their expected utility) represents a core pillar of economic thought that is particularly useful when compared to other, less structured assumptions. It makes the analysis of individual behaviour much more tractable and allows economists to derive "optimal" behaviour in a normative sense. Models of rational behaviour can also be used to explain and predict actual behaviour. Dismissing the rationality assumption altogether is not an approach most economists would favour,[80] not least because it would open the way to paternalism in a broad range of areas – under the pretext of "helping people do what is best for them".

Bearing these concerns in mind, it is widely recognized among economists and others that in the specific case of children and adolescents, the rationality assumption does not hold true (Chaloupka & Jha 2000). Children and adolescents tend not to take the future consequences of their choices into account, irrespective of whether they have information about those future consequences: they act myopically[81] and, hence, non-rationally. The result of their choices may well differ systematically from their long-term best interests. This provides a principle that justifies government intervention to help them make better choices. In other words, part of the privately borne costs does become relevant to public policy.[82]

patterns involve social "communicability". Studies have found peer smoking to be a significant determinant of one's own smoking (Molyneux et al. 2002). This could be interpreted as a negative external effect – but one that has to be balanced against the positive benefits to the individual that derive from being part of the peer group.

80. This is not to overlook the relatively new and growing strand of economics concerning the concept of "bounded rationality". This term is used to designate models of rational choice that take into account the limitations of both knowledge and cognitive capacity. Bounded rationality is a central theme in behavioural economics and concerns the ways in which the actual decision-making process influences the decisions that are eventually reached. To this end, behavioural economics departs from one or more of the neoclassical assumptions underlying the theory of rational behaviour.

81. Consumers are considered myopic if they ignore the effects of current consumption on future utility when they determine the optimal or utility-maximizing quantity of an addictive good in the present. In technical terms, their discount rate is infinite. Some authors define myopic individuals as those who have a very high discount rate and attribute very little value to future consumption. In that definition, myopic behaviour can still be rational (as long as the discount rate does not become infinitely high).

82. For an in-depth treatment of the issue see, for example, O'Donoghue & Rabin (2000).

This rationale is reinforced by the lasting impact that health and health behaviours in childhood and adolescence have over a lifetime. This is most obvious in the consumption of addictive goods, particularly tobacco. There is innumerable evidence that smoking behaviour is established in adolescence. In the United States, for instance, some 80% of adult smokers reportedly started smoking before the age of 18. Young people do not take into account the risk of becoming addicted to nicotine because they act myopically (even if informed of future consequences). Government intervention is further supported by evidence that the later the onset, the less likely a person is to become addicted (US DHHS 1994).

Even in the absence of addiction, empirical evidence strongly suggests that health behaviours adopted while young are reliable predictors of health and health behaviours in adulthood. Examples include diet and physical activity (Case, Fertig & Paxson 2005; van Dam et al. 2006; Whitaker, Wright & Pepe 1997).

Based on this justification, governments in many high-income countries have banned the sale of cigarettes and alcohol to minors in order to prevent them from damaging their health. Similarly, there is growing support and recognition in many of those countries for stronger regulation of advertising and sales of unhealthy foods to children (Ofcom 2006).

While this market failure is focused on children and adolescents, some of the most promising measures to remedy the situation are much harder to target exclusively to this group. For instance, tobacco taxation invariably will also reduce adult consumption. And in any case, since parents have a major influence on the health behaviour of their children, it is difficult to change children's behaviour in a way that circumvents parents (Hardy et al. 2006).

The next section turns to potential violations of the "perfect information" assumption. Although this concept is independent from that of rationality, the examples above show that, at least in the case of children, non-rationality and imperfect information may well converge.

Insufficient and asymmetric information

Insufficiency and asymmetry of information are interrelated market problems that differ in important ways. With asymmetric information, one party to the exchange has information that it deliberately does not share with the other party. With insufficient information, the information is not deliberately hidden, but some individuals cannot use or interpret it adequately. These differences bear very different policy implications; in the case of asymmetry, a mechanism must be developed to ensure that the party with hidden information reveals it. Insufficient information can be corrected by, for example, comprehensive or targeted information campaigns.

Two key features of insufficient and possibly asymmetric information are potentially relevant in the context of chronic disease: (1) insufficient awareness about the health risks involved in consumption choices; and (2) inadequate information about the addictive or dependence-inducing nature of some unhealthy goods. The former potentially applies to all unhealthy behaviours, while the latter is arguably more relevant to smoking and alcohol consumption than diet or physical inactivity.

Whether or not consumers in a given country are sufficiently informed about the health consequences of risky behaviour is an empirical question. Government intervention to provide health information can be justified because information is a "public good"[83] and would therefore – if consumers were left to their own devices – be undersupplied compared to the socially optimal level.

Insufficient and/or asymmetric information is more likely to prevail:

• where the health effects of a behaviour are insufficiently understood and researched (for example, because of a long lag time between behaviour and outcome);[84]

• in less developed countries;

• among children and teenagers;

• where producers of goods distort information, intentionally or otherwise.[85]

Undoubtedly, a case exists for public provision of information, which can take many forms, including product labelling, comprehensive or targeted public information campaigns and restricting the marketing of unhealthy food. However, while the information deficit will be reduced in most cases, doubts remain as to how much such reduction will actually change people's behaviour. Even perfectly well-informed people might decide to consume unhealthy

---

83. A pure "public" good is one for which consumption is non-rival (consumption by one individual does not reduce someone else's consumption) and non-excludable (a consumer cannot be excluded from consuming the good either by having to pay or through some other mechanism).

84. The health effects of smoking have only gradually come to be understood by scientists over the course of decades. A similarly thorough understanding of alcohol and the relatively new phenomenon of obesity will take more time to materialize.

85. The history of the tobacco industry, recently revealed in several studies, offers plenty of examples of a concerted effort to conceal information that would reveal the negative health impacts of smoking. See, for example, Diethelm, Rielle & McKee (2005). For the effect of food promotion on the dietary or lifestyle behaviour of children, see Hastings et al. (2003).

goods if the pleasure derived from consumption exceeds the short- and long-term private costs, particularly if the private costs do not fully account for the social costs. In this case, informational interventions will be insufficient to produce the desired behaviour change.

Time-inconsistent preferences/internalities

A potentially powerful justification for government intervention to prevent unhealthy lifestyles comes from the recently proposed hypothesis of time-inconsistent individual preferences. It posits on the basis of experimental evidence that in some situations individuals succumb to the temptation to accept immediate gratification at the expense of their long-term best interests. This means that preferences are such that the discount factor applied in an intertemporal decision (one that involves a present and a future date) is much lower than the discount rate applied on the same decision but involving two future dates. This feature is also known as "nonhyperbolic discounting". This practice characterizes individual preferences only and is not the result of insufficient or asymmetric information.

In this model, a commitment to act in a particular way in the future – made today by a perfectly well-informed and perfectly rational individual who has time-inconsistent preferences – will be reneged upon when the time comes to meet the commitment. For example, a smoker asked today to stop smoking immediately would probably decline, but might agree to stop smoking in a year. However, after that year, reminded of the commitment, the smoker would prefer to continue smoking rather than meet the commitment. In the first decision the discount factor applied to the value of future health improvements is low enough to make the individual opt for the present enjoyment of one more year of smoking, and the discount rate applied is high enough to make the individual "decide" to quit a year later and enjoy health improvements after a year. As time progresses and each future date comes to the present, the preference for immediate enjoyment prevails: the individual's "present self" disagrees with his or her "future self". Moreover, the decisions by the present self are harmful for the future self: such externalities between the time-contingent selves are called "internalities". Gruber & Koszegi (2001) used the value-of-life valuation method to estimate that the "internal" effect totals around US$ 35 per pack of cigarettes.

Empirical evidence from the United States supports this hypothesis: eight out of ten smokers express the desire to quit, but few actually do so. Gruber (2002) reports that over 80% of smokers try to quit in a typical year, and the average smoker tries to quit every eight and a half months. Strikingly, 54% of serious cessation attempts fail within a week.

The same contrast between the current and future selves can be detected indirectly in the well-documented difficulty to commit to diets. Cutler, Glaeser & Shapiro (2003:p.112–113), examining the United States situation, argue that eating decisions often appear inconsistent:

> People overeat, despite substantial evidence that they want to lose weight. The diet industry has $30–$100 billion annual revenues … Food brings immediate gratification, while health costs of overconsumption only in in the future. Maintaining a diet can be very difficult. People on diets frequently yo-yo; their weight rises and falls as they start and stop dieting.

If time-inconsistent preferences do occur, a case exists for an intervention (such as a tax) that stimulates individuals to do what they would like to do but are unable to do without external "help". Time-inconsistency can easily be confused with insufficient information, especially in the case of addictive goods.[86] The outcomes of both market failures may be identical, but the causes – and hence the policy implications – differ significantly. While the solution to limited information is to provide more information, in particular to young people who are most likely to be ill informed, the solution to time-inconsistent preferences is to provide individuals with effective commitment devices: mechanisms that require a previously adopted decision to be respected. Examples include: approaches whereby individuals can bet on their ability to stop smoking, announce publicly their intent to quit, impose punishments on themselves if they fail or reward themselves for succeeding. Clearly, such devices are weak and easily bypassed as they cannot be enforced externally.

Governments have some advantages with respect to individuals: given their enforcement powers, governments are generally able to provide fully effective commitment devices. Introducing per-unit taxes[87] is one such example – taxes would lower the individual's present benefit, offsetting the immediate enjoyment.[88]

---

86. When taking up consumption, individuals – especially young people – might have insufficient information to precisely assess the addictive power and may think that they will be able to quit in the future, although in reality they will by then have lost control over their actions. This implies, for instance, that individuals will never quit smoking (because they do not have enough self-control) – this is the same result as that observed under time-inconsistent preferences. Nevertheless, time-inconsistency is unrelated to limited information: the former is simply a feature of the preferences of individuals who otherwise are fully informed about the consequences of their actions. They are also aware of their contradictory behaviour attributable to the non-hyperbolic discount rate.

87. Not only legislative and executive branches but also courts can (indirectly) introduce a type of "tax". In the United States, the large compensation payments by the tobacco industry to settle disputes with deceased smokers' families were added to the price of cigarettes: the price per pack increased by US$ 1.31 between 1997 and 2002 to give the industry sufficient funds to make these payments. At the same time formal taxation increased only US$ 0.21 per pack (Gruber 2002).

Gruber (2002) suggests that taxes should be accompanied by a portfolio of other measures that would decrease the contemporary enjoyment associated with smoking, such as banning smoking in public places or the workplace. This suggestion can be generalized to cover the full set of unhealthy behaviours, such as introducing measures that change the private decision-making incentives without prohibiting unhealthy choices. Individuals' self-control can be reinforced to achieve the same effect as a commitment device, while conserving individual freedom to make choices.

While private benefits are (by definition) outside the scope of public intervention, both immediate and future costs can be manipulated, helping make healthy choices easier. Wider use of standardized nutritional certification programmes would reduce the time costs of gathering nutritional information. Making running lanes, gym facilities, swimming pools and cycling paths widely available would reduce the immediate cost of physical activity (for instance, by reducing search and transportation costs). Similarly, taxation and clean-air regulation increases the immediate costs of health-damaging behaviour.

Expected future costs are also important: in spite of the low discount factor adopted to assess the consequences of deteriorating health, if rational individuals realize that the future welfare lost due to current smoking is sufficiently high, they will have another incentive to not smoke. Conversely, if future economic conditions look grim, then the health costs of current smoking are too low to discourage this habit. It is widely documented that lower socioeconomic groups are more likely to display unhealthy lifestyles. However, the socioeconomic environment may itself induce unhealthy lifestyles, which opens up a much broader area for public intervention: improving the prospect for future economic conditions is very effective in discouraging unhealthy lifestyles today.

How should we invest?

Chapter 3 described health challenges in CEE-CIS, and Chapter 4 argued that improving health in the Region would help promote economic development and reduce poverty there. But how could health improvements be achieved? And would the cost be justifiable? Providing an exhaustive and detailed health investment plan that would do justice to the many specific contexts that prevail across the CEE-CIS Region exceeds the scope here. This section seeks to

---

88. Taxes that adjust for time-inconsistent preferences are "Pareto improving", that is, they give those with little self-control an effective commitment device able to increase their consumer surplus. At the same time, if the proceeds of the tax are returned evenly to everyone in the society, individuals with high self-control are (more than) compensated for the loss suffered by the tax, providing a further incentive to be self-controlled (O'Donoghue & Rabin 2006).

give selected, broadly based policy recommendations and examples on the structure and contents of health investment plans, based on the existing evidence and international best practice. It is ultimately for countries themselves to develop a consensus on their national investment strategies, given their existing health, socioeconomic and political context. Even if the current scale of the programmes may not be sufficient to tackle all health challenges, there *are* several, albeit small-scale, examples that have made visible differences in several countries of the Region, many described in a recent report (Anderson et al. 2006) commissioned by the United States Agency for International Development (USAID).

This chapter's overall message is that there are certain basic steps that need to be part of the process of developing and implementing a national investment plan, with the aim of investing more (where needed) and better in health. This involves considering investment within the health system but also beyond it, taking into account the underlying determinants of health. Highly cost-effective and evidence-based interventions (addressing the different levers of the health determinants) do exist and can be applied in CEE-CIS.

Since a sound assessment should always be part of the initial phase of an investment strategy, the first subsection reviews the various determinants of health in the Region. As it is hard to separate the discussion of the determinants of health from that on policy interventions, this section makes occasional reference to relevant, evidence-based interventions and policy measures that could help address some of these determinants of health.

The second subsection focuses directly on what should be done, by first stressing the need for a response across the government sphere if there is to be an effective approach to tackling the Region's health challenges and second by giving examples of cost-effective interventions. The section thereafter explores two issues that highlight why "investing in health" means more than investing in the health system. The first issue is the role of the quality of governance in mediating health expenditure and health outcomes while the second is the importance of social capital in improving health outcomes.

Determinants of health in CEE-CIS

Determinants of health act at different levels, as illustrated by a widely used diagram by Dahlgren & Whitehead (1993), shown in Figure 5.1. It shows how health is the result of interactions between causal factors acting at different levels, from the individual to communities and to countries.

At the centre of the picture are individuals, endowed with age, sex and genetic factors that undoubtedly influence their health potential. The next layer

Figure 5.1 *Main determinants of health (Source: Dahlgren and Whitehead, 1993. Reproduced with permission.).*

represents personal behaviours and lifestyles. People in disadvantaged circumstances often exhibit a higher prevalence of health-damaging behaviours, such as smoking and poor diet, and face greater financial and other barriers to choosing a healthier lifestyle. The next layer portrays social and community influences, social interactions and peer pressures that influence personal behaviours, for better or worse. People living in deprived areas may have fewer networks and support systems, generally a situation exacerbated by poor access to social services and community amenities. At the next level are factors related to living and working conditions, food supplies and access to essential facilities and services. In this layer, poorer housing conditions, exposure to more dangerous and/or stressful working conditions and poorer access to services create greater risks for the socially disadvantaged.

Overarching all these levels are the economic, cultural and environmental conditions prevalent in society as a whole. These conditions, such as the country's economic situation and its labour market conditions, influence every other layer. Thus, the standard of living achieved in a society will influence an individual's choice of housing, work and social interactions, as well as eating and drinking habits. Similarly, cultural beliefs about the place of women in society and the status of minority ethnic communities can influence their standard of living and socioeconomic position.

As noted previously, there is no single explanation for the high level of premature death and disability in this Region (McKee 2005a). Many factors contribute, acting in different ways and at the diagram's different layers. The exercise described next illustrates the multiple and simultaneous influences of a large set of factors in the transition country context.

Table 5.1 presents the results of a logistic regression trying to explain what determines self-rated health – "good health" in this case – in the eight CIS countries that participated in the LLH survey described earlier (see case studies on page 103). The set of "determinants" includes a range of demographic, socioeconomic, lifestyle and health system variables. Virtually all the variables covering different layers in the Dahlgren & Whitehead diagram enter into the model, displaying a significant association in the expected direction.[89] While this simple approach makes no effort to disentangle the various interdependencies between the explanatory variables or to tackle the endogeneity problem, the results can nevertheless be taken as support for the hypothesis that there is a need to look at all levels of the determinants of health given in the diagram.

Several of these determinants are explored in much greater detail in reviews commissioned to inform this book and published separately (i.e., as they relate to CVDs, injuries and violence, nutrition and social inequalities in health).[90] Those volumes provide evidence on the scale of the problem as well as information that can inform the development of effective policies to bring about health improvement.

Globally, the single most important determinant of the health of a country's population is its economic wealth. Differences in economic progress (or regress) are also a powerful explanatory factor in the Region's severe mortality crisis of the early 1990s, with countries that managed to contain the economic collapse able to limit the mortality increase much more than in those hit hardest in economic terms. However, since the relationship between health and the economy runs both ways, the low level of health is, in itself, a factor in each country's poor economic situation. And current or future economic growth cannot be relied on to improve health to the level needed to sustain economic

---

89. A notable exception in Table 5.1 is the distance from the nearest doctor, feldsher or polyclinic, which turns out not to be significant. However, when another health variable is used ("presence of health problems") as the dependent variable, this "access" measure becomes highly significant, while the self-control measure becomes insignificant. (These results are available upon request.)

90. Two literature reviews synthesize the evidence base on the effectiveness of interventions to reduce the burden of cardiovascular diseases and injuries: Knai, McKee & Bobak (2005); Bozicevic et al. (2005). Hawkes (2004) reviews food policies as a determinant of nutrition and health in the CEE-CIS Region.

Table 5.1 *Living Conditions, Lifestyles and Health survey results of a logistic regression with "good health" as the dependent variable, 2001*

	Explanatory variable	Coefficient
	Female	-0.59***
	> 10 cigarettes per day	-0.15***
Reference: youngest age group (18–27 years)	Age group 28–37 years	-0.75***
	Age group 38–47 years	-1.38***
	Age group 48–57 years	-1.80***
	Age group 58–67 years	-2.28***
	Age group 68–77 years	-2.35***
Reference: secondary or less	Secondary, vocational or some higher	0.27***
	Higher	0.46***
Reference: single	Married/cohabit	-0.05
	Widowed/divorced	-0.20**
	Total grams alcohol intake	0.001***
	Total grams alcohol intake ^2	0.000***
(Higher = more deprived)	Deprivation index	-5.01***
	Distance from nearest doctor/feldsher/polyclinic	0.04
	Definitely dissatisfied with the health system	-0.34***
	Know someone who can help in crisis	0.36***
	Control of my life/freedom of choice	0.15***
	Muslim religion	0.48***

Source: Authors' calculations using Living Conditions, Lifestyles and Health (LLH) survey data.

Notes: Results for country dummies not shown; *** Indicates statistical significance at 1% level; ** Indicates a 5% level of statistical significance.

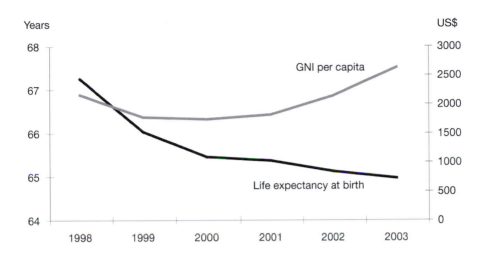

Figure 5.2 *Life expectancy and gross national income per capita in the Russian Federation, 1998–2003 (Sources: WHO Regional Office for Europe, 2006; World Bank, 2005b).*

Note: GNI: gross national income.

growth. This is confirmed by the observation of a recently diverging evolution of GDP per capita on one hand and population health indicators (e.g. life expectancy) on the other in several countries of the former USSR. A particularly striking example is the Russian Federation, as shown in Figure 5.2.

Pathways to disease and premature death

Since economic decline is not the only cause of disability and premature death, it is necessary to look further into the pathways from health to disability and premature death. As the Dahlgren and Whitehead (1993) diagram illustrates, the health of a population is shaped by factors acting at different levels. The complexity of the varying effects of these factors can be viewed starting with the context of the human genome. Decoding the human genome has focused attention on the contribution that genes make to disease. Evolutionary pressures acting over hundreds of thousands of years have shaped the susceptibility of different populations to specific diseases, often when a gene confers protection against infection with a particular microorganism while increasing the risk of another disease (Diamond 1997). The enormous reduction in the threat from microorganisms means that today's populations no longer benefit from the protection conferred by the gene but suffer its adverse consequences. However, genetic factors make only a small contribution to our understanding of poor health in CEE-CIS. Since the 1980s, life expectancy in the Russian

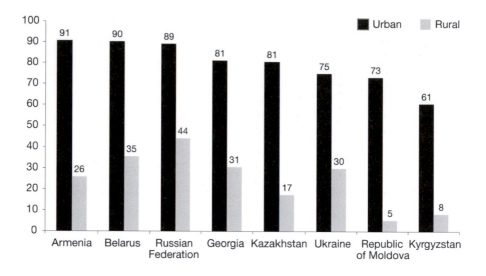

Figure 5.3 *Percentage of households with indoor piped water, 2001 (Source: McKee et al., 2006).*

Federation (as well as in the former USSR more generally) has fluctuated markedly, with that for men ranging from 58 years to over 65 (Shkolnikov, McKee & Leon 2001). Other former Soviet states had broadly similar experiences. Clearly, fluctuations of this magnitude over such a short period could not have been caused by changes in the population's genetic composition.

Turning from the genetic to the social and economic determinants of health finds many such determinants outside the health system proper. At a global level, much premature death is attributable to lack of access to the basic prerequisites for health: shelter, food, water and clothing. The substantial progress made in ensuring access to these essentials in the USSR in the 1950s and 1960s contributed substantially to the major gains in life expectancy. However, those achievements were still inadequate to meet the challenge then faced and, especially in rural areas, the quality of basic infrastructure remains poor, with many households still having no indoor access to piped water (Figure 5.3) (McKee et al. 2006). In many places the situation has deteriorated further since independence, as the sharp economic recession drained funds for infrastructure investment (UNICEF 1998). In some countries, such as Armenia and Georgia, communal systems of heating no longer function.

Based on information collected through household surveys, the recent World Bank analysis reveals continued reliance on dirty (i.e., solid) fuels for heating, especially in secondary cities and rural areas and among the poor (Alam et al. 2005). Figure 5.4 illustrates the disproportionate use of dirty fuels in the

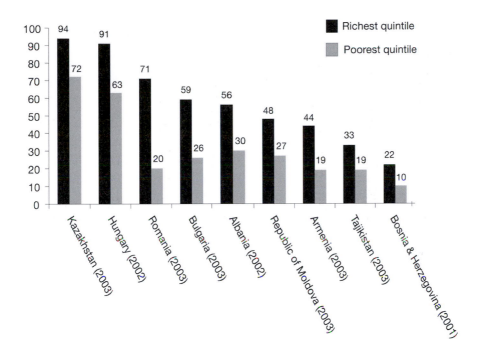

Figure 5.4 *Use of clean fuels for heating (percentages), selected years and countries (Source: Alam et al., 2005).*

poorest quintile compared to the richest in selected countries for which this information had been collected. A broadly similar picture emerges from a recent global assessment of indoor use of solid fuels (Rehfuess, Mehta & Prüss-Üstün 2006) in 181 countries. These data also show that a comparatively low regional average for CEE-CIS – 16% of households using solid fuels – hides the extremely high shares of solid fuel use in several of these countries (see Figure 5.5). Interestingly, no close link appears between solid fuel use and a country's economic wealth, implying that reducing indoor air pollution is affordable for poor countries, too.

Household reliance on dirty fuels increased sharply in the early transition years, mostly due to loss of access to district heating, irregular supply of electricity, high cost of electricity and lack of access to other clean fuel sources, such as gas. The lack of reliable energy sources and the increased costs of the existing choices (such as electricity) pushed many households into lower-quality choices of energy, such as solid fuels. The negative effects of indoor pollution due to the use of solid fuels on health status are well documented in other regions (Ezzati & Kammen 2002), and it is expected that similar effects

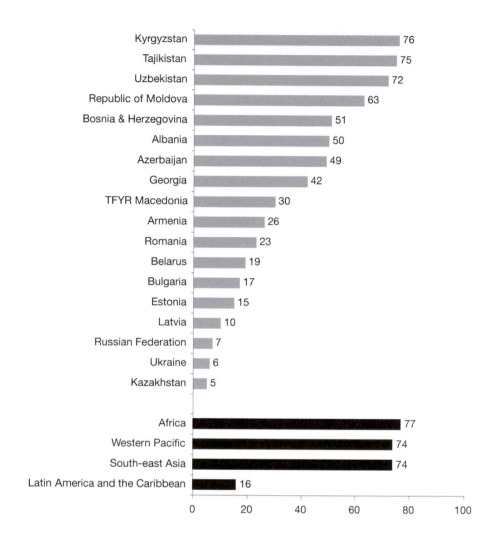

Figure 5.5 *Percentage of population using solid fuels: CEE-CIS countries and benchmark regions (Source: Rehfuess, Mehta & Prüss-Üstün, 2006).*

Note: The percentages in the following countries were classified as "below 5%": Hungary, Lithuania, Poland, Slovakia and Turkmenistan.

are emerging here, especially as communal heating systems are withdrawn. However, this issue has not yet been subject to adequate research.

Failures of the food distribution system, which worked imperfectly even in the Soviet period, has made a bad situation worse for many. For some, especially those in cities, the opening to international markets has enabled access to an unprecedented range of consumer goods, although for many they remain unaffordable. Thus, while in some countries families have been able to maintain their nutritional intake by adopting a variety of adaptive strategies (Dore, Adair & Popkin 2003), in others a significant number of people, especially the elderly, have faced shortages of life's basic essentials (McNabb et al. 1994).

Even for those with enough to meet their basic needs, economic hardship exerts a profound influence on health. Such hardship constrains the ability to make healthy choices. Poverty induces a sense of hopelessness, removing the incentive to assume a healthy lifestyle as the transient pleasures of risk-taking outweigh the prospect that it will shorten what is already perceived to be a brief life. As a consequence, many health-damaging behaviours are concentrated among those already most disadvantaged, in particular men with low levels of education and few social support networks whose world is changing in ways they cannot control (McKee & Shkolnikov 2001). Rapid economic change also contributes: research in the Russian Federation measured the sum of jobs lost and gained in medium and large enterprises (Walberg et al. 1998); it shows that the decline in life expectancy in the early 1990s was greatest in areas that experienced the most rapid pace of economic change.

Lifestyle-related risk factors

The major so-called "lifestyle"-related risk factors include alcohol, tobacco and nutrition. These factors should not be viewed in isolation, but rather as products of individuals' or communities' socioeconomic context. There is now no doubt that alcohol, acting in many different ways, is a major contributor to poor health in this Region (McKee, Shkolnikov & Leon 2001). Most obviously, those who are drunk are most at risk of injuring themselves, especially if accompanied by companions who are also drunk and unable (or unwilling) to help or in a climate where death comes quickly to those who fall in the snow. Also, the frequency of very heavy drinking is linked directly to high death rates from alcohol poisoning. Increasing evidence shows alcohol's role in the high levels of CVDs, in particular sudden cardiac death, in this Region (Britton & McKee 2000). It also results in a predisposition to other disorders such as pneumonia, liver cirrhosis, stroke and suicide. Heavy alcohol consumption affects not only those who are drinking but also those they harm, contributing substantially, for example, to the very high murder rate in this Region (Chervyakov et al. 2002) and to the number injured or killed by drunk drivers (Chenet et al. 1998). Last but not least, families of heavy drinkers risk impoverishment and domestic violence.

Hazardous patterns of drinking have characterized Russian, and subsequently Soviet, society for several centuries, with the Imperial Russian authorities deriving substantial revenues from what was then an alcohol monopoly (McKee 1999). The magnitude of the problem increased markedly in the

1950s and 1960s, in part because it was one of the few available consumer goods but also in response to worsening social conditions. It has played a particularly important role in the fluctuations in mortality since the 1980s, beginning with the sharp decline in deaths from, especially, injuries and violence and CVDs following the 1985 anti-alcohol campaign (Leon et al. 1997), followed by the subsequent increase that accompanied the break-up of the Soviet Union and, later, the 1998 Russian currency crisis. Strong evidence exists to implicate the widespread consumption of surrogate alcohols – which are inexpensive, widely available and contain high concentrations of ethanol – in the high levels of premature male mortality in the Russian Federation (McKee et al. 2005) and some of its neighbours (Lang et al. 2006). However, as the temporal relationship with these events shows, levels of hazardous drinking must be viewed in the context of the prevailing social and economic circumstances and with recognition that its ill effects are concentrated among a population's most vulnerable members.

A second major risk factor is smoking. During the Soviet period smoking rates were high among males, reaching up to 70% of adult men. Rates were much lower among women (McKee et al. 1998; Gilmore et al. 2001), but the situation changed markedly in the 1990s when western tobacco companies moved into these countries, initially developing a sales presence (Gilmore & McKee 2004a) formerly held by smuggled goods and subsequently a manufacturing presence (Gilmore & McKee 2004b).

The consequences for tobacco policy are considerable. Recognizing that the greatest potential for growth is among young women, the tobacco companies have targeted this group, with the result that smoking rates among young women have increased markedly in many countries (Gilmore et al. 2004). In addition, tobacco companies have undermined control efforts (Gilmore & McKee 2004c), advising on text in advertising legislation so as to weaken it. Their ability to do so is strengthened by their substantial economic power. For example, one major international tobacco company has a privileged position in Uzbekistan, to a large extent because it contributes 31% of total foreign direct investment to government revenues (Gilmore, McKee & Collin 2006).

Tobacco companies argue that they contribute to national economies, in particular to employment, but this argument is not supported by sound evidence (Jha & Chaloupka 1999). Tobacco production is a small part of most economies. For all but a few agrarian countries in sub-Saharan Africa that are heavily dependent on tobacco farming, there would be no net loss of jobs, and gains in employment would be likely if tobacco consumption fell: money previously spent on tobacco would be transferred to other job-creating goods and services. In poor households, particularly where tobacco expenditure accounts for a significant share of the household budget, a reduction in tobacco use would even free up essential resources for more productive investments that could help lift the household out of poverty.

Similarly, the argument that tobacco control would reduce fiscal revenue is not borne out by available evidence. On the contrary, increasing tobacco taxation is highly effective in increasing fiscal revenues (Jha & Chaloupka 1999), in addition to the positive and well-documented health effects it entails.

It is indeed hard to see any positive social or economic benefit from the tobacco industry based on recent transition country experience. In Uzbekistan, an international tobacco company's increased role was associated with a marked worsening of conditions for tobacco growers.[91] Furthermore, the power of these companies enables them to influence tax policies in ways that minimize contributions to government revenue while allowing them to repatriate most of their earnings. Consequently, even without accounting for future costs from the disease and premature deaths that their products foster, no economic case exists for encouraging inward investment by international tobacco companies. Unfortunately, the countervailing arguments have not been made forcefully enough, enabling these companies, often working closely with agriculture and trade ministries, whose primary responsibilities do not traditionally incorporate health, to argue tobacco's contribution.

A third element of "lifestyle" is diet. For some people, and especially the newly emerging middle classes in some of the larger cities, diet is changing rapidly. In some ways this is beneficial, in particular the greater availability of fresh fruit and vegetables all year round. In other ways it is detrimental, as western-style fast food outlets expand (Box 5.2), bringing with them the risk of rising levels of obesity from consumption of energy dense foods, including saturated fats (Pomerleau et al. 2003) and sugar-laden soft drinks (Hawkes 2002).

For others, diet is largely unchanged or has even deteriorated, especially in rural areas, where access to many basic foods has often declined. One reason is the reduction or shift in agricultural production as a result of withdrawal of subsidies or the break-up of collective farms, with the new small-scale farmers unable to access funds for investment in the necessary equipment. Another is the withdrawal of subsidized transport links. The situation is especially harmful to health in relation to fruit and vegetables. Low consumption levels of these products play a substantial role in the high levels of many diseases in

---

91. For more information on the situation in Uzbekistan, see the British Helsinki Human Rights Group web site at www.bhhrg.org/CountryReport.asp?CountryID=23 (accessed 14 January, 2007).

Box 5.2 Inward investment by the global food industry

Soft drinks

"Pepsi-Cola was historically the soft drinks market leader in Eastern Europe—production of Pepsi-Cola began in Romania in 1965, and in 1973 Pepsi-Cola became the first American consumer good licensed for production in the Soviet Union. Prior to 1990 Coca-Cola was virtually absent from the Region. At the end of the Cold War, Coca-Cola took the opportunity to expand. It now has now [sic] overtaken Pepsi throughout most of Eastern Europe, leading sales two to one. The company invested heavily, US$ 1.5 billion between 1989 and 1995. Investment in Russia has been particularly high: a total of US$ 600 million by the end of 1997. The company entered the former Soviet Republics in 1994–96. After a series of consolidations and buy-outs, the Greek-based Coca-Cola HBC is the Region's major bottler, covering Eastern Europe, Russia and the Baltic states."

Fast food

"Following the dismantling of the communist bloc, the number of fast food outlets in Eastern Europe expanded rapidly during the 1990s, stimulated by the entry of McDonald's, Burger King, Kentucky Fried Chicken (KFC) and Pizza Hut. The rate of multinational penetration varies significantly between countries, from 13.9% in Russia to 38.9% in Hungary. Drawing on the popularity of red meat, McDonald's is now the leading fast food operator in Eastern Europe. Their latest country of entry was Azerbaijan, in 1999. Yum! – mainly KFC – is the second ranked player in each eastern European country except for Russia, where it has only a few outlets, and Hungary, where Burger King is second. The largest regional market for McDonald's is Poland, where they operate 189 restaurants and invested US$ 125 million between 1992 and 1999. Poland is also the most important regional market for Yum! KFC, Pizza Hut and Taco Bell operate as "multi-branded" restaurants, and the company is currently expanding. Russia has been a highly visible market for McDonald's ever since it opened in 1990 as a joint venture between McDonald's Canada and the city of Moscow. It took a US$ 50 million investment to get the outlet up and running. There are now 73 restaurants, mainly in the Moscow region. Hungary is another major fast food market in the Region. McDonald's opened in Budapest in 1988, and soon became the number one McDonald's worldwide for transactions. Having invested over US$ 100 million, McDonald's is the market leader, with 78% market share of fast food sales in 2000. Burger King, which opened in 1991, is their major competitor."

Source: Extract from Hawkes, 2002.

CEE-CIS, including CVD, stroke and some cancers (Lock et al. 2005). In many places fruit and vegetables are almost unobtainable in winter (Powles et al. 1996), and even in summer an increasing number of people are dependent on food they grow themselves (Pomerleau et al. 2002).

Psychosocial stress may underlie much of the observed patterns of smoking, hazardous drinking and poor diet in CEE-CIS countries (Bosma 1994). The difficult social situation experienced by countries during economic and political transition may have affected people's sense of control, particularly control of health (Bobak & Marmot 1996). Psychosocial factors, including stress, may also act directly through neuroendocrine pathways and may be an important risk factor for high CVD levels (Bobak & Marmot 1996). This hypothesis also finds support in other European contexts. The Malmo Preventive Project (1974–1980) found stress to be an independent risk factor for CVD, particularly fatal stroke, in middle-aged men (Ohlin et al. 2004).

Evidence emerging since 1990 indicates that the distribution of psychosocial factors (such as perceived control, depression, mastery, hopelessness) was less favourable in CEE-CIS than in western European countries (Carlson 1998; Steptoe & Wardle 2001; Pikhart et al. 2004). In an ecological analysis, coronary heart disease (CHD) mortality was found to be associated with low perceived control (Carlson 1998); risk of CHD was associated with job strain (Bobak et al. 1998). Increases in death rates in both Hungary (Hajdu, McKee & Bojan 1995) and Poland (Watson 1995) in the 1980s were greatest among people who were unmarried and thus might be expected to have low levels of social support, while the increase in deaths from CVD in the Russian Federation in the early 1990s was greatest in those regions with the fastest pace of transition (Walberg et al. 1998). However, it is extremely difficult to tease out the complex and mutually interacting relationships between social, psychological and biological risk factors given the current state of knowledge, and effective action would in any case need to address each of them.

Immediate causes of disability and death

Having looked at several of the proximate and underlying determinants of health, the next step is to look at the diseases they give rise to. As noted in Chapter 3, CVDs, injuries and violence are the major contributors to the gap in mortality between CEE-CIS and western Europe. Some cancers also contribute, although here the situation is more complicated, with higher death rates from lung cancer in men but lower in women, reflecting the different stages of the tobacco epidemic. In addition, some cancers, such as breast and prostate – diseases of affluence – are still low, while others (e.g., stomach cancer) are very high, reflecting conditions several decades earlier and the long lag time between infection with the bacteria that cause most stomach cancers and the emergence of disease.

Many of the reasons underlying the high level of CVD have already been mentioned. These include poor nutrition, in particular lack of year-round access to fresh fruit and vegetables and a high consumption of saturated fat. A broad range of solutions is required, including agricultural development, strengthening the retail distribution system, relief of poverty and information about the effects of unhealthy behaviours and how to change them.

Another factor is the high rate of smoking, affecting not only those who smoke, but also those exposed to second-hand smoke, an effect now recognized as much more dangerous, especially in relation to CVD, than previously thought (Whincup et al. 2004). The high level of hazardous drinking also plays a major role, predisposing in particular to sudden cardiac death.

Consideration must also be given to the treatment and management of people with established risks for CVD, in particular those with high levels of blood cholesterol and high blood pressure. Appreciable evidence shows that neither problem is managed effectively in much of the CEE-CIS Region, calling for policies that increase access to health care that includes needed advice and treatment. A particular problem is the cost of medicines, with evidence from some countries that the high mark ups that occur during distribution, coupled with high levels of poverty, make drugs unaffordable for many (Gelders et al. 2006). People on life-sustaining drugs, such as anti-hypertensives, often take them only when they feel unwell, almost certainly contributing to the high levels of cerebrovascular disease.

Looking beyond the leading contemporary causes of premature death in the Region reveals a human history ripe with examples of diseases that have emerged or disappeared. As described in Chapter 3, the collapse of the communist system was accompanied by the re-emergence of many infectious diseases that had previously been controlled. Diphtheria re-emerged in the 1990s as immunization programmes broke down. Deaths from TB in several countries have risen to levels not seen since the 1970s, with the added complication that many cases are now resistant to the standard, and relatively inexpensive, antibiotics (Coker, Atun & McKee 2004). Malaria, once eliminated in the former USSR, has reappeared in such countries as Azerbaijan and Tajikistan. However, the greatest emerging threat is from HIV, with infection rates increasing faster in this Region than anywhere else in the world. An epidemic that originated among intravenous drug users is spreading widely, by way of "bridges" created by the large numbers of commercial sex workers (Aral et al. 2003), with subsequent spread through heterosexual sex to populations that are not considered to be at high risk (Kelly & Amirkhanian 2003). The potential consequences are extremely worrying as, apart from the countless (and rising) human tragedies, disease on this predicted scale will have substantial demographic and economic implications.

The next disability/death factor is the ability of the health care system to respond to disease. While the achievements of the Soviet health system in the 1950s and early 1960s, which brought basic health care to a widely dispersed population, have rightly been applauded, this system could not take advantage of the opportunities created internationally by scientific progress from the 1970s onwards (Field 1990). These opportunities included new pharmaceuticals, in particular those that could control a wide range of chronic disorders (asthma, hypertension, epilepsy); new techniques that made anaesthesia and surgery much safer; and, crucially, evidence-based health care, where services are based on the best available research. In much of the rest of the world, treatments that were harmful were rejected, while those that were beneficial were widely adopted.

The USSR missed out on many of these developments, despite its major, and very visible, achievements in space and defence. It was unable to develop a modern pharmaceutical industry, importing much of what it needed from eastern Europe and the Indian subcontinent. Medical technology was far behind that in the West, in part because of a failure to invest in research and development but also because of a lack of access to western information technology, imposed because of concerns about the transfer of technology with military potential. The Soviet scientific system, with its emphasis on Marxist–Leninist principles (Krementosov 1997), was unsympathetic to the concepts underlying clinical research, in particular randomized controlled trials. Furthermore, access to international journals was extremely limited, both for those unable to read them due to language difficulties and those who could. The consequence was widespread use of treatments, such as those based on the administration of light, X-rays or magnetism, which are not effective but had the advantages of being obtainable and of giving the impression that something was being done (McKee In press).

In these circumstances, it is unsurprising that the achievements of western countries in reducing deaths from causes amenable to medical care were not seen in the USSR. Figure 5.6 shows that death rates from these causes were similar in the USSR and the United Kingdom in the early 1970s, but the trajectories then steadily diverge. By 2000 the avoidable mortality in the Russian Federation was more than double that of the United Kingdom.

The period since independence has witnessed improvements in many of these problems, in particular the opening of markets to modern pharmaceuticals. Access to the international literature is also greatly improved, largely as a result

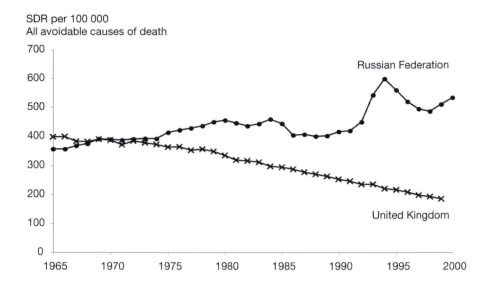

SDR per 100 000
All avoidable causes of death

Figure 5.6 *Trends in avoidable mortality in the Russian Federation and the United Kingdom, 1985–2000 (Source: Andreev, McKee & Shkolnikov, 2003).*

Note: SDR: standardized death rate.

of the Internet, although its uptake is hampered by language problems. In some places, therefore, and for some people, the delivery of health care has improved. In the Russian Federation at least, the transition to a functioning health insurance system has been achieved, although some people remain excluded (Balabanova, Falkingham & McKee 2003). Yet, in some countries it has become much worse, as economic decline, coupled with falling government revenues, markedly reduced resources for health care. In such countries as Armenia and Georgia, the majority of interactions with a health professional involve OOP payments (Balabanova et al. 2004) that, in the case of severe illness, can be catastrophic (Xu et al. 2003). See Chapter 3, Subsection "CEE-CIS health expenditure from a global perspective" for more CEE-CIS evidence on catastrophic payments.

In many places medical advances have not arrived, or health care providers have no prospect of obtaining needed resources, so many ineffective practices persist. Sometimes payment systems foster perverse incentives, such as rewarding facilities on the basis of number of beds, even when many are empty or occupied by people who should be treated in the community (Danishevski et al. 2006). Widespread informal payments exacerbate the situation, as does fee splitting with pharmacists, which encourages the administration of unnecessary drugs, in particular those administered by infusion or injection.

The need for a response at all levels

The Dahlgren & Whitehead (1993) diagram on page 152 shows that the determinants of health act at different levels. Consequently, effective action to promote health should also occur at different levels, taking into account the extent to which the higher layers may influence the lower ones.

Starting with the most fundamental layer "general socioeconomic, cultural and environmental conditions", it is apparent that health system institutions, including ministries of health and others, have limited direct ability to affect change. However, health ministries are not powerless and can act as advocates for action. A starting point for them would be making the case for the routine assessment of the health impact of policies in other ministerial areas. The importance of health impact assessment is widely accepted in western countries, with some making it a statutory requirement for major projects. Over the past decade, assessment use has reached CEE, stimulated in part by the requirements for EU accession (Lock et al. 2003; Lock & McKee 2005).

Assessments give health ministries access to information on the impact of policies in areas such as taxation (for example, the extent to which it encourages or discourages smoking and whether it increases or decreases poverty), trade and regional development. Furthermore, the process of developing an assessment reminds health policy-makers of the need to take full account of the socioeconomic, cultural and environmental context in which the population's health is formed. Unless policies are adapted to the real contexts – capabilities and constraints – of the countries concerned, they are unlikely to achieve the desired results.

The next layer down, "living and working conditions", affords more room for intervention by health sector actors. The more complex health challenges of the CEE-CIS Region can be addressed successfully only through intersectoral action, requiring not only policies and actions managed from within the health sector, but also integration with policies and actions in other sectors targeting health advancement among their goals: education, transport, housing and others.

For health system actors to act effectively at these levels, they must acquire the necessary knowledge and skills. They must also establish reforms that will allow them to speak with authority, including doing as much as possible within their sphere of responsibility to promote health: providing equitable and effective care, creating health-promoting workplaces and adopting policies that promote the health of their own staff, such as smoking cessation programmes and exercise facilities.

Social and community networks have a growing role in promoting health, an

> **Box 5.3 Community action: growing vegetables on rooftops in St Petersburg**
>
> Rooftop gardening can prove fruitful for urban people lacking access to land. It took root in St Petersburg with technical assistance from Educational Concerns for Hunger (ECHO). This civil society group advised on shallow bed methods, such as soil mix, and arranged independent testing for contaminants: these vegetables had lower levels than those in markets. The potential of rooftop gardening is huge: a single district in St Petersburg could grow 2000 tonnes of vegetables. One study identified about 15 rooftop gardens in that particular city.
>
> *Source: WHO Regional Office for Europe, 2001.*

issue explored in more detail later in relation to social capital. The communist ideology saw no role for civil society and, at various times, social networks outside state control were viewed as subversive. Although the situation has changed in some CEE-CIS countries, an active civil society is still seen as a threat in others. Where community organizations have been able to develop, they have often been able to engage in health-promoting activities (Box 5.3).

Individual lifestyle factors must also be addressed through policy-making but while taking into account the situations that constrain people from making healthy choices. Success will be achieved only if governments play a major role by increasing the scope for individuals and communities to make healthy choices and by improving living and working conditions and the general socioeconomic, cultural and environmental conditions. This requires engagement by all branches of government. Failure to address worsening health in the Region will have consequences for all government ministries as it will remain an obstacle to future economic growth; equally, success will bring benefits to them all. Each has a role to play, whether through changes in agricultural policy to improve the availability and nutritional quality of food; changes to transport policy to reduce deaths from traffic injuries; or changes in fiscal policy, such as increasing cigarette taxes. The role of health ministries will be to define the scale and nature of poor health and to propose policies to improve it.

A step-wise approach to action

A first step is to develop a clear picture of the health challenges that face populations. This should go beyond the usual measures, such as overall death rates from major diseases, to look at the underlying determinants of disease and health: immediate risk factors, such as the extent of unrecognized or inadequately treated blood pressure and the quality of nutrition, and the more distal factors, such as the extent of social exclusion. It is also important to develop a picture of the distribution of health and disease within a country, to help better target interventions. (Chapter 3 has shown that significant within-country inequalities in health and health care access do exist and may be growing.)

Once data on all these factors are collected, an assessment must be made by sifting through the collection to prioritize the factors that have the greatest impact on health. Regional data must be disaggregated to identify the significance of different factors in different regions.

It is then necessary to design effective interventions, again taking account of the social and economic context where they will be implemented, starting with what can be afforded and provides good value for money. In many cases, implementation of new programmes will first require an outlay of the money and resources required to make them work. However, to properly evaluate the use of this money, it is essential to compare programmes to the benefits they can provide in terms of future economic output and welfare – as is described in Chapter 4 and as is routinely carried out in other areas of infrastructure investment (as in road or railway construction).

Initial expense will often require investment in a skilled workforce having transferable expertise in the design and implementation of health-related programmes. Many CEE-CIS countries lack skills in modern public health, and health management remains a major obstacle and must be overcome early on (McKee 2005a).

The principle of community participation is an important aspect of decision-making (and of implementation) in health interventions. However, the explicit inclusion and participation of civil society is an area where the legacy of the CEE and even more so of the CIS leaves much room for improvement. These countries have a recent history of highly formalized, state-centred systems, with only a limited presence of civil society and formulaic approaches to participation in social and public life. Strengthening community participation might reinforce the rights of the citizen, but this dimension goes beyond the individual perspective to consider the role of the community, reflecting the wider democratization of the CEE and CIS. Apart from the fast-growing evidence on the positive contribution of social networks to health status, a significant amount of knowledge has also accumulated as to how best to empower communities and how to create social capital as a resource for health.[92]

---

92. See subsections on "Social capital", "Social capital in transition countries" and "Social capital and health" for empirical evidence on the impact of social capital on health in the Region or Wallerstein (2006) for a comprehensive synthesis of the evidence on how to promote social capital.

A third step is to establish systems to monitor the effects of change, which enable identifying when changes to programmes are warranted (McKee 2005b). Occasionally, changes in death rates follow rapidly from the implementation of a new policy, such as the effective imposition of seat-belt wearing or speed limits. More often, however, such changes take much longer: reducing smoking uptake by adolescents now will reduce lung cancer deaths in several decades (Shkolnikov et al. 1999). The longer the lag time, the more important it is to have monitoring systems indicating gains in benchmarks along the way to improved mortality. Such indicators would measure reductions in risk factors and in morbidity both at population level and among groups within the population.

Since this Region's situation differs in important respects from that in low-income tropical countries where impressive gains can result from implementation of relatively simply measures (e.g. wider distribution of insecticide-treated bed nets), more complex interventions are required. These involve a series of linked initiatives that address the underlying determinants of disease, certain risk factors and weaknesses in the health care system's ability to respond to established disease. In each case, the precise policies should be developed in the light of the health needs of each country, what is already in place and what is feasible with available resources. The papers prepared as background to this book can inform these decisions, just as Chapter 3's review of the health situation and trends, along with other evidence on the burden of disease, can be used for priority setting.

It will be important to begin with actions that can be implemented relatively easily. Tobacco control offers many opportunities. However, it is important not to underestimate the political challenges here, in particular the powerful influence of tobacco companies with strong links to other ministries and even heads of government. In these cases, effectively using the clear economic arguments for reducing tobacco consumption, as set out by, among others, the World Bank, will be important.

Appropriate tobacco control actions are set out in the Framework Convention on Tobacco Control, an international treaty signed by the majority of countries in the CEE-CIS Region (and others). An increase in tobacco taxes has the double benefit of reducing consumption while increasing government revenue (Guindon, Tobin & Yach 2002). Tobacco companies argue that higher taxes increase smuggling, an activity in which they have been complicit. Also, the Framework Convention offers a range of other activities that would improve the tobacco situation. Labelling products with country of origin, supplemented by increased law enforcement, would be highly effective in reducing smuggling. A ban on tobacco advertising and sponsorship would reduce consumption and, in particular, help to prevent smoking initiation by youths. The tobacco industry's argument that advertising is undertaken simply to promote brand switching, rather than to increase consumption, is contradicted by its own internal documents (Pollay 2000). The growing evidence of the harm caused by second-hand smoke justifies bans on smoking in public places. The tobacco industry argues against this, contending falsely that any risks that they reluctantly concede exist can be removed by improved ventilation (Dearlove, Bialous & Glantz 2002). It argues that people can choose whether to go into a smoking area, ignoring the hazards to those who enter these areas for employment or other needs. Furthermore, it contends that sales in bars and restaurants will fall with the implementation of smoking bans, resulting in job losses. All of these arguments have been shown to be entirely false (McKee, Hogan & Gilmore 2004). These actions can be implemented at little cost, and, indeed, a change in taxation would bring immediate benefits from higher taxes. However, for all these policies to be effective, enforcement is essential. This is likely to prove difficult in countries where the criminal justice system is weak and, especially, where there is widespread corruption, which is unfortunately the case in several countries in the Region.

A comprehensive tobacco policy goes even further, helping the majority of smokers who want to quit do so through promotional campaigns such as the WHO-supported Finnish Public Health Institute's "Quit and Win" initiative (see http://www.quitandwin.org/portal/en for further details). Where possible, these efforts can be linked to the provision of pharmacological measures, such as nicotine replacement therapy, for example. Finally, there is one policy that should not be adopted: claiming corporate social responsibility, the tobacco industry is promoting youth "antismoking" campaigns in many countries, with messages that smoking is acceptable for adults but not children. As children aspire to be adults, the message they take home is that smoking is desirable (WHO 2002b).

Action on tobacco control is thus, technically, quite straightforward. Action in other areas is more complicated. As noted above, policies to improve nutrition require a multifaceted approach involving the agricultural, rural development and retail sectors. Policies to reduce injuries require action to reduce hazardous drinking as well as actions by law enforcement agencies, consumer and occupational safety agencies, schools and employers (Sethi et al. 2006).

The problem of alcohol should be a high priority, yet here action may be more difficult, given the ease with which illegal alcohol can be produced or otherwise obtained. Key measures in any alcohol policy include increases in price by means of taxation and reductions in availability by reducing the number of sales outlets and their hours of operation (Edwards 1994; Anderson &

Baumberg 2006). Strong support for the effectiveness and cost–effectiveness of comprehensive action also comes from a recent ex ante assessment of alcohol policies in the EU (Horlings & Scoggins 2006). This study recommends the application of a wide variety of policy instruments (legislation, self-regulation, information and education campaigns, exchange of best practice, and stakeholder involvement) across all relevant policy domains (internal market, taxation, transport, education, research, and consumer policy). It also suggests that the strategy focus on drink-driving, coordinated campaigns, protection of third parties, commercial communication, consumer information, and availability and prices.

Surrogates (alcohol-containing substances not intended for consumption) and *samogon* (home-produced spirits) must be dealt with, to combat their widespread and highly dangerous use. The former are especially dangerous as they contain highly concentrated ethanol (typically 96% in the Russian Federation and 75% in the Baltic states) and, escaping taxation, are cheap. There is a compelling argument for some of these substances to be taxed, in the same way that controlled spirits are. Alternatively, since these substances are not intended for human consumption, it would be justifiable to require that they be denatured with an emetic agent (to induce vomiting if ingested). Similarly, there is a strong argument for prohibiting the sale of this type of alcohol where there are alternatives, as is now being carried out in the Russian Federation. Examples include charcoal lighter fluid, which has been replaced in most western countries with paraffin wax blocks, or the substitution of ethylene glycol for ethanolalcohol-containing substances used for de-icing.

While surrogate alcohols kill people rather quickly, conventional alcoholic beverages likely play a major role in putting people onto the downward spiral that leads to alcohol-related deaths. Policies are required to reduce the hazards of alcohol consumption, reducing demand (through social marketing, poverty alleviation strategies, effective treatment of alcohol dependence), reducing access (by limiting sales outlets, increasing price) and reducing the risks of harm among drinkers (preventing sales to those who are already intoxicated, enforcing restrictions on drink-driving). However, if sustained reductions in alcohol-related injuries are to be achieved, other policies will also be needed to reduce the many hazards in the environment (improved street lighting, road maintenance and improved vehicle safety) and increase the support networks available to those who are most vulnerable, in particular through policies that empower women to intervene to reduce the risks to (and from) male family members reluctant to reduce their consumption.

Cost-effective interventions

This book addresses the economic argument for investing in health in the CEE-CIS Region. Thus, when moving beyond the broader policy initiatives outlined in the previous section, many of which will cost little or may even increase government revenues (such as those involving increased taxation), it is important to consider the costs of possible interventions, as well as their effects.

When doing so, balancing the costs of possible interventions against their effects is key. Examining cost–effectiveness enables implementation of actions in a prioritized fashion. Outside high-income countries, international development assistance has provided much of the support for research on the effectiveness and cost–effectiveness of health-related interventions. Since the level of DAH in this Region has been very low and is coupled with an extremely weak research base, there is a severe paucity of directly relevant research that can inform policy with reasonable assurance. Consequently, this section draws on evidence from low- and middle-income countries in other parts of the world, recognizing the specifics of this Region but also that many parts of it have much more in common with these countries than with those in western Europe or North America.

Several methods can be used to weigh the outcome of a health intervention against its cost to determine "value for money". Of them all, cost–effectiveness analysis (CEA) is the most widely used, although others, in particular cost–benefit analysis (CBA) can also provide important insights, especially when comparing interventions with different outcomes. CEA assesses how much it costs to obtain a certain amount of health improvement. In contrast, CBA transforms the health benefits into a monetary measure.[93] In CEA analyses "health" is typically measured in DALYs[94] or in years of life saved. Cost–effectiveness is defined as the cost per unit of health benefit that results from a specific health intervention. Hence, the lower the cost–effectiveness ratio, the more health improvement can be bought with a given amount of money. A key objective of health policy-makers should be maximizing the health improvement that can be achieved with a given budget, although it is not the

---

93. See, for example, Drummond et al. (2005) for a detailed explanation of the different methodologies. Kenkel (1997), among others, argues for the application of CBA instead of CEA.

94. DALYs, disability-adjusted life years, are years attributable to a disease and are calculated as the sum of the years of life lost due to premature mortality in a population plus the years lost due to disability for incident cases of the disease/condition.

only relevant criterion (Musgrove 1999; Goddard et al. 2006).[95]

The fundamental principle of CEA is straightforward, but gathering the data needed to perform the analysis can be challenging. The CMH (2001) and its comprehensive background material have contributed greatly to the accumulation and synthesis of evidence on CEA of interventions to address communicable diseases as well as child and maternal conditions in resource-constrained settings. By contrast, CEA of interventions that address non-communicable diseases in low- and middle-income countries is comparatively limited (Mulligan, Walker & Fox-Rushby 2006). From the CEE-CIS perspective this is unfortunate, since these diseases are overwhelmingly the major burden of disease in the Region.

The recently published Disease Control Priorities Project makes strides in overcoming the long neglect of this topic. Jamison et al. (2006) reviewed an extensive body of evidence on the cost–effectiveness of interventions addressing noncommunicable disease (and injury) burden in low- and middle-income countries. The significance of this and related work[96] is that policy-makers in low- and middle-income countries, including most transition countries, now have a reasonable enough body of evidence of cost–effectiveness to guide them. At the same time – not surprisingly – scope for expanding the evidence remains.

Table A5.1 and Table A5.2 in the Annex to Chapter 5 provide an overview of a selection of population-based and personalized interventions that have been shown to provide good value for money in the areas of CVD, injury[97] and

---

95. There is no universally defined cost–effectiveness ratio, below which a given intervention is unambiguously considered "cost-effective". There are only different degrees of cost–effectiveness, and what is acceptable to decision-makers and the public ultimately depends on the specific country context. Several thresholds, however, have been introduced in national and international institutions. The values discussed range from US$ 100 per life year saved in the World Bank definition (1993) up to country-specific values such as € 80 000 per quality-adjusted life year (QALY) saved in the Netherlands and the implicit threshold of GBP 30 000, used in the United Kingdom's National Institute for Clinical Excellence (NICE) (Office of Health Economics and Kings Fund 2003). The richer the country, the higher the preferred threshold will be (although other contextual factors also enter into play). The CMH used a threshold of three times the country's per-capita income. It may be questionable whether a single threshold is an appropriate benchmark for the entire continuum of health-related activities. For example, a society may agree to accept higher cost–effectiveness thresholds for care relative to the age of its recipient or to the severity of illness or other factors (Eichler et al. 2004; Devlin & Parkin 2004).

96. See, for example, Suhrcke et al. (2006).

97. For more in depth CEA of injury interventions, using a modeling approach, see Bishai & Hyder (2006).

alcohol- and tobacco-related harm. Those tables as well as the summary that follows are largely based on Jamison et al. (2006) and in particular on Laxminarayan et al. (2006). Given the complexity of the challenge, a multi-pronged strategy spanning prevention, treatment and rehabilitation is needed, rather than single, isolated interventions. Vertical or "silo" interventions in health care delivery have proven not as effective as they might have been had more comprehensive approaches been taken. This should be borne in mind when sifting through the examples of cost-effective interventions discussed below.

Cardiovascular diseases

In the domain of population-based, primary prevention of CVDs, a few inter-ventions designed to modify lifestyles can lower the risk of coronary artery dis-ease and stroke cost-effectively and without expensive health infrastructure. They include lowering the proportion of fat in the diet, limiting salt intake, avoiding tobacco use and engaging in regular physical activity.

Interventions that target individuals at high risk of CVD can also be cost-effective in low-resource settings, and they can be particularly effective when accompanied by population-based measures.[98] Single-pill combinations of blood pressure-lowering medications, statins and aspirin offer the dual benefit of being highly effective at lowering cardiovascular risk while facilitating patient compliance with the drug regimen.

The effective management of acute myocardial infarction with basic care costs, for instance, less than US$ 25 per DALY averted in all regions. The combina-tion of aspirin and a beta-blocker is highly cost-effective in preventing the recurrence of a vascular event. In regions with poor access to hospitals, this combination is particularly cost-effective (US$ 386–545 per DALY averted). In all regions, treating congestive heart failure using a calcium antagonist and a beta-blocker is also enormously cost-effective (approximately US$ 200 per DALY averted).

The cost of treating acute ischemic stroke using aspirin is US$ 150 per DALY averted. Aspirin is the lowest-cost option for secondary prevention of stroke (US$ 3.80 per single percentage point decrease in the risk of a second stroke within two years or US$ 70 per DALY averted).

---

98. Although cost–effectiveness of these interventions varies greatly by risk factors, age of patient and cost of medication, targeted interventions may sometimes be even more cost-effective than population-based ones, simply because the smaller number of individuals to which they are applied can reduce total costs.

Injuries

To prevent unintentional road-based injuries, speed bumps appear to be the most cost-effective intervention, costing less than US$ 5 per DALY averted in all low- and middle-income regions if installed at the most dangerous junctions (accounting for 10% of deaths). Increased speeding penalties, media coverage and enforcement of traffic laws are only slightly less cost-effective. Motorcycle helmet legislation (US$ 467 per DALY averted in Thailand), bicycle helmet legislation (US$ 107 per DALY averted in China) and improved enforcement of traffic codes through a combination of enforcement and information campaigns (US$ 5–69 per DALY averted) are relatively more expensive but deserve more attention than they currently receive, given the growing injury burden associated with rising levels of vehicle ownership. Seat-belts and child restraints are known to be effective in the developed world, and lowering their costs to encourage routine use may improve their cost–effectiveness in low- and middle-income countries.

Alcohol and tobacco use

The growing prevalence of smoking, especially among women in low- and middle-income countries, is a serious threat to health to both women and their children. Interventions to reduce tobacco use are important not just because they are highly cost-effective but also because the burden of disability and number of deaths that they can avert are sizeable. As mentioned several times in this book, tobacco control through tax increases has dual benefits, increasing tax revenues as well as discouraging smoking initiation and encouraging smoking cessation. The cost–effectiveness of a policy to increase cigarette prices by 33% ranges from US$ 13 to US$ 195 per DALY averted globally, with a better cost–effectiveness ratio (US$ 3–42 per DALY averted) in low-income countries. In comparison, nicotine replacement therapy (US$ 55–751 per DALY averted) and non-price interventions, including banning advertising, providing health education information and prohibiting smoking in public places, are relatively less cost-effective (US$ 54–674 per DALY averted) in low-income countries but are still important components of any tobacco control programme.

In regions with at least a relatively high prevalence of high-risk alcohol use, of which the CEE-CIS Region is perhaps the most extreme example, tax increases to lower alcohol use are extremely cost-effective (US$ 105–225 per DALY averted). Advertising bans are among the most cost-effective (but least studied) of all interventions to reduce high-risk drinking in all regions (US$ 134–280 per DALY averted). In east Asia and the Pacific, a comprehensive ban on advertising and reduced access to retail outlets are highly cost-effective (US$

123–146 per DALY averted). Random breath testing is one of the less cost-effective interventions to reduce the alcohol-related disease burden (US$ 973–1856 per DALY averted). It is, of course, dependent on a police service that functions well and is not corrupt. Providing high-risk drinkers with brief advice from a physician in primary care settings is of intermediate cost–effectiveness (US$ 480–819 per DALY averted) in all regions, but combining this intervention with a tax on alcohol increases cost–effectiveness (US$ 260–533 per DALY averted) in all regions except sub-Saharan Africa.

Most of the cost–effectiveness findings discussed here and synthesized in the Annex to Chapter 5 (Table A5.1 and Table A5.2) are global results that vary among regional and national contexts. A comprehensive assessment of the overall cost–effectiveness of a major health investment programme in CEE-CIS would be an eminently worthwhile focus of further work. The basic idea of setting priorities according to their greatest value for money is highly rational and compelling: following this course – while incorporating appropriate weighting according to other relevant criteria – would make limited resources go further in improving health and would free up substantial resources for hitherto neglected but urgent purposes. Moreover, if the intention is to attract increased spending on health from aid agencies and development partners, demonstrating improved efficiency in health spending would improve the likelihood of success.

The core message from this section is how important it is that governments develop an effective public health function that can assess the health needs of the population; inform decisions on the interventions needed to tackle them, based on evidence of effectiveness and cost–effectiveness; and monitor the results. The details of the policies to develop are a matter for each country: this chapter facilitates the process by summarizing information that can assist governments, civil society organizations and private companies in reaching decisions about what works and what is worth the investment. These public health functions should be seen as part of the essential role of a government, on a par with economic policy. In reality, measures to improve the health of populations have typically been given a far lower priority, for many reasons (McKee et al. 2000), including the fact that they are seen as expenditure offering little prospect of economic return. Previous chapters make a case that this view is incorrect. What is needed now is a new approach where investment in the prerequisites for health is viewed in the same way as investment in physical infrastructure, which may have been given too high a priority in previous investment decisions.

Increasing health expenditure may be necessary but not sufficient

In arguing that there is substantial scope for scaling up and improving health policy efforts, Chapter 3 devotes substantial quantitative analysis to health expenditure as a proxy for health policy. This choice was motivated by the idea that the amount of resources dedicated to the health sector serves as a good proxy for a government's political will to "do something" for health. It was further assumed – fairly uncontroversially so – that some minimum level of resources must be available for the health sector to fulfil a set of even the most basic, essential functions.

However, this should not overlook the fact that the policies that matter for health far exceed what can be captured by health expenditure. Even if health expenditure might be considered a viable proxy for political engagement with health, this does not necessarily mean that more money spent on the health system directly buys better health outcomes. Several studies find a weak empirical link between health expenditures and health outcomes (Filmer, Hammer & Pritchett 1998).[99] They attribute this weak link to the possibility that public resources are used inefficiently and inequitably, and thus have little effect on the well-being of the poor. (Evidence to support this hypothesis in the CEE-CIS context is discussed in Chapter 3.) Also, public money may be crowding out private outlays on health care.

If health expenditures matter only to a limited extent for health outcomes, we need to look beyond them and ask how to most effectively and efficiently improve health. The previous sections identified some of the many evidence-based policy interventions that could potentially be applied to some of the Region's health challenges. This section complements them by focusing on two more general issues that are often overlooked when considering how to invest in health: the quality of governance and social capital. These are just two areas where policy-makers could take a broad and visionary approach in addressing the serious health-related threats to the Region's economies.

The first section adds directly to the debate on the effectiveness of health expenditure in promoting health outcomes by introducing the quality of governance as a mediating link in the chain. The underlying idea is that quality of governance improves the effectiveness of health expenditure in affecting health outcomes. The subsequent section highlights the importance of social capital for health in the Region. Both in terms of quality of governance and social capital, many countries in CEE-CIS have substantial scope for catching up with their neighbours and economic competitors.

---

99. However, the debate on the contribution of health expenditures to health outcomes continues. For a more optimistic account, see Bokhari et al. (2006)

Governance, health expenditure and health outcomes

Considerable cross-country evidence shows little independent effect of public health expenditure on child mortality rates or other health outcomes, after controlling for factors such as national per-capita incomes, income inequality and levels of education (Filmer, Hammer & Pritchett 1998). More recently, not least as a consequence of progress in measurement, the role of the quality of governance was brought into the debate about the link between health expenditure and outcomes. Governance may be defined in broad terms as the traditions and institutions by which authority in a country is exercised. This includes:

• the process by which governments are selected, monitored and replaced;

• the capacity of the government to effectively formulate and implement sound policies; and

• the respect of citizens and the state for the institutions that govern economic and social interactions among them (Kaufmann, Mastruzzi & Kraay 2004).

The underlying idea has been that as the quality of governance improves, the link between health expenditures and outcomes becomes stronger. In other words, health expenditure is good for health, but only if the quality of governance is "sufficient". A recent World Bank study (Wagstaff & Claeson 2004) confirms this hypothesis for a worldwide sample and for several health outcomes (under-five mortality, maternal mortality, underweight and TB mortality).[100] The authors find that the link between health expenditures and outcomes becomes significant once the quality of governance reaches a certain threshold. While the precise numbers should not be interpreted too literally, the findings do suggest that in some countries, typically those below this threshold, an increase in health expenditure by itself might not effectively improve health.

What does this result mean for the CEE-CIS countries? In particular, is their level of governance quality lower or higher than the threshold? To answer this question, the Wagstaff & Claeson (2004) analysis was replicated for this study with slight modifications and with more recent data. The health outcomes considered were under-five mortality and adult mortality rates (by gender) – a variable not included in the previous study.[101] "Government effectiveness", taken from the World Bank's governance database (2005c), was used as the

---

100. For similar approaches and findings, see, for example, Raikumar & Swaroop (2002) or Gupta, Davoodi & Tiongson (2000).

101. It was necessary to re-do the study (with more recent data) for at least two reasons: first, because the governance data Wagstaff & Claeson used (2004) are not publicly accessible and second, because the interest of this study was to see how the results compare when using adult mortality as an indicator, given that this health indicator is of particular relevance to the CEE-CIS Region.

indicator of quality of governance.[102] Government effectiveness captures the quality of public service provision, the quality of the bureaucracy, the competence of civil servants, the independence of the civil service from political pressures and the credibility of the government's commitment to policies. The main focus of this index is on the inputs required for a government to be able to produce and implement good policies and deliver public goods.

The results of this analysis confirm that the quality of governance significantly affects the ability of health expenditure to improve health, both for under-five mortality and adult mortality. (See the Annex to Chapter 5 for detailed methodology and full empirical results.) In the worldwide sample, the level of government effectiveness beyond which health expenditure contributes significantly to a reduction in under-five mortality is 0.53, while it is 1.03 for adult mortality. Figure 5.7 shows that the level of government effectiveness in the vast majority of the countries is below the threshold, except primarily for the three Baltic states. The same figure also shows that the level of government effectiveness in many CEE-CIS countries is lower than what would be expected when compared to other countries with a similar level of economic development.

The limitations of this approach are important. In particular, the results should not be interpreted too precisely in terms of the numerical values. Clearly, it is a daunting challenge to properly quantify primarily qualitative concepts such as the quality of governance. Moreover, the fact that these results and others indicate a limited or no impact of public health expenditure on health does not mean that money does not matter. Some studies have demonstrated that what matters is the composition of the overall amount of public money. For instance, Gupta, Verhoeven & Tiongson found that shifting spending towards primary care has a favourable effect on infant and child mortality rates (1999). Other studies show that public spending may not improve average population health indicators but that it appears to have a positive effect on the health of the poor (Bidani & Ravallion 1997; Gupta, Verhoeven & Tiongson 2003).

The broad message remains unambiguous, although more detailed analysis is warranted. In the specific case of the CEE-CIS countries, substantial health gains can accrue from "investing" in improved governance quality, in- and outside the health system. This would not only be good for health, but also for

---

102. See details and access the World Bank's governance database at www.worldbank.org/wbi/governance/ (World Bank 2005c) (accessed 30 May 2005). The World Bank produces indicators along six dimensions of governance quality: voice and accountability, political stability, government effectiveness, regulatory quality, rule of law, and control of corruption. These indicators are closely related, with bilateral correlation coefficients between 0.69 and 0.96 for the 2002 indicators.

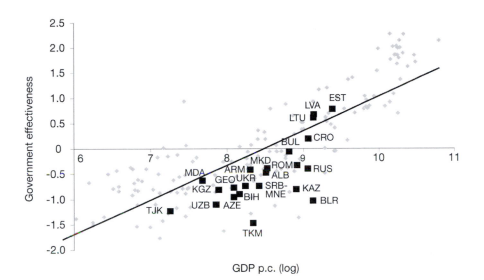

Figure 5.7 *Government effectiveness versus GDP per capita, 2002 (Source: World Bank, 2005c).*

Note: For details of country name abbreviations, see List of abbreviations; GDP: gross domestic product; p.c.: per capita.

other social and economic development outcomes. The latter is a feature that is potentially also true of social capital.

Social capital

Growing evidence indicates that the organization of society and the relationships therein may impact considerably on health, particularly for the most disadvantaged groups in society. This section contributes to this new but rapidly growing field[103] by looking at the role of social capital in health in the CEE-CIS countries. On the basis of the evidence presented here, there is: (1) significant scope for improving social capital in this part of the world; and (2) much to suggest that at least some social capital indicators do matter for health in a causal sense.

Social capital, defined as "the institutions, relationships, attitudes, and values that govern interactions among people and contribute to economic and social development" (Grootaert & van Bastelaer 2001) is increasingly recognized as having a positive effect on individual health (Putnam et al. 1993; Wilkinson 1996). Social capital is manifest through formal and informal networks. A

---

103. For a collection of papers on the importance of social capital for a large set of development outcomes, see the World Bank's Social Capital web site at www1.worldbank.org/prem/poverty/scapital/ (accessed 19 January 2006).

Box 5.4 How social capital manifests

Considering social capital requires, first, determining whether it is "structural" or "cognitive" social capital (Uphoff 2000), and second, examining it according to the scope of its unit of observation (micro, meso or macro).

Structural social capital refers to relatively objective, externally observable social structures, such as networks, associations and institutions, and the rules and procedures they embody. Sports and musical groups, and neighbourhood associations are all examples of this form of social capital. Cognitive social capital comprises more subjective, intangible elements such as generally accepted attitudes and behaviour norms, shared values, reciprocity and trust. Although these two forms of social capital may reinforce each other, either can exist without the other. Government-mandated organizations, for instance, represent structural social capital where the cognitive element is not necessarily present. Similarly, many relationships of mutual "cognitive" trust persist without being formalized in organizations.

Grootaert & van Bastelaer (2001) further distinguishes three levels at which social capital may act: at the individual (micro) level, the inter-group (meso) level (where relations among groups are both vertical and horizontal), and the macro level in the form of the institutional and political environment that serves as a backdrop for all economic and social activity and the quality of government arrangements (Olson 1982; North 1990). These three levels can have complementary or substitutional relationships with each other: national institutions may, for instance, provide an enabling environment where local associations can develop. But local forms of social capital can arise both as a response to "good" (Tendler 1997) and "bad" (Skocpol 1992) national governments. According to Rose (1998), the dysfunctional state in the Russian Federation in the early years of transition greatly "promoted" the development of informal networks at local level. On the other hand, excessive ethnic identification in local associations could be one factor that impedes successful policies at national level and may also lead to violence in some cases (Bates 1999).

---

variety of mechanisms have been proposed to explain the observed relationship between social capital and health, including formal networks, in which membership is a means of accessing social and health care, as well as informal networks, in which an individual can draw on a collective body of knowledge that will facilitate access to scarce resources, including information that will enhance the ability to make healthy choices (see Box 5.4).

Social capital in transition countries

The Region's transition from a centrally planned system to a market economy, accompanied by a transition from an authoritarian to a democratic regime, reflects a process of large-scale institutional change. Both formal and informal institutions had to adapt to the requirements of both democracy and market transactions. The resulting uncertainty placed a heavy load on social arrangements and, hence on social capital at all three of the levels identified in Box 5.4. In order to stabilize expectations and make behaviour of actual or potential counterparts more predictable, relationships other than formal ones had to be developed (Raiser et al. 2001; Wallace, Bedzik & Chmouliar 1997).[104]

In many CEE-CIS countries, especially in countries of the former USSR (except for the Baltic states) structural social capital at the macro level – that is, the quality of governance – has not fully evolved and is lagging behind what other countries at similar levels of economic development have achieved in terms of a number of governance indicators (see Subsection "Governance, health expenditure and health outcomes").

A similarly pessimistic evaluation might apply to the degree of civic engagement among individuals and groups within societies. The absence of a fully developed, vibrant civil society in communist and post-communist countries has been widely lamented by leading eastern European dissidents (such as Vaclav Havel) and western European social scientists. It has been argued that this deficit poses a major obstacle along the path of political and economic transition (Smolar 1996; Rose 1993).

Before examining the impact of social capital on health using data specific to CEE-CIS, this section presents the available quantitative information to assess where the CEE-CIS countries are in terms of social capital, defined in different ways. The fourth round of the European and World Values Surveys (EVS/WVS), carried out between 1999 and 2002, makes it possible to locate the level of social capital in the broader global picture.[104] The main question the empirical analysis seeks to answer is whether social capital is lower in CEE-CIS countries than in other countries with comparable per-capita income levels.

If this is the case, then there would be scope for improving social capital, with all the associated benefits, in health and in other aspects that this might entail.

Using the fourth round of the EVS/WVS, Table 5.2 reports country and regional means for several social capital indicators related to the degree of: (1)

---

104. The Social Capital Gateway web site has a collection of studies addressing the role of social capital in transition: see www.socialcapitalgateway.org/NV-eng-transitionmarket.htm (accessed 20 January 2006).

105. While very useful for the assessment of social capital per se, the WVS/EVS is of limited use for any more substantive analysis of the relationship between social capital and health. As a consequence, we use a different survey in the analysis below, at the cost of limited cross-country coverage.

Table 5.2 Summary statistics: social capital indicators (percentages), 1999–2002[a]

Country	Trust (2000)	Membership (2000)	Army (2000)	Confidence in:			
				Press (2000)	Unions (2000)	Police (2000)	Parliament (2000)
Albania	24	60	57	35	33	65	45
Azerbaijan	21	5	56	32	30	41	74
Armenia	25	14	72	34	19	32	30
Bosnia and Herzegovina	16	28	61	25	23	64	20
Bulgaria	27	13	58	26	15	47	27
Belarus	42	10	70	41	28	40	37
Croatia	18	32	66	18	29	53	23
Czech Republic	24	51	25	38	22	33	12
Estonia	23	27	35	42	32	34	27
Georgia	19	5	52	60	28	38	41
Hungary	22	22	46	31	24	45	34
Latvia	17	21	48	45	32	40	27
Lithuania	25	14	50	77	40	26	11
Poland	19	15	67	47	34	55	33
Romania	10	12	83	38	27	45	19
Republic of Moldova	15	31	57	44	33	35	35
Russian Federation	24	11	67	30	31	29	19
Slovakia	16	54	77	49	43	44	43
Slovenia	22	39	42	61	31	50	25
TFYR Macedonia	14	39	55	20	13	51	7

Ukraine	27	14	69	47	38	33	27
CIS average	25	14	64	42	29	34	32
CEE average	21	25	58	40	29	43	29
Low income	20	46	73	65	54	47	63
Lower-middle income	25	25	63	44	34	51	39
Upper-middle income	21	35	56	48	36	46	34
High income	36	54	59	39	40	69	40
Gap: CEE-CIS vs rest of world	ns	-46	ns	-16	-32	-30	-35
Gap: CIS vs rest of world	ns	ns	ns	Ns	-26	-41	-24
Gap: CEE vs rest of world	ns	ns	-12	-17	-31	ns	-35

Source: European Values Study Group & World Values Survey Association, 2004.

Notes: a The fourth round of the World Bank World Values Survey was carried out between 1999 and 2002; "ns": Not significant at the 5% level; The fourth round data are available for 77 countries; For Azerbaijan, Australia, Armenia, Brazil, Colombia, Dominican Republic, El Salvador, Georgia, New Zealand, Norway, Switzerland and Uruguay, the data refer to the years between 1995 and 1997 – for these countries inactive membership is coded as no membership; Armenia, Belarus, Georgia, Republic of Moldova, the Russian Federation and Ukraine are the only CIS countries for which data are available – the CIS row provides averages over these six countries; The CEE row presents averages over all the countries reported in the table; Country income classifications follow World Bank criteria; The trust variable is a dummy that takes the value 1 if the respondent indicates that most people can be trusted and 0 if the respondent says that he/she needs to be very careful in dealing with people; The membership variable is a dummy that takes the value 1 if the respondent belongs to one organization related to church, cultural activities, human rights, conservation, environment, animal rights, youth work, sports, women's group or the peace movement and 0 otherwise; The other social capital indicators measure the degree of confidence in the army, press, labour unions, police and parliament – these indicators take the value 1 if the respondent has "a great deal" or "a lot" of confidence in the organization and 0 otherwise ("not very much" or "not at all"); For each variable, the average gaps between all CEE-CIS countries and the rest of the world, between only the CIS countries and the rest of the world and between the CEE countries and the rest of the world, are reported if significantly different from zero at 95% – such gaps are derived as follows: each social capital measure was regressed on per capita GDP in 2000 and on a dummy variable taking the value 1 if a country was a CEE-CIS country (or a country from only CIS or only CEE), and subsequently, the ratio between the average of the predicted values of the CIS countries and the average of the predicted values of the rest of the world was computed; For details of country categories see List of abbreviations.

trust; (2) participation in local organization; and (3) confidence in the army, press, labour unions, police and parliament.

Most indicators report that social capital is considerably lower in the countries in transition than in the rest of the sample. The mean degree of participation in local organizations is 25% in countries in transition, comparable to that in lower-middle income countries, but substantially lower than in high-income countries (54%), and also lower than in low-income countries (46%). The mean degree of trust is 21% for the countries in transition, a level of the same order of magnitude as in low- and middle-income countries but much behind the degree of trust observable in high-income countries (36%). As regards the measures of confidence in social and political institutions, the CEE-CIS countries lag behind middle-income countries in all cases. Similar patterns emerge for the subset of CIS countries, except that the degree of participation in local organizations is sizeably lower than in the CEE countries.

The regional averages hide substantial differences within each region. In the CEE-CIS Region, for instance, the degree of trust varies between 10% in Romania and 42% in Belarus. Similarly, the national average figure for participation in local organizations ranges from a mere 5% in Azerbaijan and Georgia to as high as 60% in Albania. Heterogeneity among countries in the degree of confidence in labour unions, police and parliament is likely to be strongly related to the policies adopted by the government in power when the survey was conducted. Hence, these last indicators embody a time-contingent, fluctuating component that will not precisely reflect the actual stock of macro- or meso-social capital of the country. Table 5.2 also reports the extent of social capital differences between countries in transition and "other" countries with similar per-capita incomes (as well as between CIS countries and other countries). (The note in Table 5.2 summarizes the simple regression exercise used.) The underlying idea is that social capital tends to improve with the level of economic development in a country and that, hence, comparing social capital between countries with different per-capita incomes would not, in a sense, be "fair". The results confirm that, when controlling for per-capita GDP in 2000, the level of social capital is comparatively lower in the CEE-CIS countries. The participation in local organizations is, on average, 46% lower than in other countries with comparable per-capita incomes. Confidence in parliament is 35% lower. As regards the subgroup of CIS countries, the gap in terms of participation in local organizations amounts to 66%.

While it would have been desirable to assess changes in the social capital indicators since the onset of transition, few CEE-CIS countries have such information from the early 1990s. What little comparable information exists does suggest that at least as far as trust is concerned, a rather general deterioration seems to have occurred over the past decade.

Taken together, the indicators of social capital considered here are systematically lower in CEE-CIS than in most other parts of the world by latest counts. Although this is hard to tell based on the available data, at least in part this may be a result of the deterioration in social capital during the 1990s.

Social capital and health

The relationship between social capital and health has been documented since 1901, when Emile Durkheim identified a relationship between suicide rates and the level of social integration. Since then, research has continued to demonstrate that higher social capital and social cohesion are associated with improved health. This association has been the subject of an extensive body of research in the past decade that finds that lower trust in a population is associated with a higher level of mortality (Baum 1997).[106]

It has been argued that social capital can impact health through various channels and at various levels.[107]

- At a macro level of analysis, social capital may facilitate health care delivery. A better social network among and between each group of health care providers (i.e., the government, the market and the family/community) will make it easier to deliver effective health care if, for instance, people are more likely to seek advice from someone they trust. Community and volunteer organizations play a central role in providing services to patients in both developing and industrialized nations. Social capital may also support prevention efforts. Prevention is most effective if supported by formal and informal networks through which people receive information and health care.

- At meso and micro levels of analysis, social capital can improve health through enforcing or changing social norms. A more cohesive society, with a strong feeling of group identity is attentive to common well-being,[108] implying that environment-damaging behaviours (pollution, unhealthy waste disposal) would be avoided, and entrepreneurs would be more likely to provide a healthy workplace. Moreover, smoking, unsanitary behaviour

---

106. For an overview and a collection of studies, see, for example, Kawachi et al. (2004). For a critical account of the use of social capital for health, see Lynch et al. (2000).

107. For an extensive study on the definition, measurement and role of social capital in health, see Morgan and Swann (2004).

108. Sometimes, higher social capital has been associated with a higher degree of altruism among individuals: this allows taking into account the welfare of other members of the social group of reference in individual choices (see Durlauf and Fafchamps (2004) for an extensive discussion).

and risky sexual practices, which negatively affect public health, are less likely within a socially cohesive society. Finally, shared values and norms can also have an impact on the level of community violence and, therefore, on the frequency of injuries and violent deaths.

A rapidly growing number of studies have explored empirically the relationship between different dimensions of social capital and health. Yet few quantitative studies have explored the issue of social capital in a transition country context and even fewer have looked at the specific relationship between social capital and health in CEE-CIS.[109]

The data available allowed the investigation of only one dimension of social capital, cognitive social capital, operating at the micro level. Hence, the channels through which this dimension of social capital affects health include those of facilitating informal cooperation and information sharing. Enhanced cooperation among individuals may affect health conditions in several ways. In addition to the channels mentioned above (lower probability of smoking, risky sexual practices, crime), it could be argued that in a risky environment context, and in the absence of formal credit and insurance markets, social capital becomes a crucial ingredient for the viability of informal risk-pooling and/or risk-sharing mechanisms within a community. These mechanisms are often based on reciprocity, and they are grounded in participants' trustworthiness. Such agreements allow people to cope with shocks due to illnesses or accidents, by providing resources to cover the direct and indirect costs necessary to recovering from illness. In such circumstances, voluntary associations emerge that can contribute to caring.

Three different, but common indicators of social capital are used for the empirical assessment of its impact on health, in the survey at hand (the LLH survey):[110]

Trust in other people. This is captured by people agreeing or nearly agreeing with the view that a majority of people can be trusted. The degree of trust partly depends on the legal system, but also on certain specific economic and social characteristics of the community, such as the degree of income equality

---

109. An exception is Rose (2000).

110. Of course, these indicators do not exhaust the list of possible social capital indicators that could be relevant for health. Further analysis, subject to the availability of appropriate survey instruments, may offer the opportunity to examine more dimensions of social capital. Note that for the specific analysis of the impact of social capital on health it is not the above-mentioned EVS/WVS data that is used but the LLH survey. This is because the LLH survey offers far better possibilities for a structural analysis of the relationship, if at the cost of a smaller sample of countries.

or social cohesion (shared language, norms and interests, etc). The conditions for creating trusting relationships lie at the collective level, so this indicator can be interpreted as an asset of the community.

Membership of organizations. The focus here is on networks involving "horizontal egalitarian relationships" rather than on networks based on "vertical hierarchical relationships" (such as the employer–employee relationship). It captures respondents that are part of one of the following organizations: church, sport, art, music, neighbourhood, youth, women, charitable organizations or any other voluntary organization.[111] Social relationships between individuals sharing the same social identity ("bonding") are more likely to be associated with reciprocal trust, while relationships between individuals situated at different levels of the social scale ("bridging") are more correlated with reciprocal respect.[112] Membership also captures the collective dimension of social capital. Formal networks may facilitate the transfer of health information or limit health behaviours that differ from the network's norm, whether healthy or not. In addition, numerous authors (e.g. Pevalin & Rose 2002) have shown that social isolation is associated with psychological stress, with negative consequences for psychological and physical health.

Financial support prospects. This indicator captures those individuals who claim to be able to rely on someone outside the household in case of financial difficulties. It is based on the concept that the financial support that could be provided by informal networks (such as friends and community- and work-related ties) acts as insurance against major negative income shocks caused by sudden health deterioration. In this case, unlike the previous two indicators, the link between social support and health is likely to depend on individual factors, such as income and access to formal insurance mechanisms. This social support indicator refers to the notion of social capital as a property of the individual.[113]

In assessing the impact of social capital on health, similar econometric challenges arise, as in the microeconomic analysis in Chapter 4, when trying to assess the effect of health on labour market outcomes. First, it is usually difficult to distinguish the effect of social capital from other effects that may

---

111. The variable "membership" takes the value 0 if individual is not involved in any organizations or political or professional associations.

112. See Szreter and Woolcock (2004) for more information about the distinction between "bonding" versus "bridging" social capital.

113. In a slightly different version of this work, d'Hombres et al. (2006) use an indicator of social isolation to replace the financial support indicator. Results obtained are, however, qualitatively similar.

Table 5.3 *The impact of social capital on health in eight CIS countries (propensity score estimates), 2001*

Country	Trust	Financial support	Membership
Armenia	0.08	0	0.053
Belarus	0.133***	0.140***	0.003
Georgia	0.063***	0.093*	0.019
Kazakhstan	0.091***	0.031	0.023
Kyrgyzstan	0.067 ***	0.028	-0.05
Republic of Moldova	0.069 **	-0.02	0.06
Russian Federation	0.050***	0.090***	0.021
Ukraine	0.059 ***	0.111***	-0.011

Source: Authors' calculations based on Living Conditions, Lifestyles and Health (LLH) survey data.

Note: * significant at the 10% level; ** significant at the 5% level; *** significant at the 1% level.

influence health. Second, trust, membership in organizations and financial support are individual choices that depend on individuals' specific and unobservable preferences. Hence, they are by definition endogenously determined. Unobservable individual effects such as time preferences, personal interests, and individuals' exogenous shocks may be correlated both with self-reported health and with social capital indicators, so a basic assumption underlying the standard OLS regression method is violated. Third, there is a concern about reverse causality since health could have an impact on social participation and individual behaviours. Individuals in poor health might be more socially isolated or forced to revoke their membership of associations if they are hampered in their daily activities. One's perception of others, and thus the degree of trust, may also be a function of health.

Methodologies that help overcome these challenges have been applied to elicit the causal impact of the three social capital indicators on health, while controlling for a number of other relevant variables. The dataset set used was again the LLH survey. In contrast to the majority of the empirical approaches adopted for the work in Chapter 4, the primary technique used here is a propensity score matching (PSM) technique (see Table 5.3 for the main results and the Annex to Chapter 5 for more information on the methodology and its rationale).

While the impact of trust on health appears statistically robust across the countries (except for Armenia), only half of the countries show a significant positive influence of the financial support variable, and no single significant result is found for the membership variable. Hence, the impact of social capital on health depends to a great extent on the specific type of social capital considered. The impact of financial support might depend on three factors: (1) the availability of a formal and accessible financial market; (2) the individual financial situation; and (3) the importance of the household as a primary safety net. If formal credit is accessible, individual financial conditions are good or people mainly rely on their own household in case of need, then receiving financial support from someone outside the household will have less impact on individual health. Note that all three factors are country specific. The poor results associated with *membership* are puzzling. In principle, being member of a local association should favour the diffusion of information and reciprocal support, in turn positively affecting health. Further research will be needed to explain this result.[114]

Where results are statistically significant, the size of the impact is remarkable. In the Russian Federation, for instance, the health of those who trust others is about 8% more favourable than among those who do not; in Ukraine the figure is 12% and in Belarus 23%. The size of the impact of financial support, where significant, is even higher: Belarus, the Russian Federation, Ukraine and to a less significant extent Georgia.

Although the subject of social capital deserves further analysis, this first exercise already shows that it may be important to incorporate the concept into the broader set of policies that can promote health. Specifically, government and international organizations' efforts should not be limited to improving health infrastructures, although this is certainly crucial. Rather, it would be worthwhile to devote attention to additional aspects, at first sight unrelated to health. This includes opportunities for social interaction and cooperation, as

114. In related work, not reported here but available on request, the authors have examined in more detail the role of membership in influencing health. An instrumental variable regression is used rather than PSM, and the membership variable interacted with an index of civil liberties (available at country level) is included among the covariates, in addition to the membership variable on its own. Membership turns out to be good for individual health in countries with relatively developed civil liberties, while it is bad for health in more authoritarian countries. The interpretation is that being part of local organizations is an asset for individual health only if such organizations are favoured by the government and can indeed display their beneficial role. Conversely, if they are suspected to be a threat to a government's power and are repressed, then their members could be discriminated against in the access to health care, housing and education services, with clearly negative consequences on individual physical and psychological health.

well as the development of institutions that make it possible to enforce law and order credibly, while discouraging opportunistic behaviours. Not only do these factors have a direct positive impact on health (and therefore indirectly on economic outcomes), but they can also directly affect economic outcomes.

Conclusions

The key message from Chapter 5 is how important it is for governments to develop an effective public health function that can assess the health needs of the population, inform decisions on the interventions needed to tackle them and monitor the results. The details of the policies that will be developed are a matter for each country. These public health functions should be seen as part of the essential role of a government, on a par with economic policy. In reality, measures to improve the health of populations have typically been given a far lower priority, for many reasons: measures to improve health have undoubtedly been seen as expenditure offering little prospect of economic return. What is needed is a new approach where investment in the prerequisites for health is viewed in the same way as investment in the physical infrastructure traditionally seen as contributing to economic development. Also needed is a concept of health investment that encompasses forces beyond the health sector, such as the two examples of governance and social.

Chapter 6
Conclusions

Investing in health has untapped potential to contribute to sustained economic growth and poverty reduction in the CEE-CIS Region. Considerable evidence, highlighted herein, shows that there is substantial scope for improving the health status of this population. This scope appears particularly large for the CIS countries, where life expectancy has levelled out or even declined in recent years from already low levels. This trend runs counter to rising life expectancy in all other world regions, except where AIDS has struck hardest. While the situation is not as desperate in the CEE countries, the difference in health status between CEE and EU15 countries has increased on many counts since the start of the political and economic transition.

The enormous scale of avoidable human tragedy has indeed already been documented elsewhere, revealing a simple fact: the poor health of people in this Region is not adequately recognized. The high and rising rates of otherwise readily preventable morbidity and mortality, large and rising inequities in health systems, low levels of resources for health (at least for some countries) and a low level of international DAH in the Region all testify to the lack of serious action from these governments and international agencies.

This book brings together evidence both old and new to establish conclusively that on top of the *human* tragedy, the Region is paying an enormous and unnecessary *economic* price for its excessive burden of disease and mortality. The economic evidence documents how ill health detracts from individuals' labour market productivity and supply, both key vehicles of economic growth at the macro level. (The other ways in which ill health may hamper economic development, such as by eroding savings and restricting educational attainment, are left for another day.)

In light of the recent rebound in economic growth occurring in large parts of the Region, governments and international organizations may well continue to overlook the need to invest in health as a fundamental factor of long-term economic growth. Their doing so would fail to recognize that recent growth is very unlikely to be sustained. The challenge of establishing the long-term prerequisites for economic growth continues. Investing in health can contribute to this objective. Benefits would result for both the population at large and for those 210 million who either still live in poverty or are vulnerable to impoverishment.

Expecting health investment to function as the panacea for sustained economic growth and poverty reduction in the Region would of course be unrealistic. However, in light of the evidence presented here, health merits a firm place within each country's development strategy, a place that clearly has not been achieved to date. The increased resources that may become available through the recent growth in several countries should be used in a forward-looking manner, to lay the foundations of long-term economic growth by investing in health (among other key factors), as part of the promotion of human and institutional capital.

Improving population health is not, as some would argue, something that can be left solely to individuals. Economic (as well as other) rationales compel governments to play a role in addressing the excessive burden of noncommunicable disease in the CEE-CIS Region, alongside the other important health challenges. The numerous forces described here show that severe market failures prevail in this health domain, just as they do in those more commonly analysed, such as communicable disease.

The question then is what to do, how to begin. A framework and illustrative examples have been provided as to the steps governments should take. They include the establishment of mechanisms that will enable them to: (1) identify the health needs of their population; (2) develop effective policy responses; and (3) implement and monitor them. Selected priority actions are highlighted in order to facilitate this process. Priorities include addressing the leading risk factors – alcohol, tobacco and inadequate nutrition – for noncommunicable diseases as well as their underlying causes. (This is not to imply a disregard for communicable diseases and child and maternal conditions but rather recognizes that these are receiving both national and international attention, albeit not optimally.) Many evidence-based, cost-effective interventions addressing noncommunicable disease exist and can be implemented through actions within and outside the health system. To a large extent, they have not been tried or taken to full scale in this Region. Of course, a good health system offers a platform to address health challenges in general, irrespective of disease classification.

The book also forcefully calls attention to the need to view health investment as involving an arena broader than the health system. Two examples argue for consideration of this wider perspective: the quality of governance and social capital emerge as two areas that could propel health improvement, specifically, again, for the population of this Region. Left bereft as a legacy of the Soviet system, these areas lie both within and beyond government purview. A first step governments can take is to foster an atmosphere where civil society can thrive. In addition, poor governance, especially in its most pernicious manifestations of nepotism and corruption, should be curbed. South-east Asia is reaping the rewards of such change, and while the process is difficult, any region, including CEE-CIS, would gain from it.

The relevance of this book is not limited to national policy-makers or to this Region. While international efforts tend to neglect the threats of noncommunicable disease, they are similarly neglected in other regions, to the peril of many populations. Evidence presented here recommends interpreting the MDGs more flexibly and including noncommunicable diseases in the (many) cases where they account for the major share of the avoidable disease burden.

International support for these recommendations would not be simply a matter of altruism. Serious health challenges are poised on the EU's doorstep, and the United States is no longer far away. Relieving those challenges as part of a plan to improve the Region's economies and stability is of obvious importance. Prosperous economies remain possible worldwide, but not without investing in health and the policies that support them.

Annexes

Annex to Chapter 3

Table A3.1 *The 14 epidemiological subregions*

WHO Region	Mortality stratum*	Countries
Africa (AFR)	D	Algeria, Angola, Benin, Burkina Faso, Cameroon, Cape Verde, Chad, Comoros, Equatorial Guinea, Gabon, Gambia, Ghana, Guinea, Guinea-Bissau, Liberia, Madagascar, Mali, Mauritania, Mauritius, Niger, Nigeria, Sao Tome and Principe, Senegal, Seychelles, Sierra Leone, Togo
	E	Botswana, Burundi, Central African Republic, Congo, Côte d'Ivoire, Democratic Republic of the Congo, Eritrea, Ethiopia, Kenya, Lesotho, Malawi, Mozambique, Namibia, Rwanda, South Africa, Swaziland, Uganda, United Republic of Tanzania, Zambia, Zimbabwe
The Americas (AMR)	A	Canada, Cuba, United States of America
	B	Antigua and Barbuda, Argentina, Bahamas, Barbados, Belize, Brazil, Chile, Colombia, Costa Rica, Dominica, Dominican Republic, El Salvador, Grenada, Guyana, Honduras, Jamaica, Mexico, Panama, Paraguay, Saint Kitts and Nevis, Saint Lucia, Saint Vincent and the Grenadines, Suriname, Trinidad and Tobago, Uruguay, Venezuela (Bolivian Republic of)
	D	Bolivia, Ecuador, Guatemala, Haiti, Nicaragua, Peru

(cont.)

Table A3.1 *(cont.)*

WHO Region	Mortality stratum*	Countries
Eastern Mediterranean (EMR)	B	Bahrain, Cyprus, Iran (Islamic Republic of), Jordan, Kuwait, Lebanon, Libyan Arab Jamahiriya, Oman, Qatar, Saudi Arabia, Syrian Arab Republic, Tunisia, United Arab Emirates
	D	Afghanistan, Djibouti, Egypt, Iraq, Morocco, Pakistan, Somalia, Sudan, Yemen
Europe (EUR)	A	Andorra, Austria, Belgium, Croatia, Czech Republic, Denmark, Finland, France, Germany, Greece, Iceland, Ireland, Israel, Italy, Luxembourg, Malta, Monaco, Netherlands, Norway, Portugal, San Marino, Slovenia, Spain, Sweden, Switzerland, United Kingdom
	B	Albania, Armenia, Azerbaijan, Bosnia and Herzegovina, Bulgaria, Georgia, Kyrgyzstan, Poland, Romania, Serbia and Montenegro, Slovakia, Tajikistan, The former Yugoslav Republic of Macedonia, Turkey, Turkmenistan, Uzbekistan
	C	Belarus, Estonia, Hungary, Kazakhstan, Latvia, Lithuania, Republic of Moldova, Russian Federation, Ukraine
South-east Asia (SEAR)	B	Indonesia, Sri Lanka, Thailand
	D	Bangladesh, Bhutan, Democratic People's Republic of Korea, India, Maldives, Myanmar, Nepal
Western Pacific (WPR)	A	Australia, Brunei Darussalam, Japan, New Zealand, Singapore
	B	Cambodia, China, Cook Islands, Fiji, Kiribati, Lao People's Democratic Republic, Malaysia, Marshall Islands, Micronesia (Federated States of), Mongolia, Nauru, Niue, Palau, Papua New Guinea, Philippines, Republic of Korea, Samoa, Solomon Islands, Tonga, Tuvalu, Vanuatu, Viet Nam

Source: Adopted from Mathers et al., 2003.

Notes: A: very low child mortality and very low adult mortality; B: low child mortality and low adult mortality; C: low child mortality and high adult mortality; D: high child mortality and high adult mortality; E: high child mortality and very high adult mortality;

* These classifications have no official status and are for analytical purposes only.

Methodology for calculating the health expenditure gap

A total of 144 low- and middle-income countries (a gross national income lower than or equal to US$ 9835 per capita) were included in the analysis. Within this sample, the top 20% (best performers) for each health outcome of interest – male and female adult and under-five mortality rates – were identified.

Based on the sample of the best performers in each health outcome, a production frontier was computed, concentrating on the relationship between health expenditure per capita and gross domestic product (GDP) per capita, as in the study by Preker, Langenbrunner & Suzuki (2002). The underlying premise is that health expenditure per capita is an important determinant of the health outcomes, and we are looking for the levels of expenditure chosen by the best performers. Such a level (conditional on national per-capita incomes) should represent the target for the countries performing worse. The implicit assumption is that national heterogeneity in institutions, environment, lifestyles and anything likely to affect health expenditure effectiveness is completely captured by GDP per capita. Although this hypothesis is rather strong, it was dictated by a lack of reliable data on additional country-specific controls beyond GDP per capita, especially as regards the poorest countries. Formally, an exponential regression on a double log scale was adopted:

$$Log_{10}(government's\ health\ expenditure\ p.c.) = \alpha\ exp\ (\beta\ Log_{10}\ (GDP\ p.c.)$$

Note: p.c.: per capita.

Given this functional form, the estimates for the coefficients α and β determine what the government's health expenditure should be for any country to reach the category of best performers in terms of one health outcome. It is then simple to compute the expenditure gap by taking the difference between the ideal threshold and the actual level of health expenditure. Results are shown in Table A3.2, Table A3.3 and Table A3.4.

Table A3.2 *Health expenditure gap based on worldwide sample (US$ per capita)*

Region	Female adult mortality	Male adult mortality	Under-5 mortality	Public health expenditure per capita
Baltic states				
Estonia	–	108	86	461
Latvia	–	135	113	306
Lithuania	–	40	18	399
South-eastern Europe				
Albania	9	123	104	117
Bosnia and Herzegovina	–	15	–	161
Bulgaria	0	54	33	267
Croatia	–	–	–	513
Romania	–	46	24	309
Serbia and Montenegro	–	–	–	191
TFYR Macedonia	–	–	–	289
Western Commonwealth of Independent States				
Belarus	–	6	–	430
Republic of Moldova	–	30	18	88
Russian Federation	–	110	88	298
Ukraine	–	71	53	150
Caucasus				
Armenia	46	146	129	53
Azerbaijan	51	139	123	27
Georgia	–	–	–	–
Central Asia				
Kazakhstan	–	–	–	–
Kyrgyzstan	4	81	67	60
Tajikistan	22	72	62	13
Turkmenistan	–	77	60	129
Uzbekistan	–	71	58	65
Average (weighted)	6	92.1	73.4	229

Source: Authors' calculations.

Table A3.3 *Health expenditure gap in absolute US$ millions, worldwide sample*

Region	Female adult mortality	Male adult mortality	Under-5 mortality
Baltic states			
Estonia	–	147	117
Latvia	–	316	264
Lithuania	–	138	61
South-eastern Europe			
Albania	28	387	329
Bosnia and Herzegovina	–	62	–
Bulgaria	–	425	261
Croatia	–	–	–
Romania	–	1 002	534
Serbia and Montenegro	–	–	–
TFYR Macedonia	–	–	–
Western Commonwealth of Independent States			
Belarus	–	57	–
Republic of Moldova	–	129	78
Russian Federation	–	15 852	12 671
Ukraine	–	3 458	2 592
Caucasus			
Armenia	141	448	396
Azerbaijan	420	1 132	1 009
Georgia	235	686	608
Central Asia			
Kazakhstan	1 009	3 139	2 821
Kyrgyzstan	20	403	335
Tajikistan	137	451	391
Turkmenistan	–	369	287
Uzbekistan	–	1 805	1 468
Total	1 991	30 408	24 222

Source: Authors' calculations.

Table A3.4 *Health expenditure gap in absolute US$ millions, low- and middle-income sample*

Region	Female adult mortality	Male adult mortality	Under-5 mortality
Baltic states			
Estonia	124	38	34
Latvia	123	77	118
Lithuania	–	–	–
South-eastern Europe			
Albania	55	89	173
Bosnia and Herzegovina	–	–	–
Bulgaria	–	–	–
Croatia	–	–	–
Romania	–	–	–
Serbia and Montenegro	–	–	–
TFYR Macedonia	–	–	–
Western Commonwealth of Independent States			
Belarus	–	–	–
Republic of Moldova	–	–	–
Russian Federation	2 426	756	3 775
Ukraine	–	–	299
Caucasus			
Armenia	147	184	261
Azerbaijan	407	503	690
Georgia	–	–	–
Central Asia			
Kazakhstan	1 575	1 567	1 942
Kyrgyzstan	3	58	161
Tajikistan	108	157	246
Turkmenistan	–	–	71
Uzbekistan	–	100	612
Total	5 196	3 817	8 788

Source: Authors' calculations.

Annex to Chapter 4

Microeconomic impact studies: technical details and empirical results

Living Conditions, Lifestyles and Health survey in eight CIS countries

The methodology applied in Chapter 4 to the Living Conditions, Lifestyles and Health (LLH) dataset is based on Stern (1989). He proposes a simultaneous equation model with discrete endogenous variables. In a first version of the model, the endogenous variables are labour force participation (LFP) and self-reported health conditions. LFP is set equal to 1 if the individual is employed or looking for a job and 0 otherwise. The self-reported health variable takes on four values: good (=1), quite good (=2), rather bad (=3) and bad (=4). In a second version, the endogenous variables are LFP (as before) and the presence of limitations in daily working activities. The latter is set equal to 1 if limitations are reported by the respondent and 0 otherwise. Description of the model (both versions) and variables are reported in Table A4.1.

The two-equation model permits taking into account both the impact of self-reported health conditions or activity limitations on the LFP decision and also the potential effect of LFP on the self-reporting of health conditions. It is plausible that someone not participating in the labour force would be more likely to report illness to justify this. Neglecting the issue of reciprocal influence between the endogenous variables would produce inconsistent estimates. In both versions of the model, the estimation procedure follows two steps. First, the reduced form model is estimated, and the predicted values of the endogenous variables are determined (the predicted values of the endogenous latent variables, as either probit or ordered probit estimators were used). Second, the predicted values substitute the corresponding right-hand side endogenous variables of the structural model. Next the structural model is estimated.

Regarding the first version, Table A4.2 reports the first-stage estimation for self-reported health conditions (ordered probit) and Table A4.3 reports the second-stage estimation for LFP (probit). As the main interest is in the impact of health conditions on LFP, the first-stage estimation for LFP (probit) and the second-stage estimation for self-reported health (ordered probit) are omitted. As for the second version, Table A4.4 reports the first-stage estimation for the presence of limitations on daily working activities (probit) and Table A4.5 reports the second-stage estimation on LFP (probit).

In both Table A4.3 and Table A4.5, a variable denoted "Smith and Blundell test" is reported (see Stern (1989) for details). If its coefficient is statistically different from 0, then the hypothesis of exogeneity (of self-reported health conditions and the presence of limitations, respectively) is rejected.

Table A4.1 *Variables and model description*

Regressors		First version		Second version	
		LFP equation (dependent variable: LFP)	Health equation (dependent variable: self-reported health)	LFP equation (dependent variable: LFP)	Limitations equation (dependent variable: presence of limitations)
	LFP		x		x
Self-reported health condition dummies Reference: very bad health	Good health	x			
	Rather good health	x			
	Bad health	x			
	Limitations (yes=1)			x	
	Age	x	x	x	x
	Sex (male=1)	x	x	x	x
	Nationality (member of the majority nationality=1)	x	x	x	x
Education dummies Reference: no education	Primary education	x		x	
	Secondary education	x		x	
	Secondary vocational education	x		x	
	Unfinished higher education	x		x	
	Higher education	x		x	
	Married (married or living together=1)	x		x	
	Married interacted with sex	x		x	

Medically diagnosed non-communicable diseases (set of dummies)	NCD heart	x
	NCD stroke	x
	NCD high pressure	x
	NCD respiratory	x
	NCD diabetes	x
	NCD stomach	x
	NCD liver	x
	NCD bone	x
	NCD cancer	x
	NCD mental	x
	Communicable diseases in the past (yes=1)	x
Disabilities	Some difficulties walking 1 km	x
	Major difficulties walking 1 km	x
	Some difficulties going up stairs	x
	Major difficulties going up stairs	x
	Some problems of insomnia	x
	Major problems of insomnia	x

Source: Authors' calculations.

Notes: LFP: labour force participation; NCD: noncommunicable disease.

Table A4.2 *First-stage ordered probit with dependent variable of self-reported health: eight countries, 2001*

Independent variables	Armenia	Belarus	Georgia	Kazakhstan	Kyrgyzstan	Republic of Moldova	Russian Federation	Ukraine
Sex	-0.060 (0.58)	0.283*** (3.12)	0.370*** (3.22)	0.050 (0.51)	0.296*** (2.91)	-0.03 (0.31)	0.169*** (2.58)	0.341*** (4.05)
Age	0.015*** (8.46)	0.015*** (7.16)	0.028*** (13.56)	0.019*** (8.78)	0.019*** (9.07)	0.018*** (8.67)	0.016*** (10.99)	0.018*** (10.55)
Nationality	0.242 (1.55)	0.077 (1.21)	-0.504*** (5.53)	-0.234*** (4.24)	-0.163*** (2.77)	0.063 (1.04)	0.084* (1.81)	-0.001 (0.02)
Primary education	-0.037 (0.28)	-0.380*** (3.14)	0.035 (0.15)	-0.071 (0.46)	-0.205 (1.10)	-0.062 (0.60)	-0.127 (1.54)	-0.290** (2.45)
Secondary education	-0.242** (2.05)	-0.466*** (4.29)	-0.379* (1.94)	-0.353*** (2.61)	-0.066 (0.47)	-0.153 (1.56)	-0.237*** (3.21)	-0.371*** (3.96)
Secondary vocational education	-0.376*** (3.10)	-0.595*** (5.62)	-0.381* (1.93)	-0.454*** (3.50)	-0.068 (0.48)	-0.137 (1.46)	-0.411*** (5.75)	-0.524*** (5.67)
Unfinished higher education	-0.751*** (4.58)	-0.581*** (3.12)	-0.607*** (2.59)	-0.786*** (4.61)	-0.368** (2.12)	-0.302** (1.97)	-0.409*** (3.52)	-0.568*** (4.06)
Higher education	-0.644*** (5.29)	-0.683*** (6.12)	-0.451** (2.31)	-0.596*** (4.40)	-0.129 (0.89)	-0.337*** (3.34)	-0.513*** (6.87)	-0.723*** (7.53)
Married	-0.146 (1.46)	-0.021 (0.25)	-0.213* (1.95)	-0.174* (1.88)	-0.226** (2.38)	-0.310*** (3.46)	-0.094 (1.49)	0.023 (0.29)
Married interacted with sex	0.197 (1.61)	0.026 (0.23)	0.126 (0.94)	0.184 (1.59)	0.045 (0.38)	0.242** (2.10)	0.089 (1.12)	-0.088 (0.85)

NCD heart	0.637*** (9.53)	0.499*** (7.26)	0.930*** (11.08)	0.556*** (7.03)	0.528*** (5.71)	0.326*** (4.54)	0.395*** (8.21)	0.412*** (7.07)
NCD stroke	1.228*** (4.85)	0.722*** (3.48)	0.880** (2.51)	0.688** (2.25)	0.569* (1.82)	0.585*** (2.19)	0.983*** (7.06)	0.287* (1.83)
NCD high pressure	0.603*** (7.75)	0.524*** (6.59)	0.570*** (5.76)	0.346*** (4.07)	0.260*** (2.71)	0.566*** (7.14)	0.400*** (7.63)	0.479*** (7.17)
NCD respiratory	0.506*** (5.40)	0.255*** (3.62)	0.600*** (5.08)	0.390*** (5.44)	0.325*** (3.85)	0.353*** (5.00)	0.274*** (5.72)	0.280*** (4.83)
NCD diabetes	0.933*** (4.78)	0.815*** (4.39)	0.809*** (4.59)	0.299 (1.63)	0.302 (1.11)	0.19 (1.03)	0.458*** (3.82)	0.736*** (4.53)
NCD stomach	0.442*** (5.51)	0.414*** (6.84)	0.427*** (4.29)	0.361*** (5.34)	0.189** (2.55)	0.321*** (5.28)	0.358*** (8.52)	0.298*** (5.44)
NCD liver	0.387*** (3.85)	0.313*** (3.81)	0.381*** (2.61)	0.243*** (3.09)	0.295*** (3.23)	0.191** (2.47)	0.134** (2.57)	0.206*** (3.08)
NCD bone	0.274*** (3.02)	0.351*** (4.25)	0.319*** (3.07)	0.175** (2.04)	0.293*** (2.95)	0.266*** (3.95)	0.237*** (4.40)	0.138** (2.11)
NCD cancer	1.688*** (3.76)	0.649 (1.51)	1.323*** (3.32)	1.687*** (3.76)	0.521 (1.42)	0.703*** (2.38)	0.637*** (3.06)	0.374 (1.52)
NCD mental	0.430*** (7.12)	0.258*** (4.68)	0.644*** (6.51)	0.239*** (4.04)	0.290*** (4.36)	0.223*** (4.02)	0.293*** (7.75)	0.203*** (4.07)
Communicable diseases in the past	0.027 (0.12)	-0.005 (0.04)	0.515** (2.10)	0.019 (0.19)	0.330*** (2.71)	0.044 (0.47)	-0.018 (0.24)	-0.037 (0.37)
Observations	1961	1888	1863	1945	1950	1930	3878	2318

Source: Authors' calculations.

Notes: * significant at 10%; ** significant at 5%; *** significant at 1%; Absolute value of z statistics in parentheses; NCD: noncommunicable disease.

Table A4.3 Second-stage probit with dependent variable of labour force participation: eight countries (using self-report as health indicator), 2001

Independent variables	Armenia	Belarus	Georgia	Kazakhstan	Kyrgyzstan	Republic of Moldova	Russian Federation	Ukraine
Predicted good health	-0.014	—	0.186***	-0.076	0.081	—	0.225	—
	(0.20)		(3.29)	(0.50)	(0.54)		(1.05)	
Predicted rather good health	0.160***	0.341***	0.126***	0.235*	0.191	0.290***	0.372***	0.136**
	(3.47)	(5.27)	(2.92)	(1.77)	(1.33)	(4.35)	(6.02)	(2.39)
Predicted bad health	0.076*	0.192***	0.066	0.099	-0.001	0.159***	0.173***	0.079
	(1.67)	(3.40)	(1.46)	(0.83)	(0.01)	(2.65)	(3.07)	(1.58)
Sex	0.012	0.230***	-0.087**	-0.024	0.032	0.065	0.103***	0.184***
	(0.24)	(5.33)	(2.20)	(0.58)	(0.66)	(1.36)	(3.31)	(4.00)
Age	-0.014***	-0.011***	-0.008***	-0.012***	-0.010***	-0.009***	-0.010***	-0.016***
	(14.51)	(10.5)	(7.86)	(11.51)	(9.11)	(8.51)	(14.34)	(15.10)
Nationality	-0.099	-0.020	0.036	0.029	-0.024	0.011	-0.005	0.001
	(1.36)	(0.62)	(0.99)	(1.13)	(0.86)	(0.36)	(0.20)	(0.03)
Primary education	0.1	0.205***	-0.054	0.167**	-0.156*	0.235***	0.166***	0.217***
	(1.58)	(3.60)	(0.59)	(2.15)	(1.67)	(5.40)	(4.07)	(2.95)

	(1)	(2)	(3)	(4)	(5)	(6)	(7)
Secondary education	0.340***	0.213***	0.308***	-0.037	0.243***	0.103	0.282***
	(5.56)	(5.67)	(7.25)	(0.52)	(3.34)	(1.54)	(5.12)
Secondary vocational education	0.383***	0.347***	0.274***	0.119*	0.368***	0.180***	0.372***
	(6.27)	(9.81)	(6.50)	(1.71)	(5.11)	(2.83)	(7.17)
Unfinished higher education	-0.129	-0.083	-0.036	-0.203**	0.127	-0.523***	0.036
	(1.56)	(1.45)	(0.49)	(2.43)	(1.42)	(5.21)	(0.42)
Higher education	0.425***	0.395***	0.330***	0.227***	0.410***	0.140**	0.370***
	(7.14)	(11.98)	(8.22)	(3.34)	(6.92)	(2.08)	(7.86)
Married	0.415***	0.312***	0.276***	0.282***	0.320***	0.218***	0.410***
	(9.61)	(10.02)	(6.06)	(6.57)	(7.34)	(5.02)	(9.70)
Married interacted with sex	-0.313***	-0.223***	-0.124**	-0.144***	-0.221***	-0.121**	-0.331***
	(5.69)	(5.57)	(2.15)	(2.64)	(4.10)	(2.34)	(5.88)
Smith & Blundell test	-0.016	-0.034***	-0.040**	-0.044***	0.014	-0.028**	-0.010
	(1.07)	(2.93)	(2.53)	(2.65)	(0.85)	(2.06)	(0.62)
Observations	2291	3861	1921	1936	1938	1828	1881

Source: Authors' calculations.

Notes: * significant at 10%; ** significant at 5%; *** significant at 1%; Absolute value of z statistics in parentheses.

Table A4.4 First-stage probit with dependent variable of limitations: eight countries, 2001

Independent variables	Armenia	Belarus	Georgia	Kazakhstan	Kyrgyzstan	Republic of Moldova	Russian Federation	Ukraine
Sex	-0.145 (1.08)	0.268** (2.36)	0.261* (1.71)	0.274** (2.14)	0.211 (1.62)	0.275** (2.26)	0.13 (1.63)	0.286*** (2.74)
Age	0.009*** (3.94)	0.013*** (5.03)	0.007** (2.46)	0.017*** (6.26)	0.017*** (6.52)	0.010*** (3.75)	0.015*** (8.53)	0.014*** (6.82)
Nationality	0.064 (0.33)	-0.105 (1.36)	-0.369*** (3.23)	-0.013 (0.19)	-0.141** (1.97)	-0.085 (1.15)	0.012 (0.21)	-0.158** (2.37)
Primary education	-0.19 (1.23)	0.456*** (3.04)	-0.720** (2.47)	0.274 (1.40)	0.123 (0.52)	0.478*** (3.82)	0.107 (1.04)	0.345** (2.44)
Secondary education	-0.164 (1.18)	0.509*** (3.75)	-0.707*** (2.95)	0.134 (0.79)	0.493*** (2.83)	0.339*** (2.80)	0.193** (2.08)	0.384*** (3.43)
Secondary vocational education	0.161 (1.12)	0.596*** (4.50)	-0.639*** (2.62)	0.115 (0.70)	0.612*** (3.46)	0.463*** (4.04)	0.307*** (3.39)	0.430*** (3.85)
Unfinished higher education	0.046 (0.23)	0.672*** (2.87)	-0.773*** (2.63)	-0.244 (1.06)	0.784*** (3.70)	0.492*** (2.62)	0.287** (2.00)	0.558*** (3.24)
Higher education	-0.062 (0.43)	0.639*** (4.54)	-0.378 (1.58)	0.192 (1.12)	0.595*** (3.29)	0.598*** (4.83)	0.371*** (3.93)	0.487*** (4.16)

Married	-0.099 (0.77)	0.065 (0.59)	0.027 (0.18)	0.189 (1.54)	0.075 (0.61)	0.172 (1.52)	0.025 (0.32)	0.095 (0.93)
Married interacted with sex	-0.014 (0.09)	-0.015 (0.11)	-0.091 (0.51)	-0.274* (1.82)	-0.095 (0.62)	-0.314** (2.19)	0.011 (0.11)	-0.174 (1.37)
Some difficulties walking 1km	0.501*** (5.16)	0.455*** (3.75)	0.487*** (4.32)	0.345*** (2.96)	0.318*** (2.61)	0.332*** (3.20)	0.483*** (5.94)	0.391*** (3.97)
Major difficulties walking 1km	1.081*** (7.26)	0.950*** (3.63)	0.931*** (3.99)	0.531* (1.84)	0.823*** (3.60)	0.485*** (2.62)	0.714*** (4.49)	0.439** (2.52)
Some difficulties going up stairs	0.334*** (3.67)	0.641*** (6.59)	0.387*** (3.56)	0.565*** (5.87)	0.292*** (2.88)	0.509*** (5.18)	0.395*** (5.76)	0.390*** (4.45)
Major difficulties going up stairs	0.208 (1.53)	0.613*** (2.98)	0.144 (0.63)	0.996*** (4.60)	0.358** (1.99)	0.614*** (3.56)	0.563*** (4.04)	0.545*** (3.35)
Some problems of insomnia	0.177** (2.29)	0.389*** (5.17)	0.577*** (6.92)	0.352*** (4.57)	0.401*** (5.19)	0.436*** (6.05)	0.482*** (9.70)	0.372*** (5.54)
Major problems of insomnia	0.475*** (5.17)	0.780*** (4.83)	1.110*** (7.77)	0.364** (2.23)	0.529*** (3.83)	0.681*** (5.43)	0.563*** (6.39)	0.540*** (5.14)
Constant	-1.490*** (5.65)	-1.883*** (8.88)	-0.907*** (2.91)	-1.776*** (7.86)	-2.109*** (8.67)	-1.796*** (8.58)	-1.603*** (11.39)	-1.708*** (9.22)
Observations	1992	1975	1981	1983	1978	1978	3992	2357

Source: Authors' calculations.

*Notes: * significant at 10%; ** significant at 5%; *** significant at 1%; Absolute value of z statistics in parentheses.*

Table A4.5 Second-stage probit with dependent variable of labour force participation: eight countries (using activity of daily living as health indicator), 2001

Independent variables	Armenia	Belarus	Georgia	Kazakhstan	Kyrgyzstan	Republic of Moldova	Russian Federation	Ukraine
Predicted limitations	-0.163*** (4.41)	-0.251*** (7.14)	-0.069** (2.07)	-0.304*** (8.05)	-0.188*** (4.55)	-0.223*** (7.08)	-0.230*** (9.73)	-0.167*** (5.27)
Sex	0.002 (0.04)	0.235*** (5.47)	-0.092** (2.33)	-0.017 (0.41)	0.080* (1.73)	0.084* (1.76)	0.105*** (3.38)	0.190*** (4.15)
Age	-0.013*** (14.46)	-0.010*** (9.52)	-0.008*** (10.04)	-0.008*** (7.48)	-0.007*** (6.69)	-0.009*** (8.29)	-0.009*** (12.75)	-0.014*** (14.30)
Nationality	-0.088 (1.20)	-0.019 (0.59)	0.046 (1.28)	0.017 (0.68)	-0.032 (1.19)	-0.002 (0.08)	-0.014 (0.60)	-0.009 (0.31)
Primary education	0.103 (1.62)	0.237*** (4.39)	-0.062 (0.67)	0.200*** (2.75)	-0.129 (1.40)	0.255*** (5.94)	0.182*** (4.57)	0.248*** (3.43)
Secondary education	0.152*** (2.58)	0.320*** (6.06)	0.105 (1.56)	0.260*** (3.71)	0.009 (0.12)	0.318*** (7.57)	0.243*** (6.65)	0.365*** (6.06)
Secondary vocational education	0.266*** (4.78)	0.412*** (8.31)	0.182*** (2.87)	0.374*** (5.33)	0.168** (2.48)	0.291*** (6.94)	0.382*** (11.18)	0.415*** (6.97)

	(1)	(2)	(3)	(4)	(5)	(6)	(7)	(8)
Unfinished higher education	-0.146* (1.79)	0.095 (1.14)	-0.524*** (5.21)	-0.01 (0.11)	-0.190** (2.29)	-0.021 (0.29)	-0.046 (0.82)	-0.094 (1.13)
Higher education	0.314*** (6.01)	0.395*** (8.96)	0.142** (2.11)	0.405*** (6.97)	0.265*** (4.03)	0.346*** (8.81)	0.419*** (13.32)	0.457*** (8.07)
Married	0.299*** (5.90)	0.407*** (9.61)	0.227*** (5.28)	0.285*** (6.47)	0.269*** (6.30)	0.288*** (6.39)	0.313*** (10.05)	0.401*** (9.29)
Married interacted with sex	-0.244*** (4.09)	-0.327*** (5.81)	-0.126** (2.46)	-0.194*** (3.59)	-0.133** (2.44)	-0.144** (2.50)	-0.217*** (5.43)	-0.308*** (5.58)
Smith & Blundell test	-0.011 (0.84)	0.001 (0.03)	-0.035*** (2.83)	0.049*** (2.79)	-0.033** (1.97)	-0.019 (1.19)	-0.024** (2.02)	0.004 (0.26)
Observations	1955	1883	1828	1938	1944	1921	3861	2299

Source: Authors' calculations.

Notes: * significant at 10%; ** significant at 5%; *** significant at 1%; Absolute value of z statistics in parentheses.

Tajikistan

Haveman et al.'s (1994) model was applied to data from the Tajikistan Living Standards Measurement Survey (LSMS) 2003, an extensive dataset containing information on employment, education, health conditions and consumption/savings decisions at individual and household levels. This model accounts for the multiple relationships between individual health conditions and the labour market. The estimations were based on the subsample of people reporting having performed any work activity in the past 14 days. Only slightly above 50% of the respondents reported having worked in the past 14 days, and only about 25% reported having worked for someone else in the past 14 days.

The Haveman model consists of three simultaneous equations, one for each of the three variables: health condition, labour supply and the log of the wage rate. The reason for adopting a simultaneous equation model is that health affects both labour supply and the wage rate (interpreted as a measure of individual productivity), but at the same time labour supply might affect individual health conditions and, as standard economic reasoning prescribes, labour supply depends on the wage rate. These interdependencies are properly taken into account in this three-equation model.

The model assumes that health conditions depend on labour supply but not wage rate. This exclusion hypothesis might seem critical at first, as health is in principle affected by individual labour earnings, that is, by the product of labour supply and wage rates. However, in Haveman et al.'s view, labour earnings should be captured by other variables, such as the kind of occupation and the individual's educational background. Labour supply was introduced not (or not only) to capture an income effect on health but to capture the effect due to prolonged hours of physical and psychological stress or prolonged exposure to unhealthy workplaces. In this perspective it seems reasonable to exclude wage rates as they do not affect health per se but only via their effect on labour earnings.

The model specification and estimates are reported in Table A4.6. The unique substantial departure from Haveman et al.'s specification is represented by the inclusion of the mean self-reported health of the other household members ("household mean self-rep. health") into the labour supply equation, in order to capture individuals' behaviour in response to the health conditions prevailing in their families. Own labour supply is expected to increase when overall household health deteriorates, in order to offset eventual earning loss and to cover additional health expenditures. The results presented in Table A4.6 confirm this hypothesis.

A three-stage least squares (3SLS) method is adopted, which accounts for the

Table A4.6 *Three-stage least squares results, Tajikistan, 2003*

Independent variables	Health equation	Labour supply equation	Wage equation
	Self-reported	Labour supply	Log wage rate
Labour supply (hours per week)	0.044*** (11.45)		
Logarithm of wage rate		-1.892*** (2.60)	
Self-reported health conditions		-2.817 (1.03)	-0.081*** (3.45)
Sex (male=1)	-0.322*** (9.74)	5.333*** (6.48)	0.584*** (20.82)
Age	0.009*** (8.37)		
Occupation_2	0.201** (2.11)		
Occupation_3	0.004 (0.03)		
Occupation_4	0.156 (1.15)		
Occupation_5	0.094 (1.01)		
Occupation_6	-0.146 (1.03)		
Occupation_7	0.273*** (2.74)		
Occupation_8	0.101 (0.97)		
Occupation_9	0.109 (1.20)		

(cont.)

Table A4.6 *(cont)*

Independent variables	Health equation Self-reported	Labour supply equation Labour supply	Wage equation Log wage rate
Divorced (divorced=1)	0.165** (2.11)		
Years of schooling	0.004 (0.69)		0.048*** (8.80)
Tenure (years)			0.04 (1.00)
Squared tenure			-0.014*** (2.72)
Sogdian region			0.007 (0.13)
Kahtlon region			-0.328*** (6.59)
Dushanbe region			0.581*** (9.94)
RRS region			0.141** (2.36)
Number of children under 7		0.448*** (2.68)	
Self-employed		-0.784 (0.84)	
Household mean self-reported health		11.515*** (4.79)	
Constant	-0.367 (1.55)	33.168*** (14.73)	2.717*** (23.99)
Observations	4800	4800	4800

Source: Authors' calculations.

Notes: * significant at 10%; ** significant at 5%; *** significant at 1%; Absolute value of z statistics in parentheses.

correlation structure in the disturbances across the equations, by consistently estimating the covariance matrix from the residuals obtained by the two-stage least squares (2SLS) estimation of each structural equation. This procedure is more efficient (i.e., the produced estimates are more precise), but it requires that each equation of the model be correctly specified: otherwise, if even a single equation is misspecified, the covariance matrix will be inconsistent and in turn the estimated coefficients will be biased and inconsistent. For a more in-depth discussion of the relative benefits of 3SLS in this context, the reader is referred to Haveman et al. (1994).

In interpreting the sign of the coefficients in Table A4.6, it is important to know that the variable self-reported health is a categorical variable, which takes on values from 1 ("very good health") to 5 ("very bad health"). Hence, the higher the value, the worse the self-assessed health status.

As wages increase, labour supply decreases in the given case. This implies that the income effect more than outweighs the substitution effect that would have predicted an increase in labour supply in response to higher wages. The income effect implies that as people earn more in a given time, they can reduce their amount of work and still get the same overall income. This finding must be interpreted in the context of widespread home production as well as short-term paid jobs: almost all respondents reported owning land, and none reported having worked more than 12 weeks in the past 12 months. In a context where waged labour is not the main activity, it is likely that the income effect dominates the substitution effect.

Table A4.7 *GDP per capita forecasts: five selected CEE-CIS countries*

Year	Scenario 1 (benchmark - no change)	Scenario 2 (2% increase p.a.)	Scenario 3 (3% increase p.a.)
Georgia (FE)			
2000	4 904	4 904	4 904
2005	7 667	7 667	7 667
2010	10 214	10 310	10 358
2015	12 279	12 664	12 864
2020	13 819	14 680	15 135
2025	14 907	16 393	17 201
Georgia (OLS)			
2000	4 904	4 904	4 904
2005	5 645	5 645	5 645
2010	6 373	6 403	6 418
2015	7 076	7 193	7 254
2020	7 744	8 015	8 156
2025	8 369	8 867	9 131
Kazakhstan (FE)			
2000	7 394	7 394	7 394
2005	8 182	8 182	8 182
2010	8 732	8 814	8 856
2015	9 105	9 391	9 539
2020	9 352	9 935	10 243
2025	9 514	10 463	10 978
Kazakhstan (OLS)			
2000	7 394	7 394	7 394
2005	7 448	7 448	7 448
2010	7 495	7 529	7 547
2015	7 535	7 660	7 724
2020	7 570	7 836	7 974
2025	7 601	8 053	8 292
Lithuania (FE)			
2000	7 242	7 242	7 242
2005	9 109	9 109	9 109
2010	10 555	10 653	10 703
2015	11 601	11 965	12 154
2020	12 326	13 094	13 501
2025	12 816	14 093	14 788

(cont.)

Table A4.7 (cont.)

Lithuania (OLS)			
2000	7 242	7 242	7 242
2005	7 618	7 618	7 618
2010	7 959	7 996	8 015
2015	8 264	8 402	8 472
2020	8 537	8 837	8 992
2025	8 780	9 302	9 578
Romania (OLS)			
2000	4 287	4 287	4 287
2005	4 920	4 920	4 920
2010	5 540	5 566	5 579
2015	6 137	6 239	6 291
2020	6 703	6 938	7 060
2025	7 233	7 663	7 891
Romania (FE)			
2000	4 287	4 287	4 287
2005	6 767	6 767	6 767
2010	9 071	9 155	9 198
2015	10 947	11 291	11 469
2020	12 351	13 121	13 528
2025	13 346	14 676	15 400
Russian Federation (FE)			
2000	8 013	8 013	8 013
2005	9 179	9 179	9 179
2010	10 016	10 110	10 157
2015	10 592	10 925	11 097
2020	10 980	11 664	12 026
2025	11 236	12 356	12 965
Russia Federation (OLS)			
2000	8 013	8 013	8 013
2005	8 038	8 038	8 038
2010	8 059	8 097	8 116
2015	8 078	8 212	8 281
2020	8 094	8 378	8 525
2025	8 108	8 590	8 846

Source: Authors' calculations.

Note: OLS: ordinary least squares; FE: fixed effects; p.a.: per annum GDP: gross domestic product.

Annex to Chapter 5

Cost-effective interventions in low- and middle-income countries
See Table A5.1 and Table A5.2.

Estimating the impact of governance quality and health expenditure on health outcomes

A worldwide database of macroeconomic and demographic variables is used to explore how public health expenditure affects adult mortality, under-five mortality, and life expectancy, and in particular, how governance quality affects the effectiveness of health expenditure in improving those health outcomes.

The level of public health expenditure is in large part set by government, reflecting factors like its preferences and economic and health conditions. Therefore, it would be problematic from an econometric perspective to assume that public health expenditure was an exogenous variable (i.e., uncorrelated with the error term). To account for the possible endogeneity of health expenditure, an instrumental variable estimator was used for the present exercise. If i denotes the country under scrutiny and j each of the countries in the same region, public health expenditure of i is instrumented by the average j control of corruption index and health and defence expenditure. These are considered good instruments as neighbouring countries often have similar climatic and geographical characteristics and their spending decisions influence government i policies. For instance, neighbours' defence spending affects i internal defence policies and, via government budget constraint, its choices on health spending. Moreover and importantly, neighbours' choices can be considered as sufficiently independent of government i specific preferences. These considerations are supported by the fact that the chosen instruments have passed Hansen's test of overidentification (i.e., test of instruments' exogeneity) in each specification.

One equation each is estimated for: the logarithm of adult mortality, the logarithm of under-five mortality and the logarithm of life expectancy in 2003 (Table A5.3). The following regressors were included: share of government health expenditure as a proportion of gross domestic product (GDP), government health expenditure as a share of GDP interacted with an index of government effectiveness computed by the World Bank, plus a number of country-specific controls such as educational conditions, availability of clean water and sanitation systems, and regional dummies. In order to preserve a sufficiently large sample size, the missing values were filled with zeros in the variables indicated in Table A5.3 with (*) and a number of dummy variables were included in the regression in order to keep track of this operation (precisely, the variables labelled as "countries missing data on..." were included).

Table A5.1 *Selected population-based interventions*

Intervention	Intervention description	Intervention setting	Objective	Target population	Cost-effectiveness (US$/DALY)
Alcohol abuse					
Excise tax	25–50% increase in the current excise tax rate on alcoholic beverages	Policy level	Instrument of policy	Adolescents and adults	1377
Advertising ban and reduced access to beverages, retail	Reduced access to alcoholic beverages at retail outlets by reducing the hours of sale or advertising bans on television, radio, and billboards	Policy level	Instrument of policy	Adolescents and adults	404
Excise tax, advertising ban, with brief advice	50% increase in the current excise tax rate on alcoholic beverages, combined with advice, education sessions, and psychosocial counselling possible inclusion of random driver breath testing and advertising bans	Policy level	Instrument of policy	Adolescents and adults	631
Coronary artery disease					
Legislation substituting 2% of trans fat with polyunsaturated fat at US$ 0.50 per adult	Legislation replacing 2% of dietary trans fat from partial hydrogenation in manufactured foods with polyunsaturated fat, at a cost of US$ 0.50 per adult, and assuming a 7% reduction in coronary artery disease	Policy level	Instrument of policy	Adults	48
Legislation substituting 2% of trans fat with polyunsaturated fat at US$ 6 per adult	Legislation replacing 2% of dietary trans fat from partial hydrogenation in manufactured foods with polyunsaturated fat, at a cost of US$ 6 per adult, and assuming a 7–40% reduction in coronary artery disease	Policy level	Instrument of policy	Adults	838

(cont.)

Table A5.1 (cont.)

Intervention	Intervention description	Intervention setting	Objective	Target population	Cost-effectiveness (US$/DALY)
Diabetes, ischaemic heart disease, and stroke					
Legislation with public education to reduce salt content	Legislated reduction in salt content of manufactured foods and an accompanying public education campaign	Policy level	Instrument of policy	All ages	1937
Media campaign to reduce saturated fat	Media campaign to reduce saturated fat content in manufactured foods and replace part of the saturated fat with polyunsaturated fat	Policy level	Instrument of policy	All ages	2617
Tobacco addiction					
Taxation causing 33% price increase	A 33% price increase due to tobacco taxes to discourage tobacco use, prevent initiation (and subsequent addiction) among youths, increase the likelihood of cessation among current users, reduce relapse among former users and reduce consumption among continuing users	Policy level	Instrument of policy	Adolescents and adults	22
Non-price interventions	Advertising bans on television, radio, and billboards health information and advertising in the form of health warning labels on tobacco products interventions to reduce tobacco supply, such as smuggling control restrictions on smoking	Policy level	Instrument of policy	Adolescents and adults	353

(cont.)

Table A5.1 (cont.)

Intervention	Intervention description	Intervention setting	Objective	Target population	Cost-effectiveness (US$/DALY)
Traffic accidents					
Increased speeding penalties, enforcement, media campaigns, and speed bumps	Minimizing exposure to high-risk scenarios by installation of speed bumps at hazardous junctions, increased penalties for speeding and other effective road-safety regulations combined with media coverage and better law enforcement	Policy level	Instrument of policy	Adults	21
Enforcement of seat-belt laws, promotion of child restraints and random driver breath testing	Mandatory seat-belt and child-restraint laws, enforcement of drunk-driving laws, and random breath testing of drivers	Policy level	Instrument of policy	Adults	2449

Source: Laxminarayan, Chow & Shahid-Salles, 2006.

Note: DALY: disability-adjusted life year.

Table A5.2 Selected personalized interventions

	Intervention	Intervention description	Intervention setting	Objective	Target population	Cost-effectiveness (US$/DALY)
Alcohol abuse	Brief advice to heavy drinkers by primary health care providers	During primary health care visits, provision of advice by physicians through education sessions and psychosocial counselling	Clinic	Primary prevention	Adolescents and adults	642
Congestive heart failure	ACE inhibitor and beta-blocker, with diuretics	Use of ACE inhibitor and an optional beta-blocker (metoprolol), incremental to diuretics	District hospital	Secondary prevention	Adults	150
Ischemic heart disease	Aspirin, beta-blocker, and optional ACE inhibitor	Aspirin plus beta-blocker (atenolol) with optional ACE inhibitor (enalapril), with or without hospital availability	District or referral hospital	Secondary prevention	Adults	688
Myocardial infarction	Aspirin and beta-blocker	Aspirin with or without beta-blocker (atenolol)	District or referral hospital	Acute management	Adults	14
Myocardial infarction	Streptokinase, with aspirin and beta-blocker	Incremental use of streptokinase, in addition to aspirin and beta-blocker (atenolol)	District or referral hospital	Acute management	Adults	671

Myocardial infarction	Tissue plasminogen activator, with aspirin and beta-blocker	Incremental use of tissue plasminogen activator in addition to aspirin and beta-blocker (atenolol)	District hospital	Acute management	Adults	15 869
Myocardial infarction and stroke	Polypill	Combination treatment with aspirin, beta-blocker, thiazide diuretic, ACE inhibitor and statin, based on 10-year risk of cardiovascular disease	District hospital	Secondary prevention	Adults	409
Stroke (ischemic)	Aspirin	Aspirin dose within 48 hours of onset of acute stroke	Clinic or district hospital	Acute management	Adults over 15	149
Stroke (recurrent)	Aspirin and dipyridamole	Daily aspirin dose or combination of aspirin and extended-release dipyridamole	Clinic or district hospital	Secondary prevention	Adults over 15	81
Stroke and ischemic and hypertensive heart disease	Polypill by absolute risk approach	Combination treatment with aspirin, beta-blocker, thiazide diuretic, ACE inhibitor, and statin based on 10-year risk of cardiovascular disease	District or referral hospital	Primary prevention	Adults	2128
Tobacco addiction	Nicotine replacement therapy	Smoking cessation treatments in the form of nicotine replacement therapy	Clinic	Primary prevention	Adults	396

Source: Laxminarayan, Chow & Shahid-Salles, 2006.

Note: ACE: angiotensin converting enzyme.

Table A5.3 *Effectiveness of government health expenditure, instrumental variable estimates, 2003*

Source	Independent variable	Logarithm of adult mortality	Logarithm of under-5 mortality	Logarithm of life expectancy
World Bank – WDI	Government health expenditure/GDP ratio 2002	0.042 (1.40)	0.025 (0.47)	-0.008 (1.38)
World Bank – Governance and Anti-Corruption	Government effectiveness interacted with government health expenditures/GDP	-0.080*** (2.59)	-0.192*** (3.69)	0.018** (2.25)
World Bank – WDI	GDP (PPP) 2002	-0.000 (0.32)	0.000 (0.07)	-0.000 (0.50)
World Bank – WDI	Secondary school enrolment 2001 (*)	0.002 (1.33)	0.005* (1.92)	-0.001 (1.20)
World Bank – WDI	% of population with access to improved water sources 2002 (*)	0.00 (1.87*)	0.003 (0.47)	-0.001 (0.89)
World Bank – WDI	% of population with access to improved sanitation facilities 2002 (*)	-0.006* (1.93)	-0.016*** (3.70)	0.002* (1.90)
World Bank – WDI	% of urban population 2002	-0.003 (1.13)	0.002 (0.54)	0.000 (0.17)
World Bank – WDI	Age dependency ratio 2002 (dependents to working age population)	0.624* (1.82)	1.852** (3.90*)	-0.292*** (2.81)
	East Asia – Pacific	-0.259 (1.34)	-1.048*** (3.09)	0.055 (1.54)
	Eastern Europe – central Asia	-0.269 (1.18)	-1.247*** (3.34)	0.065 (1.35)
	Latin America – Caribbean	-0.615*** (2.59)	-1.719*** (4.06)	0.171*** (3.05)
	Middle East – North Africa	-0.556*** (2.74)	-1.218*** (3.31)	0.115*** (2.61)

(cont.)

Table A5.3 *(cont.)*

Source	Independent variable	Logarithm of adult mortality	Logarithm of under-5 mortality	Logarithm of life expectancy
	Southern Africa	-0.292 (1.49)	-0.957*** (2.64)	0.073** (1.99)
	Sub-Saharan Africa	0.219 (0.93)	-0.798** (2.27)	-0.127** (2.11)
	Western Europe	-0.08 (0.68)	-0.134 (0.88)	0.013 (0.87)
	Countries missing data on secondary school enrolment 2001	0.122 (1.10)	0.377* (1.83)	-0.053 (1.19)
	Countries missing data on % of population with access to improved water sources 2002	0.589 (1.56)	0.233 (0.41)	-0.114 (0.78)
	Countries missing data on % of population with access to improved sanitation facilities 2002	-0.554* (1.82)	-1.917*** (3.76)	0.203* (1.82)
	Constant	4.948*** (10.87)	3.915*** (6.22)	4.332*** (33.14)
	Observations	118	118	118

Source: Authors' calculations.

Notes: * significant at 10%; ** significant at 5%; *** significant at 1%; Robust z statistics in parentheses; WDI: World Development Indicators; GDP: gross domestic product; PPP: purchasing power parity.

Table A5.4 *Minimum levels of government effectiveness, 2003*

	Logarithm of adult mortality	Logarithm of under-5 mortality	Logarithm of life expectancy
Governance level to get 95% significant growth rate	1.03	0.53	1.51
d(log Y)/d(government health expenditure/GDP ratio 2002)	-0.04	-0.076	0.018

Source: Authors' calculations.

Note: GDP: gross domestic product.

Table A5.5 *Health expenditure impacts at different levels of government effectiveness, 2003*

Government effectiveness	Impact on adult mortality	Impact on under-5 mortality	Impact on life expectancy
0.5	0.002	-0.070	0.000
1.0	-0.038	-0.166	0.009
1.5	-0.078	-0.262	0.018
2.0	-0.118	-0.358	0.027

Source: Authors' calculations.

Table A5.4 reports the minimum level of government effectiveness required to get a statistically significant impact of health expenditure on health outcomes. In the chosen specification, the impact of health expenditure on the considered health outcomes (generally indicated with Y) is a growth rate, and it is given by:

$$d(log\ Y)/d(government\ health\ expenditure/GDP) = b_1 + b_2*(policy\ index)$$

where b_1 and b_2 are the estimated coefficients associated with the variables "government health expenditure/GDP ratio 2002" and "government effectiveness interacted with government health expenditures/GDP". An example may help to interpret Table A5.4: results in the third column reveal that it is necessary to have at least a score of 0.53 in government effectiveness to be able to observe a significant reduction of under-five mortality as a result of an increase in health expenditure. At a government effectiveness equal to 0.53, increasing by 1 percentage point the government health expenditure/GDP ratio will reduce under-five mortality by about 7.6%. (The benchmarks in the case of adult mortality and life expectancy are even higher, at about 1 and 1.5, respectively). Table A5.5 reports the impact of health expenditures on morality rates and life expectancy at selected levels of government effectiveness.

Estimating the impact of social capital on health using propensity score matching technique and simultaneous equation methods

Individuals reporting a "high" level of social capital (henceforth called the "treated" group) will differ in many respects from individuals that report a "low" level of social capital (the "control" group). In other words, the treated group might have individual-specific characteristics that affect both health and the selection into the treatment. Some of these characteristics are observable and can typically be included among the list of controls (such as age, gender and education), but others are not observable (such as preferences). If it is not possible to control for the influence of unobservable factors, one cannot simply compare the conditional mean level of health between the "treated" group and the "control" group.

In order to address this selection bias, a widely used procedure, known as "propensity score matching (PSM)", is applied. This approach allows controlling for individual unobservable heterogeneity, which is common between individuals sharing the same observable characteristics. The underlying idea is that of creating an index (the propensity score), which is based on the observable characteristics X_{it} of the surveyed individuals and is able to summarize those characteristics. Thereafter, the outcomes (in this case health) of two individuals or two subsamples with close propensity scores, one belonging to the treated and one to the control sample, are compared. The difference in the mean level of reported health between the treated group and the control group then gives an estimate of the impact of social capital.

An important assumption must hold true to be able to correctly apply PSM: *all* the variables X that simultaneously affect the outcome and the participation to the treatment must be part of the propensity score $p(X_{it})$ (Caliendo & Kopeinig 2005). This requirement implies that, conditioned on the propensity score $p(X_{it})$, the outcomes with and without treatment are random and do not depend anymore on individual characteristics. Consistent estimates of the impact of social capital on health are obtained as a result (Becker & Ichino 2002; Ichino 2002).

As mentioned above, each of the social capital indicators is considered as a treatment. The X_{it} variables used to compute the propensity scores are two individual exogenous features (age and sex), several household characteristics (household size, squared household size, marital status, urban/rural residency), some economic indicators (e.g. employment status, the nature of employer (public or private)), an individual evaluation of the household economic condition, and the individual level of education. In addition there are interaction variables between urban residence and, respectively, education, marital status, employment condition and nature of employer, in order to elicit the residence role eventually mediated through these variables. The hypothesis is that households living in urban environments experience and feel social capital in a much different way than rural families.

It is important to note that, while the PSM, if correctly applied, wipes out some econometric bias (selection bias), it does not specify the causal direction between treatment and outcome. In other words, the PSM is unable to indicate whether the treatment caused the outcome or vice versa. To address this issue, a simultaneous two-equation model of the type commonly employed in the analyses for Chapter 4 is used. The first equation models health as a function of a number of individual and community controls and as a function of a social capital indicator. The second equation models the individual social capital indicator as a function of (partly) different sets of individual and community controls and of individual health. (Since there are three social capital indicators, there are three alternative simultaneous two-equation models, one for each of the indicators.) The variables included in both the health and social capital equations are: age, age squared, household size and some indicators for sex, marital status, region of residence (urban/rural), activity and the sector of occupation.

The results of this exercise (not reported here but available from the authors upon request) show that reverse causality is hardly a problem: health affects neither trust nor membership in any country. There is evidence for reversed causality only for financial support and only in Kyrgyzstan. The implication is that in light of the simultaneous equation results, the previous propensity score estimates that on their own would not have shown causality, now do at least strongly suggest that the relationships estimated actually do represent a causal link from social capital (certainly for trust) to health.

References

Acemoglu D, Johnson S, Robinson J (2005). *Institutions as the fundamental cause of long-run growth*. Cambridge, MA, National Bureau of Economic Research (NBER Working Paper No. 10481).

Alam A et al. (2005). *Growth, poverty, and inequality: eastern Europe and the former Soviet Union*. Washington, DC, World Bank.

Aleshina N, Redmond G (2005). How high is infant mortality in central and eastern Europe and the Commonwealth of Independent States? *Population Studies*, 59:39–54.

Alesina A, Weder B (2002). Do corrupt governments receive less foreign aid? *The American Economic Review*, 92:1126–1137.

Alsan M, Bloom D, Canning D (2004). *The effect of population health on foreign direct investment*. Cambridge, MA, National Bureau of Economic Research (NBER Working Paper No. 10596).

Analytical and Information Centre of the Ministry of Health of the Republic of Uzbekistan et al. (2004). *Uzbekistan: health examination survey 2002*. Calverton, MD, MEASURE DHS.

Andersen BA, Silver BD (1997). Issues of data quality in assessing mortality trends and levels in the new independent states. In: Bobadilla J, Costello C, Mitchell F, eds. *Premature death in the new independent states*. Washington, DC, National Academy Press: 120–155.

Anderson G, Poullier J (1999). Health spending, access, and outcomes: trends in industrialized countries. *Health Affairs*, 18:178–192.

Anderson GF et al. (2006). *Noncommunicable diseases and injuries in eastern Europe and Eurasia*. United States Agency for International Development (USAID) and John Hopkins University, Bloomberg School of Public Health.

Anderson P, Baumberg B (2006). *Alcohol in Europe: a public health perspective*. London, Institute of Alcohol Studies.

Andreev E, McKee M, Shkolnikov V (2003). Health expectancy in Russia: a new perspective on the health divide in Europe. *Bulletin of the World Health Organization*, 81:778–788.

Andreeva TI et al. (2005). *Smoking and its consequences in pregnant women in Ukraine*. Washington, DC, World Bank (Economics of Tobacco Control Paper No. 30).

Andrews M, Shatalov S (2004). *Public expenditure management in the CIS-7: recent developments and prospects.* Washington, DC, World Bank (Background Paper for the CIS-7 Initiative) (www.cis7.org, accessed 6 February 2007).

Anell A, Willis M (2000). International comparisons of health care systems using resource profiles. *Bulletin of the World Health Organization,* 78:770–778.

Aral S et al. (2003). The social organization of commercial sex work in Moscow, Russia. *Sexually Transmitted Diseases,* 30:39–45.

Arrow K. (1963). Uncertainty and the welfare economics of medical care. *American Economic Review,* 53:941–973.

Atun R et al. (In press). High coverage with HAART is required to substantially reduce the number of deaths from tuberculosis: system dynamics simulation in the setting of explosive HIV epidemic and tuberculosis. *International Journal of STD & AIDS.*

Badurashvili I et al. (2001). Where there are no data: what has happened to life expectancy in Georgia since 1990? *Public Health,* 115:394–400.

Balabanova D, Falkingham J, McKee M (2003). Winners and losers: expansion of insurance coverage in Russia in the 1990s. *American Journal of Public Health,* 93:2124–2130.

Balabanova D et al. (2004). Health service utilization in the former Soviet Union: evidence from eight countries. *Health Services Research,* 39:1927–1940.

Baldwin M, Zeager L and Flacco P (1994). Gender differences in wage losses from impairments. *Journal of Human Resources,* 29:865–887.

Barkley Rosser J et al. (2000). Income inequality and the informal economy in transition economies. *Journal of Comparative Economics,* 28:156–171.

Barro R (1997). *Determinants of economic growth: a cross-country empirical study.* Cambridge, MA, The MIT Press.

Bates R (1999). *Ethnicity, capital formation, and conflict.* Washington, DC, World Bank (Working Paper No. 12).

Baum F (1997). Public health and civil society: understanding and valuing the connection. *Australian and New Zealand Journal of Public Health,* 21(7):673–675.

Beaglehole R, Yach D (2003). Globalization and the prevention and control of noncommunicable disease: the neglected chronic diseases of adults. *The Lancet,* 362:903–908.

Becker S, Ichino A (2002). Estimation of average treatment effects based on propensity scores. *Stata Journal,* 2(4):358–377.

Bell C, Devarajan S, Gersbach H (2003). *The long-run economic costs of AIDS: theory and an application to South Africa.* Washington, DC, University of Heidelberg and World Bank.

Belli P, Bustreo F, Preker A (2005). Investing in children's health: what are the economic benefits? *Bulletin of the World Health Organization,* 83:777–784.

Berkovec J and Stern, S (1991). Job exit behaviour of older men. *Econometrica,* 59: 189–210.

Berthélemy J-C, Tichit A (2002). *Bilateral donors' aid allocation decisions: a three-dimensional panel analysis.* Helsinki, UNU/WIDER (UNU/WIDER Discussion Paper No. 2002/123).

Betti G, Verma V (1999). Measuring the degree of poverty in a dynamic and comparative context: a multi-dimensional approach using fuzzy set theory. In: *Proceedings of the ICCS-VI.* Lahore, Pakistan, August 27–31. 11:289–301.

Bhargava A et al. (2001). Modelling the effects of health on economic growth. *Journal of Health Economics,* 20:423–440.

Bidani B, Ravallion M. (1997). Decomposing social indicators using distributional data. *Journal of Econometrics,* 77:125–139.

Bishai DM, Hyder AA (2006). Modelling the cost–effectiveness of injury interventions in lower and middle-income countries: opportunities and challenges. *Cost Effectiveness and Resource Allocation,* 4:2 (DOI:10.1186/1478-7547-4-2, www.resource-allocation.com/content/4/1/2, accessed 14 January 2007).

Bloom DE, Canning D, Graham B (2003). Longevity and life cycle savings. *Scandinavian Journal of Economics,* 105:319–338.

Bloom D, Canning D, Sevilla J (2001). The effect of health on economic growth: theory and evidence. Cambridge MA, National Bureau of Economic Research (NBER Working Paper No. 8587).

Bloom DE, Canning D, Sevilla J (2003). *The demographic dividend: a new perspective on the economic consequences of population change.* Santa Monica, CA, RAND Corporation.

Bobak M, Marmot M (1996). East–West health divide and potential explanations. In: Hertzman C et al., eds. *East–West life expectancy gap in Europe: environmental and non-environmental determinants.* Dordrecht, Kluwer: 17–44.

Bobak M et al. (1998). Association between psychosocial factors at work and non-fatal myocardial infarction in a population based case-control study in Czech men. *Epidemiology,* 9:43–47.

Bokhari FA, Gai Y, Gottret P (2006) Government health expenditures and health outcomes. *Health Economics,* September 26 [Epub ahead of print]. (DOI: 10.1002/hec.1157, accessed 14 January 2007.)

Bonu S et al. (2005). Does use of tobacco or alcohol contribute to impoverishment from hospitalization costs in India? *Health Policy and Planning,* 20:41–49.

Bosma JHA (1994). *A cross-cultural comparison of the role of some psychosocial factors in the etiology of coronary heart disease.* Maastricht: Universitaire Pers Maastricht (Follow-up to the Kaunas-Rotterdam Intervention Study (KRIS)).

Bozicevic I et al. (2001). What is happening to the health of the Croatian population? *Croatian Medical Journal,* 42:601–605.

Bozicevic I, et al. (2005). *The evidence base on interventions to reduce the burden of disease due to injuries in low- and middle-income, with special consideration of the ECA countries.* Venice, WHO Regional Office for Europe (Mimeo).

Britton A, McKee M (2000). The relationship between alcohol and cardiovascular disease in eastern Europe: explaining the paradox. *Journal of Epidemiology and Community Health,* 54:328–332.

Brunello G, d'Hombres B (2005). *Does obesity hurt your wages more in Dublin than in Madrid?* Evidence from ECHP. Bonn, Institute for the Study of Labour (IZA) (Discussion Paper Series IZA DP, No. 1704).

Burnside C, Dollar D (2004). *Aid, policies, and growth: revisiting the evidence.* Washington, DC, World Bank (World Bank Policy Research Working Paper No. 3251).

Caliendo M, Kopeinig S (2005). *Some practical guidance for the implementation of propensity score matching.* Bonn, Institute for the Study of Labor (IZA). (IZA Discussion Paper 1588).

Carlson P (1998). Self-perceived health in east and west Europe: another European health divide. *Social Science & Medicine,* 46(10):1355–1366.

Carlson P (2001). Risk behaviours and self-rated health in Russia. *Journal of Epidemiology and Community Health,* 55:806–817.

Case A, Fertig A, Paxson C (2005). The lasting impact of childhood health and circumstance. *Journal of Health Economics,* 24:365–389.

Cashin C (2001). *Access to health care in rural Ferghana Oblast, Uzbekistan.* Tashkent, ZdravPlus (Study prepared for USAID).

Cercone J (1994). *Alcohol-related problems as an obstacle to the development of human capital.* Washington, DC, World Bank (World Bank Technical Paper No. 219).

Chaloupka F, P Jha (2000). *Economics of tobacco: tobacco control in developing countries.* Washington, DC, World Bank.

Charlton A (1996). Children and smoking: the family circle. *British Medical Bulletin*, 52:90–107.

Chenet L et al. (1998). Death from alcohol and violence in Moscow: socioeconomic determinants. *European Journal of Population*, 14:19–37.

Chervyakov V et al. (2002). The changing nature of murder in Russia. *Social Science & Medicine*, 55:1713–1724.

Claeys V, Wuyts E (2004). *Official development assistance levels and spending for sexual and reproductive health and rights since the ICPD.* United Nations Economic Commission for Europe (UNECE) European Population Forum 2004: Population Challenges and Policy Response (Background Paper for the Session on Global Population and Development Trends: the European View).

CMH (2001). *Macroeconomics and health: investing in health for economic development.* Geneva, WHO Commission on Macroeconomics and Health.

Coker R, Atun R, McKee M (2004). Health care system frailties and public health control of communicable disease on the European Union's new eastern border. *The Lancet*, 363:1389–1392.

Coker R et al. (2006). Risk factors for pulmonary tuberculosis in Samara, Russia: a case-control study. *British Medical Journal*, 332:85–87.

Contoyannis P, Rice N (2001). The impact of health on wages: evidence from the British Household Panel Survey. *Empirical Economics*, 26:599–622.

Conway TL, Cronan TA (1992). Smoking, exercise, and physical fitness. *Preventive Medicine*, 21:723–734.

Cornia GA, Paniccià R (2000). *The mortality crisis in transitional economies.* Oxford, Oxford University Press.

Costa D, Kahn ME (2003). *Changes in the value of life, 1940–1980.* Cambridge, MA, The MIT Press.

Crafts N (2003). *The contribution of increased life expectancy to growth of living standards in the UK, 1870–2001.* London, London School of Economics [Unpublished manuscript].

Currie J, Madrian BC (1999). Health, health insurance and the labour market. In: Ashenfelter O, Card D, eds. *Handbook of labour economics.* Amsterdam, Elsevier Science BV: 3309–3415.

Cutler D, Glaeser E, Shapiro J (2003). Have Americans become more obese? *Journal of Economic Perspectives*, 17:93–118.

Cutler D, Richardson E (1997). Measuring the health of the U.S. population. *Brookings Papers on Economic Activity Microeconomics*, 29:519–539.

Dahlgren G, Whitehead M (1993). *Tackling inequalities in health: what can we learn from what has been tried?* London, King's Fund (Working paper (Mimeo) prepared for the King's Fund International Seminar on Tackling Inequalities in Health, September, Ditchley Park, Oxfordshire).

Dam RM van et al. (2006). The relationship between overweight in adolescence and premature death in women. *Annals of Internal Medicine*, 145:91–97.

Danishevski K et al. (2005). Inequalities in birth outcomes in Russia: evidence from Tula oblast. *Paediatric and Perinatal Epidemiology*, 19:352–359.

Danishevski K et al. (2006). Delivering babies in a time of transition: variations in maternal care in Tula, Russia. *Health Policy Planning*, 21:195–205.

Davis C (2004). *Economic consequences of changes in the health status of the population and economic benefits of medical programmes in the USSR during 1950–1991*. Venice, WHO Regional Office for Europe (Mimeo).

Davoodi H, Tiongson E, Asawanuchit S (2003). *How useful are benefit incidence analyses of public education and health spending?* Washington, DC, International Monetary Fund (IMF Working Paper 03/227).

Dearlove JV, Bialous SA, Glantz SA (2002). Tobacco industry manipulation of the hospitality industry to maintain smoking in public places. *Tobacco Control*, 11:94–104.

Del Gaudio Weiss A, Fantuzzo JW (2001). Multivariate impact of health and caretaking risk factors on the school adjustment of first graders. *Journal of Community Psychology*, 29:141–160.

Devlin N, Parkin D (2004). Does NICE have a cost–effectiveness threshold and what other factors influence its decisions? A binary choice analysis. *Health Economics*, 13:437–452.

D'hombres B et al. (2006). *Does social capital determine health? Evidence from eight transition countries*. Venice, WHO Regional Office for Europe (Mimeo).

Diamond J (1997). *Guns, germs, and steel: the fates of human societies*. New York, W.W. Norton & Company.

Diethelm PA, Rielle J-C, McKee M (2005). The whole truth and nothing but the truth? The research that Philip Morris did not want you to see. *Lancet*, 366: 86–92.

Disney R, Emmerson C, Wakefield M (2003). *Ill health and retirement in Britain: a panel data-based analysis*. London, Institute for Fiscal Studies.

Djipa D, Muzur M, Franklin Lytle P (2002). Bosnia and Herzegovina: war-torn lives. In: Deepa N, Petesch P, eds. *Voices of the poor: from many lands*. New York (published for the World Bank), Oxford University Press: 213–238.

Dodd R, Hinshelwood E (2004). *PRSPs: their significance for health: second synthesis report*. Geneva, World Health Organization.

Donoghoe M, Lazarus J, Matic S (2005). HIV/AIDS in the transitional countries of eastern Europe and central Asia. *Clinical Medicine*, 5:487–490.

Dore A, Adair L, Popkin B (2003). Low-income Russian families adopt effective behavioural strategies to maintain dietary stability in times of economic crisis. *Journal of Nutrition*, 133:3469–3475.

Downs A, Hamers F (2003). HIV in central and eastern Europe. *The Lancet*, 361:1035–1044.

Drummond MF et al. (2005). *Methods for the economic evaluation of health care programmes*, 3rd ed. Oxford, Oxford University Press.

Durlauf SN, Fafchamps M (2004). *Social capital*. Cambridge, MA, National Bureau of Economic Research (NBER Working paper No. 10485).

EBRD (2004). *Transition report 2004: infrastructure*. London, European Bank for Reconstruction and Development.

Edwards G (1994). *Alcohol policy and the public good*. Oxford, Oxford University Press.

EERC (2006). *Ambulance not on the way: the disgrace of health care for Roma in Europe*. Budapest, European Roma Rights Centre.

Eichler HG et al. (2004).Use of cost–effectiveness analysis in health care resource allocation decision-making: how are cost–effectiveness thresholds expected to emerge? *Value Health*, 7:518–528.

Esanov A, Raiser M, Buiter W. (2001). *Nature's blessing or nature's curse: the political economy of transition in resource-based economies.* London, European Bank for Reconstruction and Development (EBRD Working Paper No. 66).

European Values Study Group, World Values Survey Association. (2004). *European and World Values Surveys, 1999–2002.* Release I [Computer file]. 2nd ICPSR version. Cologne, Germany: Zentralarchiv fur Empirische Sozialforschung (ZA)/Tilburg; Netherlands: Tilburg University/Amsterdam, Netherlands: Netherlands Institute for Scientific Information Services (NIWI); Madrid, Spain: Analisis Sociologicos Economicos y Politicos (ASEP); and JD Systems (JDS)/Ann Arbor, MI: Inter-university Consortium for Political and Social Research [producers].

EUROSTAT (2002). *Income, poverty and social exclusion: second report.* Luxembourg, European Social Statistics: 76–92.

Evans DB et al. (2000). *The comparative efficiency of national health systems in producing health: an analysis of 191 countries.* Geneva, World Health Organization (WHO/EIP Discussion Paper No. 29).

Ezzati M, Kammen DM. (2002). The health impacts of exposure to indoor air pollution from solid fuels in developing countries: knowledge, gaps, and data needs. *Environmental Health Perspectives,* 110(11):1057–1068.

Ezzati M et al. (2005). Rethinking the "diseases of affluence" paradigm: global patterns of nutritional risks in relation to economic development. *PLoS Medicine,* 2:e133.

Favaro D, Suhrcke M (2006). Health as a driver of economic development: conceptual framework and related evidence for south-eastern Europe. In: *Health and economic development in south-eastern Europe.* Copenhagen, WHO Regional Office for Europe, and Paris, Council of Europe Development Bank: 71–85.

Feeney G (1991). Child survivorship estimation: methods and data analysis. *Asia and Pacific Population Forum,* 5:51–87.

Field M (1990). Noble purpose, grand design, flawed execution, mixed results: soviet socialized medicine after seventy years. *American Journal of Public Health,* 80:144–145.

Figueras J et al., eds. (2004). *Health systems in transition: learning from experience.* Copenhagen, WHO Regional Office for Europe on behalf of the European Observatory on Health Systems and Policies.

Filmer D (2003). *The incidence of public expenditures on health and education.* Washington, DC, World Bank (Background note for *World development report 2004: making services work for poor people*).

Filmer D, Hammer J, Pritchett L (1998*). Health policy in poor countries: weak links in the chain.* Washington, DC, World Bank (World Bank Policy Research Working Paper No. 1874).

Freedman VA, Martin L (1999). The role of education in explaining and forecasting trends in functional limitations among older Americans. *Demography,* 36(4):461–473.

Futures Group, Instituto Nacional de Salud Publica (2003). *Funding required for the response to HIV/AIDS in eastern Europe and central Asia.* Mexico City (Report prepared for the World Bank and UNAIDS Secretariat).

Gallup JL, Sachs JD, Mellinger A (1999). *Geography and economic development.* Center for International Development (CID), Harvard University (CID Working Paper No. 1, March 1999).

Gambin L (2004). Gender differences in the effect of health on wages in Britain. York, University of York Department of Economics and Related Studies (ECuity III Working Paper 20).

Gamkredlidze A et al. (2002). *Health care systems in transition: Georgia.* Copenhagen, WHO Regional Office for Europe on behalf of the European Observatory on Health Care Systems.

Gannon B, Nolan B (2003). *Disability and labour market participation.* Dublin, Economic and Social Research Institute.

Gelders S et al. (2006) *Availability and affordability: an international comparison of chronic disease medicines.* Geneva, World Health Organization and Health Action International.

Gillespie S, McLachlan M, Shrimpton R (2003). *Combating malnutrition: time to act. World Bank – UNICEF nutrition assessment.* Washington, DC, World Bank.

Gilmore AB, McKee M (2004a). Moving east: how the transnational tobacco industry gained entry to the emerging markets of the former Soviet Union – Part I: establishing cigarette imports. *Tobacco Control,* 13:143–150.

Gilmore AB, McKee M (2004b). Moving east: how the transnational tobacco industry gained entry to the emerging markets of the former Soviet Union – Part II: an overview of priorities and tactics used to establish a manufacturing presence. *Tobacco Control,* 13:151–160.

Gilmore AB, McKee M (2004c). Tobacco and transition: an overview of industry investments, impact and influence in the former Soviet Union. *Tobacco Control,* 13:136–142.

Gilmore A, McKee M, Collin J (2006). Unless Health Decree 30 is amended satisfactorily it will not be possible for this transaction to proceed: British American Tobacco's erosion of health legislation in Uzbekistan. *British Medical Journal,* 332:355–358.

Gilmore A et al. (2001). Epidemiology of smoking in Ukraine, 2000. *Preventive Medicine,* 33:453–461.

Gilmore A et al. (2004). Prevalence of smoking in eight countries of the former Soviet Union: results from the Living Conditions, Lifestyles and Health Study. *American Journal of Public Health,* 94:2177–2187.

Goddard M et al. (2006). Priority setting in health – a political economy perspective. *Health Economics, Policy and Law,* 1:79–90.

Gottret P, Schieber G (2006). *Health financing revisited: a practitioner's guide.* Washington, DC, World Bank.

Gregg P, Machin S (1998). *Child development and success or failure in the youth labour market.* London, London School of Economics Centre for Economic Performance (CEP Discussion Paper No. 397).

Grootaert C, van Bastelaer T (2001). *Understanding and measuring social capital: a synthesis of findings and recommendations from the Social Capital Initiative.* Washington, DC, World Bank (EBRD Working Paper No. 24).

Gros D, Suhrcke M (2000). *Ten years after: what is special about transition economies?* London, European Bank for Reconstruction and Development (EBRD Working Paper No. 56).

Gruber J (2002). Smoking's "internalities". *Regulation,* 25:25–27.

Gruber J, Koszegi B (2001). Is addiction 'rational'? Theory and evidence. *Quarterly Journal of Economics,* 116:1261–1303.

Guindon GE, Tobin S, Yach D (2002). Trends and affordability of cigarette prices: ample room for tax increases and related health gains. *Tobacco Control,* 11:35–43.

Gupta S, HR Davoodi, ER Tiongson (2000). *Corruption and the provision of health care and education services.* Washington, DC, Internaional Monetary Fund (IMF Working Paper No. 00/116).

Gupta S, Verhoeven M, Tiongson E (1999). *Does higher government spending buy better results in education and health care?* Washington, DC, International Monetary Fund (IMF Working Paper No. 99/21).

Gupta S, Verhoeven M, Tiongson ER (2003). Public spending on health care and the poor. *Health Economics*, 12:685–696.

Haacker M, ed. (2004). *The macroeconomics of HIV/AIDS*. Washington, DC, International Monetary Fund.

Habicht J et al. (2005). *Out-of-pocket payments in Estonia: an object for concern?* WHO Regional Office for Europe Health Systems Programme (Working document).

Haddad LJ, Bouis HE (1991). The impact of nutritional status on agricultural productivity: wage evidence from the Philippines. *Oxford Bulletin of Economics and Statistics*, 53:45–68.

Hajdu P, McKee M, Bojan F (1995). Changes in premature mortality differentials by marital status in Hungary and in England and Wales. *European Journal of Public Health*, 5:259–264

Hardy LL et al. (2006). Family and home correlates of television viewing in 12–13 year-old adolescents: the Nepean Study. *International Journal of Behavioural Nutrition and Physical Activity*, 3:24.

Hastings G et al. (2003). *Review of the research on the effects of food promotion to children*. Glasgow, University of Strathclyde Centre for Social Marketing (Report prepared for the Food Standards Agency).

Hausman JA, Taylor WE (1981). Panel data and unobservable individual effects. *Econometrica*, 49:1377–1398.

Haveman R et al. (1994). Market work, wages and men's health. *Journal of Health Economics*, 13:163–182.

Hawkes C (2002). Marketing activities of global soft drink and fast food companies in emerging markets: a review. *Globalization, Diets and Noncommunicable Diseases*. Geneva, World Health Organization (www.who.int/hpr/NPH/docs/globalization.diet.and.ncds.pdf, accessed 14 January 2007).

Heston A, Summers R and Aten B (2002). *Penn World Table Version 6.1*. Center for International Comparisons at the University of Pennsylvania (CICUP), 18 October.

Hawkes C (2004). *Food: a determinant of nutrition and health in the ECA Region*. Venice, WHO Regional Office for Europe (Mimeo).

Hay R (2003). *The 'fiscal space' for publicly financed health care*. Washington, DC, Oxford Policy Institute (Policy Brief No. 4, February).

Heller P (2005). *Understanding fiscal space*. Washington, DC, International Monetary Fund (IMF Policy Discussion Paper PDP/05/4).

Horlings E, Scoggins A (2006). *An ex ante assessment of the economic impacts of EU alcohol policies*. Cambridge (UK), Rand Europe Corporation.

Ichino A (2002). *The problem of causality in the analysis of educational choices and labour market outcomes*. Florence, European University Institute [Manuscript].

International HIV/AIDS Alliance in Ukraine and World Bank (2006). *Socioeconomic impact of HIV/AIDS in Ukraine*. Washington, DC, World Bank.

Islam N (1995). Growth empirics: a panel data approach. *Quarterly Journal of Economics*, 110:1127–1170.

Ivaschenko O (2002). *Adult health and earnings in the Ukrainian labour market*. Gothenburg, Gothenburg University School of Economics and Commercial Law (Paper presented at the 2002 ESPE conference) (www.eco.rug.nl/~espe2002/ivaschenko.pdf, accessed 30 December 2006).

Jahns L, Baturin A, Popkin B (2003). Obesity, diet, and poverty: trends in the Russian transition to market economy. *European Journal of Clinical Nutrition*, 57:1295–1302.

Jamison D, Lau L, Wang J (2004). *Health's contribution to economic growth in an environment of partially endogenous technical progress*. Bethesda, MD, National Institutes of Health Fogarty

International Center (Disease Control Priorities Project Working Paper No. 10).

Jamison DT et al., eds. (2006). *Disease control priorities in developing countries,* 2nd ed. Washington, DC, World Bank and Oxford University Press.

Jha P, Chaloupka F (1999). *Curbing the epidemic: governments and the economics of tobacco control.* Washington, DC, World Bank.

Jiménez-Martín S, Labeaga JM, Martínez Granado M (1999). *Health status and retirement decisions for older European couples.* Differdange, Centre d'Etudes de Populations, de Pauvreté et de Politiques Socio-Economiques (CEPS).

Kalemli-Ozcan S, Ryder HE, Weil DN (2000). Mortality decline, human capital investment, and economic growth. *Journal of Development Economics,* 62:1–23.

Kaufmann D, Mastruzzi M, Kraay A (2004). *Governance matters III: governance indicators for 1996–2002.* Washington, DC, World Bank.

Kawachi I et al. (2004). Commentary: reconciling the three accounts of social capital. *International Journal of Epidemiology,* 33(4):682–690; Discussion: 700–704.

Kelly J, Amirkhanian Y (2003). The newest epidemic: a review of HIV/AIDS in central and eastern Europe. *International journal of STD & AIDS,* 14:361–371.

Kenkel D (1993). Drinking, driving, and deterrence: the effectiveness and social costs of alternative policies. *Journal of Law & Economics,* 36:877–913.

Kenkel D (1997). On valuing morbidity, cost–effectiveness analysis, and being rude. *Journal of Health Economics,* 16:749–757.

Kingkade W, Sawyer C (2001). *Infant mortality in eastern Europe and the former Soviet Union before and after the break-up.* Paper prepared for the 2001 Meeting of the International Scientific Study of Population, Salvador de Bahia, Brazil, August 19–24.

Knai C, McKee M, Bobak M (2005). *Evidence base on how to improve health in low-resource settings with special attention to ECA: CVD prevention, management, rehabilitation.* Venice, WHO Regional Office for Europe (Mimeo).

Krementosov NL (1997). *Stalinist science.* Princeton, NJ, Princeton University Press.

Kulis M et al. (2004). *Truck drivers and casual sex: an inquiry into the potential spread of HIV/AIDS in the Baltic region.* Washington, DC, World Bank (World Bank Working Paper No. 37).

Ladnaia N, Pokrovsky V, Rühl C (2003). *The economic consequences of HIV in Russia: an interactive simulation approach.* Moscow, World Bank.

Lang K et al. (2006). The composition of surrogate and illegal alcohol products in Estonia. *Alcohol Alcoholism,* 47:446–450.

Law C, Yip P (2003). Healthy life expectancy in Hong Kong special administrative region of China. *Bulletin of the World Health Organization,* 81:43–47.

Laxminarayan R, Chow J, Shahid-Salles SA (2006). Intervention cost–effectiveness: overview of main messages. In: Jamison D et al. *Disease control priorities in developing countries,* 2nd ed. Washington, DC, World Bank; Oxford, Oxford University Press: 35–86.

Lechner M, Vazquez-Alvarez R (2004). *The effect of disability on labour market outcomes in Germany: evidence from matching.* London, Centre for Economic Policy Research.

Lee LF (1982). Health and wage: a simultaneous equation model with multiple discrete indicators. *International Economic Review,* 23:199–221.

Leinsalu M, Vågerö D, Kunst AE (2003). Estonia 1989–2000: enormous increase in mortality differences by education. *International Journal of Epidemiology,* 32:1081–1087.

Leite C, Weidmann J (1999). *Does Mother Nature corrupt? Natural resources, corruption, and economic growth.* Washington, DC, International Monetary Fund (IMF Working Paper No. 85).

Leon D et al. (1997). Huge variation in Russian mortality rates 1984–1994: artefact, alcohol, or what? *The Lancet*, 350:383–388.

Levin H et al. (1993). Micronutrient deficiency disorder. In: Jamison D et al., eds. *Disease control priorities in developing countries*. Oxford, Oxford University Press: 421–451.

Levine P, Gustafson T, Velenchik A (1997). More bad news for smokers? The effect of cigarette smoking on wages. *Industrial and Labor Relations Review*, 50:493–509.

Levine R, Renelt D (1992). A sensitivity analysis of cross-country growth regressions. *American Economic Review*, 80:942–963.

Lewis M (2000). *Who is paying for health care in eastern Europe and central Asia?* Washington, DC, World Bank.

Lindholm C, Burström B, Diderichsen F (2001). Does chronic illness cause adverse social and economic consequences among Swedes? *Scandinavian Journal of Public Health*, 29:63–70.

Lock K, McKee M (2005). Health impact assessment: assessing opportunities and barriers to intersectoral health improvement in an expanded European Union. *Journal of Epidemiology and Community Health*, 59:356–360.

Lock K et al. (2003). Health impact assessment of agriculture and food policies: lessons learnt from the Republic of Slovenia. *Bulletin of the World Health Organization*, 81:391–398.

Lock K et al. (2005). The global burden of disease due to low fruit and vegetable consumption: implications for the global strategy on diet. *Bulletin of the World Health Organization*, 83(2):100–108.

Lockman S et al. (2001). Clinical outcomes of Estonian patients with primary multi-resistant versus drug-susceptible tuberculosis. *Clinical Infectious Diseases*, 32:373–380.

Lokshin M, Beegle K (2006). *Forgone earnings from smoking: evidence for a developing country*. Washington, DC, World Bank (World Bank Policy Research Working Paper No. 4018).

López-Casasnovas G, Rivera B, Currais L, eds. (2005). *Health and economic growth: findings and policy implications*. Cambridge, MA, The MIT Press.

Lynch J et al. (2000). Social capital – is it a good investment strategy for public health? *Journal of Epidemiology & Community Health*, 54:404–408.

Macura M, MacDonald A, eds. (2005). *The new demographic regime: population challenges and policy responses*. New York, United Nations (United Nations Economic Commission for Europe (UNECE) and United Nations Population Fund (UNFPA)).

Mankiw RG, Romer D (1991). A quick refresher course in macroeconomics. *Journal of Economic Literature*, 28(4):1645–1660.

Manning W et al. (1991). *The costs of poor health habits*. Cambridge, MA, Harvard University Press.

Marquez PV, Suhrcke M (2005). Combating noncommunicable diseases. *British Medical Journal*, 331:174.

Mathers CD et al. (2003). *Global burden of disease in 2002: data sources, methods and results*. Geneva, World Health Organization (Global Programme on Evidence for Health Policy Discussion Paper No. 54).

Matic S, Lazarus J, Donoghoe M, eds (2006). *HIV/AIDS in Europe: moving from death sentence to chronic disease management*. Copenhagen, WHO Regional Office for Europe.

McCain MN, Mustard JF (1999). *Reversing the real brain drain: early years study, final report*. Toronto, Ontario Children's Secretariat.

McGillivray M, White H (1993). *Explanatory studies of aid allocation among developing countries: a critical survey*. The Hague, Institute of Social Studies (Institute of Social Studies Working Paper No. 148).

McGuire J (1996). *The nutrition pay-off.* Washington, DC, World Bank.

McKee M (1999). Alcohol in Russia. *Alcohol and Alcoholism*, 34:824–829.

McKee M (2001). The health effects of the collapse of the Soviet Union. In: Leon D, Walt G, eds. *Poverty, inequality and health.* London, Oxford University Press: 17–36.

McKee M (2005a). A decade of experience in eastern Europe. In: Foege W, Black R, Daulaire N, eds. *Leadership and management for improving global health.* New York: Joosey Bass/John Wiley & Sons: 167–186.

McKee M (2005b). Monitoring health in central and eastern Europe and the former Soviet Union. *Soz Praventivmed*, 50:341–343.

McKee M (2007). Cochrane on communism: the influence of ideology on the search for evidence. *International Journal of Epidemiology*, Advance Access, published online 14 March (DOI:10.10093/ijc/dym002).

McKee M, Chenet L (2002). Patterns of health. In: McKee M, Falkingham J, Healy J, eds. *Health care in central Asia.* Buckingham, Open University Press: 57–66.

McKee M, Hogan H, Gilmore A (2004). Why we need to ban smoking in public places now. *Journal of Public Health and Medecine*, 26:325–326.

McKee M, Shapo L, Pomerleau J (2004). Physical inactivity in a country in transition: a population-based survey in Tirana City, Albania. *Scandinavian Journal of Public Health*, 32:60–67.

McKee M, Shkolnikov V (2001). Understanding the toll of premature death among men in eastern Europe. *British Medical Journal*, 323:1051–1055.

McKee M, Shkolnikov V, Leon D (2001). Alcohol is implicated in the fluctuations in cardiovascular disease in Russia since the 1980s. *Annals of Epidemiology*, 11:1–6.

McKee M et al. (1998). Patterns of smoking in Russia. *Tobacco Control*, 7:22–26.

McKee M et al. (2000). Health policy-making in central and eastern Europe: lessons from the inaction on injuries? *Health Policy and Planning*, 15:263–269.

McKee M et al. (2005). The composition of surrogate alcohols consumed in Russia. *Alcoholism, Clinical and Experimental Research*, 29:1884–1888.

McKee M et al. (2006). Access to water in the countries of the former Soviet Union. *Public Health*, 120:364–372.

McNabb S et al. (1994). Population-based nutritional risk survey of pensioners in Yerevan, Armenia. *American Journal of Preventive Medicine*, 10:65–70.

Mheen H van de et al. (1999). The influence of adult ill health on occupational class mobility and mobility out of and into employment in the Netherlands. *Social Science & Medicine*, 49:509–518.

Michaud C (2001). *Development assistance for health (DAH): average commitments 1997–1999.* Geneva, World Health Organization (Background paper to CMH Working Group 6, Paper No. 1).

Miller TR (2000). Variations between countries in values of statistical life. *Journal of Transport Economics and Policy*, 34:169–188.

Mitchell J and Burkhauser, R (1990). Disentangling the effect of arthritis on earnings: a simultaneous estimate of wage rates and hours worked. *Applied Economics Letters*, 22:1291–1310.

Mitra P, Yemtsov R (2006). *Increasing inequality in transition economies: is there more to come?* Washington, DC, World Bank (World Bank Policy Research Working Paper No. 4007).

Molyneux A et al. (2002). Is smoking a communicable disease? The effect of exposure to ever-smokers in school tutor groups on the risk of incident smoking in the first year of secondary school. *Tobacco Control: An International Journal*, 11:241–245.

Monteiro C et al. (2004). Socioeconomic status and obesity in adult populations of developing countries: a review. *Bulletin of the World Health Organization*, 82:940–946.

Morgan A, Swann C, eds. (2004). *Social capital for health: issues of definition, measurement and links to health*. London, National Health Service Health Development Agency.

Mounier S et al. (2007). HIV/AIDS in Central Asia. In: Twigg J, ed. *HIV/AIDS in Russia and Eurasia*, Vol. II. New York, Palgrave.

Mullahy J (1991). Gender differences in labour market effects of alcoholism. *American Economic Review: Papers and Proceedings*, 81:161–165.

Mulligan J-A, Walker D, Fox-Rushby J (2006). Economic evaluations of noncommunicable disease interventions in developing countries: a critical review of the evidence base. *Cost Effectiveness and Resource Allocation*, 4:7 (DOI:10.1186/1478-7547-4-7) (www.resource-allocation.com/content/4/1/7, accessed 14 January 2007).

Musgrove P (1996). *Public and private roles in health: theory and financing patterns*. Washington, DC, World Bank.

Musgrove P (1999). Public spending on health care: how are different criteria related? *Health Policy*, 47:207–223.

Musgrove P, Zeramdini R, Carrin G (2002). Basic patterns in national health expenditure. *Bulletin of the World Health Organization*, 80:134–146.

National Statistical Service of the Ministry of Health, MEASURE DHS (2006). *Armenia demographic and health survey 2005: preliminary report*. Yerevan, Ministry of Health of Armenia; Calverton, MA, MEASURE DHS.

Nickel S (1981). Biases in dynamic models with fixed effects. *Econometrica*, 49:1117–1126.

Nolte E, McKee M, Gilmore A (2005). Morbidity and mortality in the transition countries of Europe. In: Macura M, MacDonald A, eds. *The new demographic regime: population challenges and policy responses*. New York, United Nations (United Nations Economic Commission for Europe (UNECE) and United Nations Population Fund (UNFPA)), 153–176.

Nordhaus W (2003). The health of nations: the contribution of improved health to living standards. In: Moss M, ed. *The measurement of economic and social performance*. New York, Columbia University Press for the National Bureau of Economic Research (NBER): 9–40.

North DC (1990). *Institutions, institutional change and economic performance*. Cambridge (UK), Cambridge University Press.

Novotny T, Haazen D, Adeyi O (2004). *HIV/AIDS in south-eastern Europe: case studies from Bulgaria, Croatia and Romania*. Washington, DC, World Bank.

O'Donoghue T, Rabin M (2000). *Risky behaviour among youths: some issues from behavioural economics*. University of California Economics Department, Berkeley (Working Paper E00-285, June 7).

O'Donoghue T, Rabin M (2006). Optimal sin taxes. *Journal of Public Economics*, 90:1825–1849.

OECD (1992). *The reform of health care: A comparative analysis of seven OECD countries*. Paris, Organisation for Economic Co-operation and Development.

OECD (1994). *The reform of health care systems: A review of seventeen OECD countries*. Paris, Organisation for Economic Co-operation and Development.

OECD (2003). OECD International Development Statistics (IDS) database [offline database]. Paris, Organisation for Economic Co-operation and Development.

OECD (2004). OECD Health Data 2004 [online database]. Paris, OECD (http://www.oecd.org, accessed 06 February 2007).

Ofcom (2006). *Child obesity – food advertising in context: children's food choices, parents' understanding and influence, and the role of food promotions.* London, Office of Communications (www.ofcom.org.uk/research/tv/reports/food_ads/, accessed 9 September 2006).

Office of Health Economics and King's Fund (2003). *Cost–effectiveness thresholds. Economic and ethical issues.* London, Office of Health Economics and King's Fund.

Öhlin B et al. (2004). Chronic psychosocial stress predicts long-term cardiovascular morbidity and mortality in middle-aged men. *European Heart Journal,* 25(10):867–873.

Olson M (1982). *The rise and decline of nations: economic growth, stagflation and social rigidities.* New Haven, Yale University Press.

OSI (2005). *Access to education and employment for people with intellectual disabilities.* Budapest/New York, Open Society Institute.

OSI (2006). *Delivering HIV care and treatment for people who use drugs: lessons from research and practice.* Budapest/New York, Open Society Institute.

Pagán R, Marchante AJ (2004). Análisis de las diferencias salariales por discapacidad en España: el caso de los varones. *Hacienda Pública Española/ Revista de Economía Pública,* 171:75–100.

Pevalin DJ, Rose D (2002). *Social capital for health: investigating the links between social capital and health using the British Household Panel Survey.* London, Health Development Agency.

Pikhart H et al. (2004). Psychosocial factors at work and depression in three countries of central and eastern Europe. *Social Science & Medicine,* 58(8):1475–1482.

Plavinski SL, Plavinskaya SI, Klimov AN (2003). Social factors and increase in mortality in Russia in the 1990s: prospective cohort study. *British Medical Journal,* 326:1240–1242.

Pollay RW (2000). Targeting youth and concerned smokers: evidence from Canadian tobacco industry documents. *Tobacco Control,* 9:136–147.

Pomerleau J et al. (2002). Food security in the Baltic republics. *Public Health Nutrition,* 5:397–404.

Pomerleau J et al. (2003). The burden of disease attributable to nutrition in Europe. *Public Health Nutrition,* 6:453–461.

Powles J et al. (1996). Protective foods in winter and spring: a key to lower vascular mortality. *The Lancet,* 348:898–899.

Prah Ruger J, Jamison D, Bloom DE (2001). Health and the economy. In: Merson M, Black R, Mills A, eds. *International public health: diseases, programmes, systems and policies.* Gaithersburg, MD, Aspen Publishers, Inc.: 617–666.

Preker SA, Langenbrunner J, Suzuki E (2002). *The global expenditure gap: securing financial protection and access to health care for the poor.* Washington, DC, International Bank for Reconstruction and Development and World Bank (Health, Nutrition and Population Discussion Paper, December 2002).

Putnam R, et al. (1993). *Making democracy work: civic traditions in modern Italy.* Princeton, NJ, Princeton University Press.

Rabin BA, Boehmer TK, Brownson RC (2006). Cross-national comparison of environmental and policy correlates of obesity in Europe. *European Journal of Public Health* [June 14, Epub ahead of print].

Raikumar AS, Swaroop V. (2002). *Public spending and outcomes: does governance matter?* Washington, DC, World Bank (World Bank Policy Research Paper 2840).

Raiser M et al. (2001). *Social capital in transition: a first look at the evidence.* London, European Bank for Reconstruction and Development (EBRD Working Paper No. 62).

Rechel B, McKee M (2005). *Human rights and health in Turkmenistan.* London, London School of Hygiene and Tropical Medicine.

Rechel B, Shapo L, McKee M (2004). *Millennium Development Goals for health in Europe and central Asia: relevance and policy implications.* Washington, DC, World Bank (World Bank Working Paper No. 33).

Rehfuess E, Mehta S, Prüss-Üstün A (2006). Assessing household solid fuel use: multiple implications for the Millennium Development Goals. *Environmental Health Perspectives,* 114: 373–378.

Republic of Moldova Ministry of Health and Social Protection, National Scientific and Applied Center for Preventive Medicine, MEASURE DHS (2006). *Moldova demographic and health survey 2005: preliminary report.* Calverton, MD, MEASURE DHS and Republic of Moldova Ministry of Health and Social Protection.

Rhodes T, Simic M (2005). Transition and the HIV risk environment. *British Medical Journal,* 331:220–223.

Riphahn RT (1998). *Income and employment effects of health shocks – a test case for the German welfare state.* Bonn, Institute for the Study of Labour (IZA).

Rivera B, Currais L (1999). Economic growth and health: direct impact or reverse causation? *Applied Economics Letters,* 6:761–764.

Rokx C, Galloway R, Brown L (2002). *Prospects for improving nutrition in eastern Europe and central Asia.* Washington, DC, World Bank.

Rose R. (1993). Rethinking civil society: post-communism and the problem of trust. *Journal of Democracy,* 1(1):18–29.

Rose R (1998). *Getting things done in an anti-modern society: social capital networks in Russia.* Washington DC, World Bank, Social Development Department (Social Capital Initiative Working Paper 6).

Rose R. (2000). How much does social capital add to individual health? A survey study of Russians. *Social Science & Medicine,* 51(9):1421–1435.

Rothschild M, Stiglitz JE (2006). Equilibrium in competitive insurance markets: an essay on the economics of imperfect information. *Quarterly Journal of Economics,* 90:629–649.

Ruel M, Rivera J, Habicht J (1995). Length screens better than weight in stunted populations. *Journal of Nutrition,* 125:1222–1228.

Sachs JD, Warner AM (1995a). *Natural resource abundance and economic growth.* Cambridge, MA, National Bureau of Economic Research (NBER Working Paper No. 5398).

Sachs JD, Warner AM (1995b). Economic reform and the process of global integration. *Brookings Papers on Economic Activity,* 1–118.

Sala-i-Martin X (2005). On the health-poverty trap. In: López-Casasnovas G, Rivera B, Currais L, eds. *Health and economic growth: findings and policy implications.* Cambridge, MA, The MIT Press: 95–114.

Sala-i-Martin X, Doppelhofer G, Miller R, (2004). Determinants of long-term growth: a Bayesian averaging of classical estimates (BACE) approach. *The American Economic Review,* 94:813–835.

Salomon J, Murray C (2002). The epidemiologic transition revisited: compositional models for causes of death by age and sex. *Population and Development Review,* 28:205–228.

Sargan JD (1958). The estimation of economic relationships using instrumental variables. *Econometrica,* 26:393–415.

Schieber G, Poullier J, Greenwald L (1991). Health systems in twenty-four countries. *Health Affairs,* 10:22–38.

Schneider F (2006). *Shadow economies and corruption all over the world: what do we really know?* Bonn, Institute for the Study of Labor (IZA) (Discussion Paper No. 2315).

Sethi D et al. (2006). *Injuries and violence in Europe. Why they matter and what can be done.* Rome and Copenhagen, WHO Regional Office for Europe.

Shkolnikov V, McKee M, Leon D (2001). Changes in life expectancy in Russia in the 1990s. *The Lancet*, 357:917–921.

Shkolnikov V et al. (1999). Why is the death rate from lung cancer falling in the Russian Federation? *European Journal of Epidemiology*, 15:203–206.

Shkolnikov V et al. (2006). The changing relationship between education and life expectancy in central and eastern Europe in the 1990s. *Journal of Epidemiology and Community Health*, 60:875–881.

Siddiqui S (1997). The impact of health on retirement behaviour: empirical evidence from West Germany. *Econometrics and Health Economics*, 6:425–438.

Skocpol T (1992). *Protecting soldiers and mothers: the political origins of social policy in the United States.* Cambridge, MA and London, Belknap Press of Harvard University Press.

Sloan F et al. (2004). *The price of smoking.* Cambridge, MA, The MIT Press.

Smolar, A. (1996). Civil society after communism: from opposition to atomization. *Journal of Democracy*, 4(1):24–38.

Stepanyan V (2003). *Reforming tax systems: experience of the Baltics, Russia, and other countries of the former Soviet Union.* Washington, DC, International Monetary Fund (IMF Working Paper No. 03/173).

Steptoe A, Wardle J (2001). Health behaviour, risk awareness and emotional well-being in students from eastern Europe and western Europe. *Social Science & Medicine*, 53(12):1621–1630.

Stern S. (1989), Measuring the effect of disability on labour force participation. *Journal of Human Resources*, 24(3):361–395.

Stern S (1996). Measuring child work and residence adjustments to parents' long-term care needs. *Gerontologist*, 36:76–87.

Strauss J, Thomas D (1998). Health, nutrition, and economic development. *Journal of Economic Literature*, 36:766–817.

Strong K et al. (2005). Preventing chronic diseases: how many lives can we save? *The Lancet*, 366:1578–1582.

Suhrcke M, Rechel B, Michaud C (2005). Development assistance for health in central and eastern Europe. *Bulletin of the World Health Organization*, 83:920–927.

Suhrcke M, Võrk A, Mazzuco S (2006). *The economic consequences of ill health in Estonia.* Copenhagen, WHO Regional Office for Europe; Tallinn, Praxis Center for Policy Studies.

Suhrcke M et al. (2005). *The contribution of health to the economy in the European Union.* Brussels, European Commission.

Suhrcke M et al. (2006). *Chronic disease: an economic perspective.* London, Oxford Health Alliance.

Suhrcke M et al. (2007). *Economic consequences of noncommunicable diseases and injuries in the Russian Federation.* Copenhagen, WHO Regional Office for Europe on behalf of the European Observatory on Health Systems and Policies.

Suhrcke M et al. (Forthcoming, 2007). *Socioeconomic differences in health, health behaviours and access to health care in Armenia: tabulations from the 2001 Living Conditions, Lifestyles and Health Survey.* Copenhagen, WHO Regional Office for Europe.

Sullivan D (1971). *A single measurement of mortality and morbidity.* Rockville, MD, Health Services and Mental Health Administration (HSMHA Health Report).

Szreter S, Woolcock M (2004). Health by association? Social capital, social theory, and the political economy of public health. *International Journal of Epidemiology*, 33(4):650–667.

Tendler J (1997). *Good government in the tropics*. Baltimore and London, Johns Hopkins University Press.

Thomas D (2001). *Health, nutrition and economic prosperity: a microeconomic perspective*. Geneva, WHO Commission on Macroeconomics and Health (CMH Working Paper No. WG1:7).

Trognon A (1978). Miscellaneous asymptotic properties of ordinary least squares and maximum likelihood estimators in dynamic error components models. *Annales d l'INSEE*, 30/31:631–657.

UNAIDS Turkmenistan (2004). *Epidemiological fact sheets on HIV/AIDS and sexually transmitted infections*. Geneva, Joint United Nations Programme on HIV/AIDS.

UNAIDS, WHO (2005). *AIDS epidemic update: December 2005*. Geneva, Joint United Nations Programme on HIV/AIDS and World Health Organization.

UNAIDS, WHO (2006). *AIDS epidemic update 2006*. Geneva, Joint United Nations Programme on HIV/AIDS and World Health Organization.

UNDP (2004). *Reversing the epidemic: facts and policy options*. Bratislava, United Nations Development Programme.

UNICEF (1998). *Safe water and hygiene for children: UNICEF's integrated assistance in rural Tajikistan*. New York, United Nations Children's Fund.

UNICEF (2001). *A decade of transition*. Florence, United Nations Children's Fund Innocenti Research Centre (Regional Monitoring Report, No. 8).

UNICEF (2003). *Social Monitor 2003*. Florence, United Nations Children's Fund Innocenti Research Centre (Innocenti Social Monitor).

UNICEF (2006). Multiple Indicator Cluster Surveys (MICS) [online database]. New York, United Nations Children's Fund (www.childinfo.org/index2.htm, accessed 11 January 2007).

UNICEF (2006a). Multiple Indicator Cluster Surveys (MICS) [online database]. New York, United Nations Children's Fund (www.childinfo.org/index2.htm, accessed 11 January 2007).

UNICEF (2006b). TransMONEE 2006 [database]. Florence, United Nations Children's Fund Innocenti Research Centre.

UNICEF, The Micronutrient Initiative (2004). *Vitamin and mineral deficiency: a global assessment*. Ottawa, United Nations Children's Fund and The Micronutrient Initiative.

Uphoff, N. (2000). Understanding social capital: learning from the analysis and experience of participation. In: Dasgupta & Serageldin, eds. *Social capital: a multifaceted perspective*. Washington DC, World Bank: 215–249.

US DHHS (1994). *Preventing tobacco use among young people: a report of the Surgeon General*. Atlanta, GA, United States Department of Health and Human Services Centers for Disease Control and Prevention.

US DHHS (2006). *The health consequences of involuntary exposure to tobacco smoke: a report of the Surgeon General*. Atlanta, GA, United States Department of Health and Human Services Centers for Disease Control and Prevention.

Usher D (1973). An imputation to the measure of economic growth for changes in life expectancy. In: Moss M, ed. *The measurement of economic and social performance*. New York, Columbia University Press for National Bureau of Economic Research (NBER): 193–226.

Viscusi W, Aldy E (2003). *The value of statistical life: a critical review of market estimates throughout the World*. Cambridge, MA, National Bureau of Economic Research (NBER Working Paper No. 9487).

Wagstaff A (1989). Estimating effciency in the hospital sector: a comparison of three statistical cost frontier models. *Applied Economics*, 21:659–672.

Wagstaff A, Claeson M. (2004). *The Millennium Goals for health: rising to the challenges*. Washington, DC, World Bank.

Wagstaff A, van Doorslaer E. (2001). *Paying for health care: quantifying fairness, catastrophe, and impoverishment, with applications to Vietnam, 1993–1998*. Washington, DC, World Bank (Policy Research Working Paper Series, No. WPS 2715).

Walberg P et al. (1998). Economic change, crime, and mortality crisis in Russia: a regional analysis. *British Medical Journal*, 317:312–318.

Wallace C, Bedzik V, Chmouliar O (1997). *Spending, saving or investing social capital: the case of shuttle traders in post-communist central Europe*. Vienna, Institute for Advanced Studies (East European Series No. 43).

Wallerstein N (2006). *What is the evidence on effectiveness of empowerment to improve health?* Copenhagen, WHO Regional Office for Europe. (Health evidence network report) (www.euro.who.int/Document/E88086.pdf, accessed 1 February 2006).

Walters S, Suhrcke M (2005). *Socioeconomic inequalities in health and health care access in central and eastern Europe and the CIS: a review of the recent literature*. Venice, WHO Regional Office for Europe (Working Paper No. 1).

Wang J et al. (1999). *Measuring country performance on health: selected indicators for 115 countries*. Washington DC, World Bank.

Wang Y (2001). Cross-national comparison of childhood obesity: the epidemic and the relationship between obesity and socioeconomic status. *International Journal of Epidemiology*, 30:1129–1136.

Watson, P (1995). Explaining rising mortality among men in eastern Europe. *Social Science & Medicine*, 41:923-934.

Whincup PH et al. (2004). Passive smoking and risk of coronary heart disease and stroke: prospective study with cotinine measurement. *British Medical Journal*, 329:200–205.

Whitaker RC, Wright JA and Pepe MS (1997). Predicting obesity in young adulthood from childhood and parental obesity. *New England Journal of Medicine*, 337:869–873.

Whitehead M, Dahlgren G (2006). *Levelling up (part 1): a discussion paper on concepts and principles for tackling social inequities in health*. Copenhagen, WHO Regional Office for Europe (Studies on Social and Economic Determinants of Population Health, No. 2).

Whitehead M, Dahlgren G, Evans T (2001). Equity and health sector reforms: can low-income countries escape the medical poverty trap? *The Lancet*, 358:833–836.

WHO (2000). *The world health report 2000 – health systems: improving performance*. Geneva, World Health Organization.

WHO (2002a). *The world health report 2002 – reducing risks, promoting healthy life*. Geneva, World Health Organization.

WHO (2002b). *Tobacco industry youth smoking prevention programs – a critique*. [World Health Organization Briefing, 23 October 2002]. Geneva, World Health Organization (http://www.ash.org.uk/html/conduct/html/yspbriefwho.html, accessed 1 December 2006).

WHO (2003). Table 3: Estimated completeness of mortality data for latest year and Table 4: Estimated coverage of mortality data for latest year [online data]. Geneva, World Health Organization (http://www.who.int/healthinfo/morttables/en/, accessed 29 October 2003).

WHO (2005a). *Preventing chronic diseases: a vital investment: WHO global report*. Geneva, World Health Organization.

WHO (2005b) WHO Statistical Information Systems (WHOSIS) [web site] Geneva, World Health Organization (National Health Accounts (NHA) indicators) (http://www3.who.int/whosis/core/core_select.cfm, accessed 1 December 2005).

WHO (2005c). *The world health report 2005: make every mother and child count.* Geneva, World Health Organization.

WHO (2005d). National health accounts (NHA) [web site]. Geneva, World Health Organization (http://www.who.int/nha/en/, accessed 1 December 2005).

WHO (2006a). Core health indicators [online database]. Geneva, World Health Organization (http://www3.who.int/whosis/core/core_select.cfm, accessed 11 January 2007).

WHO (2006b). Global child growth and malnutrition database [online database]. Geneva, World Health Organization (www.who.int/nutgrowthdb/, accessed 17 July 2006).

WHO (20006c). WHO database on health in PSRPs [online database]. Geneva, World Health Organization (www.who.int/hdp/database/, accessed 20 December 2006).

WHO Regional Office for Europe (2001). *Urban and peri-urban food and nutrition action plan. Elements for community action to promote social cohesion and reduce inequalities through local production for local consumption.* Copenhagen, WHO Regional Office for Europe (Document EUR/01/5026040).

WHO Regional Office for Europe (2002). *European country profiles on tobacco control, 2001.* Copenhagen, WHO Regional Office for Europe.

WHO Regional Office for Europe (2006). European health for all database [online database]. Copenhagen, WHO Regional Office for Europe (http://data.euro.who.int/hfadb/, accessed 1 December 2006).

Wilkinson RG (1996). *Unhealthy societies: the afflictions of inequality.* London, Routledge.

Wilkinson R, Marmot M (2003). *Social determinants of health: the solid facts,* 2nd ed. Copenhagen, WHO Regional Office for Europe, Copenhagen.

Wilson J (1980). *The politics of regulation.* New York, Basic Books, Inc.

Wooldridge JM (2002). *Econometric analysis of cross section and panel data.* Cambridge, MA, The MIT Press.

World Bank (1993). *World development report 1993: investing in health.* Washington DC, World Bank.

World Bank (2000a). *Making transition work for everyone: poverty and inequality in Europe and Central Asia.* Washington, DC, World Bank.

World Bank (2000b). Round I Country Reports on Health, Nutrition, Population Conditions among Poor and Better-Off in 45 Countries [online database]. Washington, DC, World Bank (www.worldbank.org/poverty/health/index.htm, accessed 11 January 2007).

World Bank (2000c). *Republic of Tajikistan: poverty assessment.* Washington, DC, World Bank (Report No. 20285-TJ).

World Bank (2002a). *Armenia: poverty update.* Washington, DC, World Bank (Report No. 24339-AM ed).

World Bank (2002b). *Bulgaria: poverty assessment.* Washington, DC, World Bank (Report No. 26516-BUL).

World Bank (2003a). *Averting AIDS crises in Europe and Central Asia.* Washington, DC, World Bank.

World Bank (2003b). *Azerbaijan: public expenditure review.* Washington, DC, World Bank (Report No. 25233-AZ ed).

World Bank (2003c). *Albania: poverty assessment.* Washington, DC, World Bank (Report No. 26213-AL).

World Bank (2003d). *Moldova: public economic management review.* Washington, DC, World Bank (Report No. 25423-MD).

World Bank (2003e). *Serbia and Montenegro: poverty assessment.* Washington, DC, World Bank (Report No. 26011-YU).

World Bank (2004a). *Reversing the tide: priorities for HIV/AIDS prevention in central Asia.* Washington, DC, World Bank.

World Bank (2004b). Round II Country Reports on Health, Nutrition, Population Conditions among Poor and Better-Off in 45 Countries [online database]. Washington, DC, World Bank (www.worldbank.org/poverty/health/index.htm, accessed 11 January 2007).

World Bank (2004c). *Russian Federation: poverty assessment.* Washington, DC, World Bank (Report No. 28923-RU DRAFT).

World Bank (2005a). World Development Indicators 2005 [CD-ROM]. Washington, DC, World Bank.

World Bank (2005b). *Dying too young: addressing premature mortality and ill health due to non-communicable diseases and injuries in the Russian Federation.* Washington, DC, World Bank.

World Bank (2005c). World Bank Institute (WBI) Governance & Anti-Corruption [online database]. Washington, DC, World Bank (www.worldbank.org/wbi/governance/, accessed 1 December 2005).

World Bank (2006a). *Ukraine – creating fiscal space for growth: a public finance review.* Washington, DC, World Bank.

World Bank (2006b). *Fiscal space for infrastructure borrowing in South-eastern Europe – a suggested approach.* Washington, DC, World Bank.

World Bank (2006c). *Repositioning nutrition as central to development: a strategy for large-scale action.* Washington, DC, World Bank.

Xu K et al. (2003). Household catastrophic health expenditure: a multi-country analysis. *The Lancet,* 362:111–117.

Zhirova I et al. (2004). Abortion-related maternal mortality in the Russian Federation. *Studies in Family Planning,* 35:178–188.

The European Observatory on Health Systems and Policies
produces a wide range of analytical work on health systems and policies.
Its publishing programme includes:

☐ **The Health Systems in Transition profiles (HiTs)**. Country-based reports that provide a detailed description of the health systems of European and selected OECD countries outside the region, and of policy initiatives in progress or under development.

HiT profiles are downloadable from: www.euro.who.int/observatory

☐ **Joint Observatory/Open University Press -McGraw Hill Series. A prestigious health series exploring key issues for health systems and policies in Europe.** Titles include: Mental Health Policy and Practice across Europe ■ Decentralization in Health Care ■ Primary Care in the Driver's Seat ■ Human Resources for Health in Europe ■ Purchasing to Improve Health Systems Performance ■ Social Health Insurance Systems in Western Europe ■ Regulating Pharmaceuticals in Europe

Copies of the books can be ordered from: www.mcgraw-hill.co.uk

☐ **The Occasional Studies**. A selection of concise volumes, presenting evidence-based information on crucial aspects of health, health systems and policies. Recent titles include: Patient Mobility in the EU ■ Private Medical Insurance in the UK ■ The Health Care Workforce in Europe ■ Making Decisions on Public Health ■ Health Systems Transition: learning from experience

Studies are downloadable from: www.euro.who.int/observatory

☐ **Policy briefs**. A series of compact brochures, highlighting key policy lessons on priority issues for Europe's decision-makers, such as cross-border health care, screening, health technology assessment, care outside the hospital.

Policy briefs are downloadable from: www.euro.who.int/observatory

☐ *Eurohealth*. A joint Observatory/LSE Health journal, providing a platform for policy-makers, academics and politicians to express their views on European health policy.

☐ *Euro Observer*. A health policy bulletin, published quarterly, providing information on key health policy issues and health system reforms across Europe.

✳ ✳ ✳ **Join our E-Bulletin** ✳ ✳ ✳

Are you interested in signing up for the European Observatory's listserve to receive E-Bulletins on news about health systems, electronic versions of our latest publications, upcoming conferences and other news items? If so, please subscribe by sending a blank e-mail to: subscribe-observatory_listserve@list.euro.who.int

---